The Prose Works

of

Sir Philip Sidney

In Four Volumes

Volume II

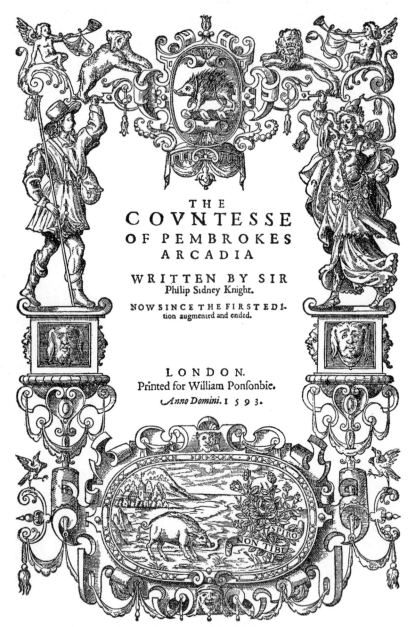

THE
COVNTESSE
OF PEMBROKES
ARCADIA

WRITTEN BY SIR
Philip Sidney Knight.

NOW SINCE THE FIRST EDI-
tion augmented and ended.

LONDON.
Printed for William Ponsonbie.
Anno Domini. 1 5 9 3.

Title-page of the first folio

SIR PHILIP SIDNEY

THE LAST PART OF THE
COUNTESSE OF PEMBROKES ARCADIA

THE LADY OF MAY

EDITED BY

ALBERT FEUILLERAT

CAMBRIDGE
AT THE UNIVERSITY PRESS
1968

PUBLISHED BY
THE SYNDICS OF THE CAMBRIDGE UNIVERSITY PRESS

Bentley House, P.O. Box 92, 200 Euston Road, London, N.W.1
American Branch: 32 East 57th Street, New York, N.Y. 10022

First printed 1912
Reprinted 1962
1963
1968

First printed in Great Britain at the University Press, Cambridge
Reprinted by offset-lithography by
Lowe & Brydone (Printers), Ltd., London. N.W.10

PUBLISHER'S NOTE

FEUILLERAT'S edition of the complete works of Sir Philip Sidney has long been out of print, but has continued to be in demand by scholars. Bibliographical research has shown that Feuillerat did not work from the best copy-texts, and that many of his readings are corrupt. Further, three more manuscripts of Sidney have been discovered since Feuillerat's edition was printed. It may, however, be many years before a new and definitive edition is published, and it has therefore been decided to reissue with minor corrections the complete prose works in Feuillerat's edition. The publisher gratefully acknowledges the advice of Professor R. W. Zandvoort and Mrs Jean Bromley in connection with this reprint.

The prose works are divided among the four volumes as follows: vol. I, *Arcadia*, 1590; vol. II, *Arcadia*, 1593 and *The Lady of May*; vol. III, *The Defence of Poesie*, Political Discourses, Correspondence and Translation; vol. IV, *Arcadia* (original version). These volumes combine with Professor Ringler's newly edited *Complete Poems* to make all Sidney's works available again.

The parts of Feuillerat's prefatory notes which are not relevant to this reprint have been removed; the remaining parts are set out below.

*   *   *

PREFATORY NOTE

In accordance with the method adopted in the first volume, the text given is that of the earliest edition. Thus, the last part of *Arcadia* is printed from the folio of 1593 and *The Lady of May* from the folio of 1598.

The text is reproduced without any deviations from the originals in the matter of spelling or punctuation. I have, however, corrected a few evident misprints, a list of which will be found on page 236.

CONTENTS

THE LAST PART OF
SIR PHILIP SIDNEY'S
ARCADIA

FROM THE FOLIO OF 1593

AFter that *Basilius* (according to the oracles promise) had received home his daughters, and settled himselfe againe in his
solitary course and accustomed company, there passed not many
dayes ere the now fully recomforted *Dorus* having waited a time
of *Zelmanes* walking alone towards her little Arbor, tooke leave
of his master *Damætas* husbandry to follow her. Neere wher-
unto overtaking her, and sitting downe together among the
sweet flowers whereof that place was very plentifull, under the
pleasant shade of a broad leaved Sycamor, they recounted one
to another their strange pilgrimage of passions, omitting nothing
which the open harted frendship is wont to lay forth, where
there is cause to cõmunicate both joyes & sorows, for indeed
ther is no sweeter tast of frendship, then the coupling of soules
in this mutualitie either of condoling or comforting: where the
oppressed minde findes itself not altogether miserable, since it is
sure of one which is feelingly sory for his misery: and the joyfull spends not his joy, either alone, or there where it may be
envyed: but may freely send it to such a well grounded object,
from whence he shall be sure to receive a sweete reflection of
the same joye, and, as in a cleere mirror of sincere good will,
see a lively picture of his owne gladnes. But after much discourse on eyther parte, *Dorus* (his hearte scarce serving him to
come to the pointe, whereunto his then comming had bene
wholie directed, as loth in the kindest sorte to discover to his
friend his owne unkindnes) at length, one word emboldening

another made knowne to *Zelmane*, how *Pamela* upon his vehement othe to offer no force unto her, till hee had invested her in the Duchie of *Thessalia*, had condiscended to his stealing her awaie to the next sea porte. That besides the straunge humors she sawe her father more and more falling into, and unreasonable restraint of her libertie, whereof she knewe no cause but light grounded jealosies, added to the hate of that manner of life, and confidence she had in his vertue, the chiefest reason had wonne her to this, was the late daunger she stoode in of loosing him, the like whereof (not unlike to fall if this course were continued) she chose rather to dye then againe to undergoe. That now they wayted for nothing else, but some fit time for their escape, by the absence of their three lothsome companions, in whome follie ingendred suspicion. And therefore now, sayd *Dorus*, my deere Cozen, to whome nature began my friendship, education confirmed it, and vertue hath made it eternall, heere have I discovered the very foundacion whereupon my life is built: bee you the Judge betwixt mee and my fortune. The violence of love is not unknowne to you: And I knowe my case shall never want pittie in your consideration. How all the joyes of my hearte doo leave mee, in thinking I must for a time be absent from you, the eternall truth is witnesse unto mee, I knowe I should not so sensiblie feele the pangs of my last departure. But this enchantment of my restlesse desire hath such authoritye in my selfe above my selfe, that I am become a slave unto it, I have no more freedome in mine owne determinacions. My thoughtes are now all bent how to carrie awaie my burdenous blisse. Yet, most beloved Cozen, rather then I should thinke I doo heerein violate that holie bande of true friendship, wherein I unworthie am knit unto you, commaund mee stay. Perchaunce the force of your commaundement may worke such impression into my hearte, that no reason of mine owne can imprint into it. For the Gods forbid, the foule word of abandoning *Pyrocles*, might ever be objected to the faithfull *Musidorus*. But if you can spare my presence, whose presence no way serves you, and by the division of these two Lodges is not oft with you: nay if you can thinke my absence may, as it shall, stand you in stead, by bringing such an armye hither, as shall make *Basilius*, willing or unwilling, to knowe his owne happe in graunting you *Philoclea*: then I will cheerefullie goe about this my most desired enterprise,

2

and shall thinke the better halfe of it alreadie atchieved, beeing begunne in the fortunate houre of my friendes contentment. These wordes, as they were not knitte together with such a constant course of flowing eloquence, as *Dorus* was woont to use : so was his voice interrupted with sighes, and his countenaunce with enterchanging coulour dismayed. So much his owne hearte did finde him faultie to unbende any way the continuall use of theyr deare friendshippe. But *Zelmane*, who had all this while gladlie hearkened to the other tydings of her friends happye successe, when this last determination of *Dorus* strake her attentive eares, she stayed a great while oppressed with a dead amazement. Ther came streight before her mind, made tender with woes, the images of her own fortune. Her tedious longings, her causes to despaire, the combersome follie of *Basilius*, the enraged Jealousie of *Gynecia*, her selfe a Prince without retinewe ; a man annoyed with the troubles of woman-kinde ; lothsomely loved, and daungerouslie loving ; And now for the perfecting of all, her friend to be taken away by himself, to make the losse the greater by the unkindnes. But within a while she resolutely passed over all inwarde objections, and preferring her friends proffitt to her owne desire, with a quiet but hartie looke, she thus aunsweared him. If I bare thee this Love vertuous *Musidorus*, for mine owne sake, and that our friendshipp grew because I for my parte, might rejoyce to enjoye such a friend : I shoulde nowe so thorowly feele mine owne losse, that I should call the heavens and earth to witnesse, howe cruelly yee robbe mee, of my greatest comforte, measuring the breach of friendshippe by myne owne passion. But because indeede I love thee for thy selfe, and in my judgement judge of thy worthines to be loved, I am content to builde my pleasure uppon thy comforte : And then will I deeme my happe in friendshippe great, when I shall see thee, whome I love happie. Let me be onely sure, thou lovest me still, the onely price of trew affection goe therefore on, worthye *Musidorus*, with the guide of vertue, and service of fortune. Let thy love be loved, thy desires prosperous, thy escape safe, and thy jornye easie. Let every thing yeeld his helpe to thy deserte, for my part absence shall not take thee from mine eyes, nor afflictions shall barre mee from gladding in thy good, nor a possessed harte shall keepe thee from the place it hath for ever allotted unto thee. *Dorus* would faine have replied againe, to

3

have made a liberall confession that *Zelmane* had of her side the advantage of well performing friendshippe: but partelie his owne griefe of parting from one he loved so dearely, partly the kinde care in what state hee should leave *Zelmane*, bredd such a conflicte in his minde, that many times he wished, he had either never attempted, or never revealed this secreat enterprise. But *Zelmane*, who had now looked to the uttermoste of it, and established her minde upon an assured determination, my onely friend said shee since to so good towardnes, your courteous destinies have conducted you, let not a ceremoniall consideration of our mutuall love, be a barre unto it. I joye in your presence, but I joye more in your good, that friendshipp brings foorth the fruites of enmitie, which preferres his owne tendernes, before his friendes domage. For my parte my greatest griefe herein shalbe, I can bee no further serviceable unto you O *Zelmane* saide *Dorus* with his eyes even covered with water, I did not think so soone to have displayed my determination unto you, but to have made my way first in your loving judgement. But alas as your sweet disposition drew me so farre: so doth it now strengthen me in it. To you therefore be the due commendation given, who can conquere me in Love, and Love in wisedome. As for mee, then shall goodnes turne to evill, and ungratefulnes bee the token of a true harte when *Pyrocles* shall not possesse a principall seate in my soule, when the name of *Pyrocles* shall not be helde of me in devout reverence.

They would never have come to the cruell instant of parting, nor to the il-faring word of farewell, had not *Zelmane* sene a farre off the olde *Basilius*, who having perfourmed a sacrifice to *Apollo*, for his daughters, but principally for his mistresse happy returne, had since bene every where to seeke her. And nowe being come within compasse of discerning her, he beganne to frame the loveliest coûtenance he could, stroking up his legges, setting his bearde in due order, and standing bolte upright. Alas said *Zelmane*, behold an evill fore-token of your sorrowfull departure. Yonder see I one of my furies, which doth daylie vexe me, farewell fare wel my *Musidorus*, the Gods make fortune to waite on thy vertues, and make mee wade through this lake of wretchednes. *Dorus* burst out into a floud of teares wringing her fast by the hande. No, no, said he, I go blindfold, whither the course of my ill happe caries me: for now too late my harte gives me this our separating can never be prosperous. But if I live, attend me here shortly with an army. Thus both appalled with the grievous renting of their long Combination, (having first resolved with thẽselves that, whatsoever fell unto them, they should never upon no occasion utter their names for the cõserving the honour of their Royal parentage, but keep the names of *Daiphantus* & *Palladius,* as before had ben agreed between thẽ) they tooke diverse waies : *Dorus* to the lodg-ward, wher his heavy eyes might be somthing refreshed; *Zelmane* towards *Basilius* : saying to her selfe with a skornefull smiling: yet hath not my friendly fortune deprived me of a pleasant companion. But he having with much searche come to her presence, *Doubt* & *Desire* bred a great quarrel in his mind. For his former experience had taught him to doubt: & true feeling of Love made doubts daungerous, but the working of his desire had ere long wonne the fielde. And therefore with the most submissive maner his behaviour could yeeld: O Goddesse, said hee towardes whom I have the greatest feeling of Religion, be not displeased at some shew of devotion I have made to *Apollo* : since he (if he know any thing) knowes that my harte beares farre more awful reverẽce to your self then to his, or any other the like *Deity.* You wil ever be deceaved in me, answered *Zelmane*: I wil make my selfe no competitor with *Apollo,* neither can blasphemies to him be duties to me. With that *Basilius* tooke out of his bosome certaine verses he had written, and kneling downe, presented them to her. They contained this:

PHæbus *farewell, a sweeter Saint I serve,*
  The high conceits thy heav'nly wisedomes breed
My thoughts forget : my thoughts, which never swerve
From her, in whome is sowne their freedomes seede,
And in whose eyes my dayly doome I reede.

Phæbus *farewell, a sweeter Saint I serve.*
Thou art farre off, thy kingdome is above :
She heav'n on earth with beauties doth preserve.
Thy beames I like, but her cleare rayes I love :
Thy force I feare, her force I still do prove.

Phæbus *yeelde up thy title in my minde.*
She doth possesse, thy Image is defaste,
But if thy rage some brave revenge will finde,

5

THE COUNTESSE OF PEMBROKES

On her, who hath in me thy temple raste,
Employ thy might, that she my fires may taste.
And how much more her worth surmounteth thee,
Make her as much more base by loving me.

This is my Hymne to you, said he, not left me by my auncestors, but begone in my selfe. The temple wherin it is daylie songe, is my soule: and the sacrifice I offer to you withall is all whatsoever I am. *Zelmane*, who ever thought shee founde in his speeches the ill taste of a medecine, and the operation of a poyson, would have suffred a disdainful looke to have bene the onely witnesse of her good acceptation; but that *Basilius* began a fresh to lay before her many pittifull prayers, and in the ende to conclude that he was fully of opinion it was onely the unfortunatenes of that place that hindered the prosperous course of his desires. And therefore since the hatefull influence; which made him embrace this solitary life, was now past over him (as he doubted not the judgment of *Philanax* would agree with his) and his late mishapes had taught him how perillous it was to commit a Princes state to a place so weakely guarded: He was now enclined to returne to his pallace in *Mantinea*, and there he hoped he should be beter able to shew how much he desired to make al he had hers: with many other such honnie wordes which my penne growes almost weary to set downe: This indeede neerely pierced *Zelmane*. For the good beginning shee had there obtained of *Philoclea* made her desire to continue the same trade, till unto the more perfecting of her desires: and to come to any publike place shee did deadly feare, lest her maske by many eyes might the sooner be discovered, and so her hopes stopped, and the state of her joyes endaungered. Therefore while shee rested, musing at the dayly chaunging labyrinth of her owne fortune, but in her selfe determined it was her onely best to keepe him there: and with favors to make him love the place, where the favors were received, as disgraces had made him apte to chaunge the *Soyle*.

Therefore casting a kinde of corner looke upon him, it is truely saide, (saide she) that age cooleth the bloud. Howe soone goodman you are terrified before you receave any hurte? Doe you not knowe that daintines is kindly unto us? And that hard obtayning, is the excuse of womans graunting? Yet speake I

6

not as though you were like to obtaine, or I to graūt. But because I would not have you imagin, I am to be wonne by
courtely vanities, or esteeme a man the more, because he hath
handsome men to waite of him, when he is affraid to live without them. You might have seene *Basilius* humbly swell, and
with a lowly looke stand upon his tiptoes ; such diversitie her
words delivered unto him. O *Hercules* aunswered he ; *Basilius*
afraide ? Or his bloud cold, that boyles in such a fournace ? Care
I who is with mee, while I enjoy your presence ? Or is any
place good or bad to me, but as it pleaseth you to blesse or curse
it ? O let me be but armed in your good grace, and I defie
whatsoever there is or can be against mee. No, no, your love
is forcible, and my age is not without vigoure. *Zelmane* thought
it not good for his stomacke, to receave a surfet of too much
favoure, and therefore thinking he had enough for the time, to
keepe him from any sodaine removing, with a certaine gracious
bowing downe of her heade towarde him, she turned away, saying, she would leave him at this time to see how temperately
hee could use so bountifull a measure, of her kindenes. *Basilius*
that thought every dropp a flood that bred any refreshment,
durst not further presse her, but with an ancient modestie left
her to the sweete repast of her owne fancies. *Zelmane* assoone
as he was departed went towarde *Pamelas* lodge in hope to have
seene her friende *Dorus*, to have pleased her selfe with another
paynefull farrewell, and further to have taken some advise with
him touching her owne estate, whereof before sorowe had not
suffered her to thinke. But being come even neere the lodge,
she saw the mouth of a cave, made as it should seeme by nature
in despite of Arte : so fitly did the riche growing marble serve
to beautifie the vawt of the first entrie. underfoot, the ground
semed mynerall, yeelding such a glistering shewe of golde in it,
as they say the ryver *Tagus* caries in his sandie bed. The cave
framed out into many goodly spatious Roomes such as the selfe-
liking men, have with long and learned delicacie founde out the
most easefull. There rann through it a little sweete River, which
had lefte the face of the earth to drowne her selfe for a smale
waye in this darke but pleasant mansion. The very first shewe
of the place entised the melancholy minde of *Zelmane* to yeelde
her selfe over there to the flood of her owne thoughtes. And
therefore sitting downe in the first entrie, of the Caves mouth,

with a song shee had lately made, shee gave a dolefull waye to
her bitter Affectes, shee sunge to this effecte:

SInce that the stormy rage of passions darcke
(Of passions darke, made darke of beauties light)
Whith rebell force, hath closde in dungeon darke
My minde ere now led foorth by reasons light:

Since all the thinges which give mine eyes their light
Do foster still, the fruites of fancies darke:
So that the windowes of my inward light
Do serve, to make my inward powers darke:

Since, as I say, both minde and sences darke
Are hurt, not helpt, with piercing of the light:
While that the light may shewe the horrors darke
But cannot make resolved darkenes lighte:
I like this place, whereat the least the durke
May keepe my thoughtes, from thought of wonted light.

   In steede of an instrument, her song was accompanied with
the wringing of her hands, the closing of her weary eyes, and
even sometime cut off with the swellinge of hir sighes, which
did not suffer the voice to have his free and native passage. But
as she was a while musing upon her songe, raising up her spirites,
which were something falne into the weakenes of lamentation,
considering solitary complaints do no good to him whose helpe
stands with out himselfe, shee might a far off, first heare a whispering sounde which seemed to come from the inmost parte of
the Cave, and being kept together with the close hollownes of
the place, had as in a Truncke the more liberall accesse to her
eares, and by and by she might perceave the same voice, deliver
it selfe into musicall tunes, and with a base Lyra give foorth
this songe:

HArke plaintfull ghostes, infernall furies harke
Unto my woes the hatefull heavens do sende,
The heavens conspir'd, to make my vitall sparke
A wreched wracke, a glasse of Ruines ende.

Seeing, Alas; so mightie powers bende
Their ireful shotte against so weake a marke,
Come cave, become my grave, come death, and lende
Receipte to me, within thy bosome darke.

For what is life to dayly dieng minde,
Where drawing breath, I sucke the aire of woe :
Where too much sight, makes all the bodie blinde,
And highest thoughts, downeward most headlong throw ?
  Thus then my forme, and thus my state I finde,
  Death wrapt in flesh, to living grave assign'd.

And pawsing but a little, with monefull melodie it continued this octave :

Like those sicke folkes, in whome strange humors flowe,
Can taste no sweetes, the sower onely please :
So to my minde, while passions daylie growe,
Whose fyrie chaines, uppon his freedome seaze,
  Joies strangers seeme, I cannot bide their showe,
  Nor brooke oughte els but well acquainted woe.
  Bitter griefe tastes me best paine is my ease,
  Sicke to the death, still loving my disease.

O *Venus*, saide *Zelmane*, who is this so well acquainted with mee, that can make so lively a portracture of my miseries ? It is surely the spirit appointed to have care of me, which doth now in this darke place beare parte with the complaints of his unhappie charge. For if it be so, that the heavens have at all times a measure of their wrathefull harmes, surely so many have come to my blistlesse lot, that the rest of the world hath too small a portion, to make with cause so wailefull a lamentation. But saide she ; whatsoever thou be, I will seeke thee out, for thy musique well assures me wee are at least-hand fellowe prentises to one ungracious master. So raise shee and went guiding her selfe, by the still playning voice, till she sawe uppon a stone a little waxe light set, and under it a piece of paper with these verses verie lately (as it should seeme) written in it :

HOwe is my Sunn, whose beames are shining bright
Become the cause of my darke ouglie night ?
Or howe do I captiv'd in this darke plight,
Bewaile the case, and in the cause delight ?

My mangled mind huge horrors still doe fright,
With sense possest, and claim'd by reasons right :
Betwixt which two in me I have this fight,
Wher who so wynns, I put my selfe to flight.

9

THE COUNTESSE OF PEMBROKES

Come clowdie feares close up my daseled sight,
Sorrowes suck up the marowe of my might,
Due sighes blowe out all sparkes of joyfull light,
Tyre on despaier uppon my tyred sprite.
  An ende, an ende, my dulde penn cannot write,
  Nor mas'de head thinke, nor faltring tonge recite.

And hard underneath the sonnet, were these wordes written:

This cave is darke, but it had never light.
This waxe doth waste it selfe, yet painelesse dyes.
These wordes are full of woes, yet feele they none.

I darkned am, who once had clearest sight.
I waste my harte, which still newe torment tryes.
I plaine with cause, my woes are all myne owne,

  No cave, no wasting waxe, no wordes of griefe,
  Can holde, shew, tell, my paines without reliefe.

She did not long stay to reade the wordes, for not farre off from
the stone shee might discerne in a darke corner, a Ladie liéng
with her face so prostrate upon the ground, as she could neither
know, nor be knowen. But (as the generall nature of man is
desirous of knowledge, and sorrow especially glad to find fellowes,) she went as softely as she could convey her foot, neere
unto her, where she heard these words come with vehement
sobbings from her. O darkenes (saide shee) which doest light somly
(me thinks) make me see the picture of my inward darknes:
since I have chosen thee, to be the secret witnesse of my sorows,
let me receive a safe receipte in thee; and esteeme them not
tedious, but if it be possible, let the uttering them be some discharge to my overloaden breast. Alas sorrowe, nowe thou hast
the full sack of my conquered spirits, rest thy selfe a while, and
set not stil new fire to thy owne spoiles: O accursed reason,
how many eyes thou hast to see thy evills, and thou dimme,
nay blinde thou arte in preventing them? Forlorne creature
that I am! I would I might be freely wicked, since wickednesse
doth prevaile, but the foote steppes of my overtroden vertue, lie
still as bitter accusations unto me: I am devided in my selfe,
howe can I stande? I am overthrowne in my selfe, who shall
raise mee? Vice is but a nurse of new agonies, and the vertue
I am divorsed from, makes the hatefull comparison the more

manyfest. No, no vertue, either I never had but a shadow of thee, or thou thy selfe, art but a shadow. For how is my soule abandoned? How are all my powers laide waste? My desire is payned, because it cannot hope, and if hope came, his best shoulde bee but mischiefe. O strange mixture of humaine mindes! onely so much good lefte, as to make us languish in our owne evills. Yee infernall furies, (for it is too late for mee, to awake my dead vertue, or to place my comforte in the angrie Gods) yee infernall furies I say, aide one that dedicates her selfe unto you, let my rage bee satisfied, since the effecte of it is fit for your service. Neither bee afraide to make me too happie, since nothing can come to appease the smart of my guiltie cōscience. I desire but to asswage the sweltring of my hellish longing, dejected *Gynecia*. *Zelmane*, no sooner heard the name of *Gynecia*, but that with a colde sweate all over her, as if she had ben ready to treade upon a deadly stinging Adder, she would have withdrawne her selfe, but her owne passion made her yeelde more unquiet motions, then she had done in comming. So that she was perceaved, & *Gynecia* sodainely risne up, for in deed it was *Ginecia*, gotten into this Cave, (the same Cave, wherein *Dametas* had safelie kept *Pamela* in the late uprore) to passe her pangs, with change of places. And as her minde ranne still upon *Zelmane*, her piercing lovers eye had soone found it was she. And seeing in her a countenance to flye away, she fell downe at her feete, and catching fast hold of her: Alas, sayd she, whether, or from whome doost thou flye awaye? the savagest beastes are wonne with service, and there is no flint but may be mollifyed: How is *Gynecia* so unworthie in thine eyes? or whome cannot aboundance of love, make worthie? O thinke not that crueltie, or ungratefulnes, can flowe from a good minde! O weigh, Alas! weigh with thy selfe, the newe effectes of this mightie passion, that I unfit for my state, uncomely for my sexe, must become a suppliant at thy feete! By the happie woman that bare thee, by all the joyes of thy hart, and successe of thy desire, I beseech thee turne thy selfe to some consideration of me; and rather shew pittie in now helping me, then into late repenting my death which hourely threatens me. *Zelmane* imputing it, to one of her continuall mishaps, thus to have met with this Lady, with a full weary countenance; Without doubt Madame, said she, where the desire is such, as may be obtained, and the partie well deserving as your selfe, it must be a great excuse that may well cullour a deniall; but when the first motion carries with it a direct impossibilitie, then must the only answere be, comfort without helpe, and sorrow to both parties; to you not obtaining to me not able to graunt. O sayd *Gynecia*, how good leisure you have to frame these scornefull answeres? Is *Ginecia* thus to be despised? am I so vile a worme in your sight? no no, trust to it hard harted tigre, I will not be the only Actor of this Tragedy: since I must fall, I will presse downe some others with my ruines: since I must burne, my spitefull neighbors shall feele of my fire. Doest thou not perceave that my diligent eyes have pierced through the clowdie maske of thy desguisemēt? Have I not told thee, ô foole, (if I were not much more foole) that I know thou wouldest abuse us with thy outward shew? Wilt thou still attend the rage of love in a womans hart? the girle thy well chosen mistresse, perchaunce shall defend thee, when *Basilius* shal know how thou hast sotted his minde with falsehood, and falsely sought the dishonour of his house. Beleeve it, beleeve it unkind creature, I will end my miseries with a notable example of revenge, and that accursed cradle of mine shal feele the smart of my wound, thou of thy tiranny, and lastly (I confesse) my selfe of mine owne work. *Zelmane* that had long before doubted her selfe to be discovered by her, and now plainely finding it, was as the proverbe saith, like them that hold the wolfe by the eares, bitten while they hold, and slaine if they loose. If she held her off in these wonted termes, she sawe rage would make her love worke the effects of hate; to graunt unto her, her hart was so bounde upon *Philoclea*, it had ben worse then a thousand deaths. Yet found she it was necessarie for her, to come to a resolution, for *Gynecias* sore could bide no leasure, and once discovered, besides the dāger of *Philoclea*, her desires should be for ever utterly stopped. She remēbred withall the words of *Basilius*, how apt he was to leave this life, & returne to his court, a great barre to her hopes. Lastly she considered *Dorus* enterprise, might bring some strange alteration of this their well liked fellowship. So that encompassed with these instant difficulties, she bent her spirits to thinke of a remedie, which might at once both save her from them, and serve her to the accomplishment of her only pursuite. Lastly, she determined thus, that there was no way but to yeeld to the violence of their desires, since striving did the more chafe them. And that following their owne current, at length of it selfe it would bring her to the other side of her burning desires.

Now in the meane while the divided *Dorus*, long divided betwene love and frendship, and now for his love divided frō his frend, though indeed without prejudice of frendships loyaltie, which doth never barre the minde from his free satisfaction: yet still a cruell judge over himselfe, thought he was somewayes faultie, and applied his minde how to amend it, with a speedie and behovefull returne. But then was his first studie, how to get away, whereto already he had *Pamelas* consent, confirmed and concluded under the name of *Mopsa* in her owne presence, *Dorus* taking this way, that whatsoever he would have of *Pamela* he would aske her, whether in such a case it were not best for *Mopsa* so to behave her selfe, in that sort making *Mopsas* envie, an instrument of that she did envie. So having passed over, his first and most feared difficultie, he busied his spirites how to come to the harvest of his desires, whereof he had so faire a shew. And thereunto (having gotten leave for some dayes of his maister *Damætas*, who now accompted him as his sonne in lawe,) he romed round about the desart, to finde some unknowne way, that might bring him to the next Sea port, as much as might be out of all course of other passengers: which all very well succeeding him, and he having hired a Bark for his lives traffick, and provided horsses to carrie her thither, returned homeward, now come to the last point of his care, how to goe beyond the loathsome watchfulnes of these three uncomely companions, and therin did wisely consider, how they were to be taken with whom he had to deale, remembring that in the particularities of every bodies mind & fortune, there are particuler advantages, by which they are to be held. The muddy mind of *Damætas*, he found most easily sturred with covetousnes. The curst mischevous hart of *Miso*, most apt to be tickled with jealousie, as whose rotten brain could think wel of no body. But yong mistres *Mopsa*, who could open her eys upon nothing, that did not all to bewonder her, he thought curiositie the fittest bait for her. And first for *Damætas*, *Dorus* having imploid a whole days work, about a tenne mile off from the lodge (quite contrary way to that he ment to take with *Pamela*) in digging & opening the ground, under an auncient oke that stood there, in such sort as might longest hold *Damætas* greedy hopes, in some shewe of comfort, he came to his master, with a countenance mixt betwixt cherefulnes and haste, and taking him by the right hand, as if he had a great matter of secrecie to reveale unto him: Master said he, I did never thinke that the gods had appointed my mind freely brought up, to have so longing a desire to serve you, but that they minded therby to bring some extraordinary frute to one so beloved of them, as your honesty makes me think you are. This bindes me even in conscience, to disclose that which I perswade my self is alotted unto you, that your fortune may be of equal ballance with your deserts. He said no further, because he would let *Damætas* play upon the bit a while, who not understanding what his words entended, yet well finding, they caried no evil news, was so much the more desirous to know the matter, as he had free scope to imagin what measure of good hap himselfe would. Therefore putting off his cap to him, which he had never done before, & assuring him he should have *Mopsa*, though she had bene all made of cloath of gold, he besought *Dorus* not to hold him long in hope, for that he found it a thing his hart was not able to beare. Maister, answered *Dorus*, you have so satisfied me, with promising me the uttermost of my desired blisse, that if my duty bound me not, I were in it sufficiently rewarded. To you therefore shall my good hap be converted, and the fruite of all my labor dedicated. Therewith he told him, how under an auncient oke, (the place he made him easily understand, by sufficient marks he gave unto him) he had found digging but a little depth, scatteringly lying a great number of rich Medailles, and that percing further into the ground, he had met with a great stone, which by the hollow sound it yeelded, seemed to be the cover of some greater vaut, and upon it a boxe of Cypres, with the name of the valiant *Aristomenes* graven upon it: and that within the box, he found certaine verses, which signified that some depth againe under that all his treasures lay hidden, what time for the discord fell out in *Arcadia* he lived banished. Therwith he gave *Damætas* certaine Medailles of gold he had long kept about him, and asked him because it was a thing much to be kept secret, and a matter one man in twenty houres might easily performe, whether he would have him go and seeke the bottome of it, which he had refrained to do till he knew his mind, promising he would faithfully bring him what he found, or else that he himselfe would do it, and be the first beholder of that comfortable spectacle. No man need doubt which part *Damætas* would choose, whose fancie had alredy devoured all this great riches, and even now began to grudge at a partenor, before he saw his owne share. Therefore taking a strong Jade, loaden with spades and mattocks, which he ment to bring back otherwise laden, he went in all speed thetherward, taking leave of no body, only desiring *Dorus* he would looke wel to the Princes *Pamela.* Promising him mountaines of his owne labor, which neverthelesse he little ment to performe, like a foole not considering, that no man is to be moved with part, that neglects the whole. Thus away went *Damætas*, having alreadie made an image in his fancie, what Pallaces he would build, how sumptuously he would fare, and among all other things imagined what money to employ in making coffers to keepe his money, his tenne mile seemed twise so many leagues, and yet contrarie to the nature of it, though it seemed long, it was not wearysome. Many times he curssed his horses want of consideration, that in so important a matter would make no greater speede: many times he wished himself the back of an Asse, to help to carrie away the new sought riches, (an unfortunate wisher, for if he had aswell wished the head, it had bene graunted him.) At length being come to the tree, which he hoped should beare so golden Akornes, downe went all his instruments, and forthwith to the renting up of the hurtlesse earth, where by and by he was caught with the lime of a fewe promised Medailles, which was so perfect a pawne unto him of his further expectation, that he deemed a great number of howers well employed in groping further into it, which with loggs and great stones was made as cumbersome as might be, till at length with sweatie browes he came to the great stone. A stone, God knowes, full unlike to the cover of a Monument, but yet there was the Cipres box with *Aristomenes* graven upon it, and these verses written in it.

A Banisht man, long bard from his desire
    By inward letts, of them his state possest,
Hid heere his hopes, by which he might aspire
To have his harmes with wisdomes helpe redrest.

Seeke then and see, what man esteemeth best,
All is but this, this is our labours hire,

THE COUNTESSE OF PEMBROKES

Of this we live, in this wee finde our rest,
Who hold this fast no greater wealth require.
Looke further then, so shalt thou finde at least,
A baite most fit, for hungrie minded guest.

He opened the box, and to his great comfort read them, and
with fresh courage went about to lift up that stone. But in the
meane time, ere *Damætas* was halfe a mile gone to the treasure
warde, *Dorus* came to *Miso*, whom he found sitting in the
chimneys ende, babling to her selfe, and shewing me all her
gestures that she was loathsomly weary of the worlde, not for
any hope of a better life, but finding no one, good neyther in
minde nor body, where-out she might nourish a quiet thought,
having long since hated each thing else, began now to hate her
selfe. Before this sweete humour'd Dame, *Dorus* set himselfe,
and framed towardes her, such a smiling countenance, as might
seeme to be mixt betwene a tickled mirth, and a forced pittie.
Miso, to whome cheerefulnes in others, was ever a sauce of
envie in her selfe, tooke quicklie marke of his behaviour, and
with a looke full of foreworne spite: Now the Devill, sayd she,
take these villaynes, that can never leave grenning, because I am
not so fayre as mistresse *Mopsa*, to see how this skipjacke lookes
at me. *Dorus* that had the occasion he desired, Truly mistresse
aunswered he, my smiling is not at you, but at them that are
from you, and in deede I must needes a little accord my countenance with other sport. And therewithall tooke her in his
armes, and rocking her too and fro, In faith mistresse, sayd he,
it is high time for you, to bid us good night for ever, since others
can possesse your place in your owne time. *Miso* that was never
voide of mallice enough to suspect the uttermost evill, to satisfye
a further shrewdnes, tooke on a present mildnes, and gentlie desired him, to tell her what he meant, for, said she, I am like
enough to be knavishly dealt with, by that churle my husband.
Dorus fell off from the matter againe, as if he had meant no such
thing, till by much refusing her intreatie, and vehemently stirring
up her desire to knowe, he had strengthned a credit in her to
that he should saye. And then with a formall countenance, as
if the conscience of the case had touched himselfe: Mistresse,
sayd he, I am much perplexed in my owne determination, for
my thoughts do ever will me to do honestlie, but my judgement

fayles me what is honest: betwixt the generall rule, that entrusted secreacies are holilie to be observed, and the particuler exception that the dishonest secreacies are to be revealed : especially there, whereby revealing they may eyther be prevented, or at least amended. Yet in this ballance, your judgement wayes me downe, because I have confidence in it, that you will use what you know moderately, and rather take such faults as an advantage to your owne good desert, then by your bitter using it, be contented to be revenged on others with your own harmes. So it is mistresse said he, that yesterday driving my sheepe up to the stately hill, which lifts his head over the faire Citie of *Mantinea*, I hapned upon the side of it, in a little falling of the ground which was a rampier against the Sunnes rage, to perceave a yong maid, truly of the finest stamp of beawtie, & that which made her bewtie the more admirable, there was at all no arte added to the helping of it. For her apparell was but such as Shepheards daughters are wont to weare : and as for her haire, it hoong downe at the free libertie of his goodly length, but that sometimes falling before the cleare starres of her sight, she was forced to put it behinde her eares, and so open againe the treasure of her perfections, which that for a while had in part hidden. In her lap there lay a Shepheard, so wrapped up in that well liked place, that I could discerne no piece of his face, but as mine eyes were attent in that, her Angellike voice strake mine eares with this song:

M*Y true love hath my hart, and I have his,*
By just exchange, one for the other giv'ne.
I holde his deare, and myne he cannot misse :
There never was a better bargaine driv'ne.

His hart in me, keepes me and him in one,
My hart in him, his thoughtes and senses guides :
He loves my hart, for once it was his owne :
I cherish his, because in me it bides.

His hart his wound receaved from my sight :
My hart was wounded, with his wounded hart,
For as from me, on him his hurt did light,
So still me thought in me his hurt did smart :
    Both equall hurt, in this change sought our blisse :
    My true love hath my hart and I have his.

17

But as if the Shepheard that lay before her, had bene organes, which were only to be blowen by her breath, she had no sooner ended with the joyning her sweete lips together, but that he recorded to her musick this rurall poesie:

O *Words which fall like sommer deaw on me,*
O breath more sweete, then is the growing beane,
O toong in which, all honyed likoures bee,
O voice that doth, the Thrush in shrilnes staine,
  Do you say still, this is her promise due,
  That she is myne, as I to her am true.

Gay haire more gaie then straw when harvest lyes,
Lips red and plum, as cherries ruddy side,
Eyes faire and great, like faire great oxes eyes,
O brest in which two white sheepe swell in pride:
  Joyne you with me, to seale this promise due,
  That she be myne, as I to her am true.

But thou white skinne, as white as cruddes well prest,
So smooth as sleekestone-like, it smoothes each parte,
And thou deare flesh, as soft as wooll new drest,
And yet as hard, as brawne made hard by arte:
  First fower but say, next fowr their saying seale,
  But you must pay, the gage of promist weale.

And with the conclusion of his song, he embraced her about the knees, O sweet *Charita* said he, when shall I enjoy the rest of my toyling thoughts? And when shall your blisfull promise now due, be verified with just performance? with that I drew neerer to them, and saw (for now he had lifted up his face to glasse himselfe in her faire eyes) that it was my master *Damætas*, but here *Miso* interrupted his tale, with rayling at *Damætas*, with all those exquisite termes, which I was never good skolde inough to imagine. But *Dorus*, as if he had ben much offended with her impaciěce, would proceed no further till she had vowed more stillnes. For said he, if the first drumme thus chafe you, what will you be when it commes to the blowes? Then he told her, how after many familiar entertainments betwixt them, *Damætas*, laying before her, his great credit with the Duke, and withall giving her very faire presents, with promise of much more, had in the ende concluded together to meete as that night at *Mantinea*, in the *Oudemian* streete, at *Charitas* uncles house, about tenne of the clocke. After which bargaine *Damætas* had spied *Dorus*, and calling him to him, had with great bravery told him all his good happe, willing him in any case to returne to the olde witch *Miso* (for so indeede mistresse of livelinesse, and not of ill will he termed you) and to make some honest excuse of his absence, for sayde he, kissing *Charita*, if thou didst know what a life I lead with that drivell, it would make thee even of pittie, receave me into thy only comfort. Now Mistresse sayde he, exercise your discretion, which if I were well assured of, I would wish you to goe your selfe to *Mantinea*, and (lying secrete in some one of youre gossypps houses, till the time appoynted come) so may you finde them together, and using mercie, reforme my Maister from his evill wayes. There had nothing more en-raged *Miso*, then the prayses *Dorus* gave to *Charitas* bewtie, which made her jealousie swell the more, with the poyson of envye. And that being increased with the presents she heard *Damætas* had given her (which all seemed torne out of her bowells) her hollow eyes, yeelded such wretched lookes, as one might well thinke *Pluto* at that time, might have had her soule very good cheape. But when the fire of spite had fully caught hold of all her inward partes, then whosoever would have seene the picture of *Alecto*, or with what maner of countenance *Medea* kild her owne children, needed but take *Miso* for the full satis-faction of that point of his knowledge. She that could before scarce go, but supported by crutches, now flew about the house, borne up with the wings of Anger, there was no one sort of mortall revenge, that had ever come to her eares, but presented it selfe nowe to her gentle minde. At length with few words, for her words were choakt up with the rising of her revengefull hart, she ran downe, and with her own hands sadled a mare of hers, a mare that 7. yeare before had not bene acquainted with a sadle, & so to *Mantinea* she went, casting with her selfe, how she might couple shame with the punishmẽt of her accursed husband: but the person is not worthie in whose passion I should too long stand. Therefore now must I tell you that Mistresse *Mopsa* (who was the last party *Dorus* was to practise his cunning withal) was at the parting of her parents, attending upon the Princes *Pamela*, whom because she found to be placed in her fathers house, she knew it was for suspicion the Duke had of

her. This made *Mopsa* with a right base nature (which joyes to
see anie hard hap happen to them, they deeme happie) grow
prowd over her, & use great ostentation of her own diligēce, in
prying curiously into each thing that *Pamela* did. Neither is
there any thing sooner overthrows a weak hart, then opiniō of
authority, like too strong a liquor for so feebl a glasse, which
joined it self to the humor of envying *Pamelas* beauty, so far,
that oft she would say to her self, if she had ben borne a Duchesse
as well as *Pamela*, her perfections then should have beene as well
seene as *Pamelas*, with this manner of woman, and placed in
these termes, had *Dorus* to play his last parte, which hee would
quickly have dispatched in tying her up in such a maner, that
she should litle have hindred his enterprise. But that the vertuous
Pamela, (whē she saw him so minded,) by countenaunce absolutlie
forbad it, resolutely determining, she would not leave behinde
her any token of wrong since the wrong done to her selfe was
the best excuse of her escape. So that *Dorus* was compelled to
take her in the maner hee first thought of, and accordingly
Pamela sitting musing at the strange attempt shee had condiscended unto, and *Mopsa* harde by her, (looking in a glasse
with very partiall eyes) *Dorus* put himselfe between them, and
casting up his face to the top of the house, shrugging all over
his bodie, and stamping somtimes upon the ground, gave *Mopsa*
occasion (who was as busie as a Bee to know any thing) to aske
her lover *Dorus* what ayled him, that made him use so strange
a behaviour, he, as if his spirits had beene ravished with some
supernaturall contemplation, stoode still muett, somtimes rubbing
his forehead, sometime starting in him selfe, that hee set *Mopsa*
in such an itche of inquirie, that she would have offred her
maydenhead, rather then be longe kept from it. *Dorus* not yet
aunswearing to the purpose, still keeping his amazement. O
Hercules, saide he, resolve me in this doubt. A tree to graunt
ones wishes? Is this the cause of the Kinges solitarie life? Which
parte shall I take? Happie in either, unhappie because I cannot
know which were my best happ. These doubtful selfe-speches,
made *Mopsa* yet in a further longing of knowing the matter, so
that the prettie pigge, laying her sweete burden about his neck,
my *Dorus*, saide she, tell mee these words, or els I know not
what will befal mee, honny *Dorus* tell them me. *Dorus* having
stretched her minde upon a right laste, extremely loved *Mopsa*,

20

saide hee, the matters be so great, as my harte failes me in the telling them, but since you holde the greatest seate in it, it is reason your desire should adde life unto it. Ther with he told her a farre fet tale how that many millions of yeares before, *Jupiter* fallen out with *Apollo* had throwne him out of heaven, taking from him the priveledge of a God. So that poore *Apollo* was faine to leade a verie miserable life, unacquainted to worke and never used to begge, that in this order having in time learned to bee *Admetus* heardman, he had upon occasion of fetching a certaine breed of beastes out of *Arcadia*, come to that verie deserte, where wearied with travaile, and resting himselfe in the boughes of a pleasaunt Ashe tree, stoode little of from the lodge, hee had with pittifull complaintes gotten his father *Jupiters* pardon, and so from that tree was receaved againe to his golden spheare. But having that right nature of a God, never to be ungratefull, to *Admetus* hee had graunted a double life, and because that tree was the chappel of his prosperous prayers, he had given it this equality, that whatsoever of such estate, and in such maner as he then was, sate downe in that tree, they should obtaine whatsoever they wished. This *Basilius* having understoode by the oracle, was the onely cause which had made him trie, whether framing himselfe to the state of an heardman, he might have the previledge of wishing onely graunted to that degree, but that having often in vaine attempted it, because indeede hee was not such, he had now opened the secret to *Dametas*, making him sweare hee should wish according to his direction. But because said *Dorus*, *Apollo* was at that time with extreme griefe muffled, round aboute his face, with a skarlet cloake, *Admetus* had given him, and because they that must wish must be muffled in like sorte, and with like stuffe, my master *Dametas* is gone I know not whither to provide him a skarlet cloake, and to morrow doth appointe to returne with it, my Mistresse I cannot tell how, having gotten some inckling of it, is trudged to *Mantinea* to get her selfe a cloake before him : because she woulde have the first wishe. My master at his parting of great trust tould me this secret, commaunding me to see no bodie should clime that tree. But now my *Mopsa*, said he, I have here the like cloake of mine owne and am not so verie a foole as though I keep his commaundement in others to barre my selfe, I rest onely extreemely perplexed, because having nothing in the worlde I wish for, but the enjoying you & your favour, I think it a much pleasanter conquest to come to it by your owne consent, then to have it by such a charming force, as this is. Now therefore choose since have you I will, in what sorte I shall have you. But never child was so desirous of a gay puppet, as *Mopsa* was to be in the tree, and therefore without squeamishnes, promising all he woulde, shee conjured him by all her precious Loves, that she might have the first possession of the wishing tree, assuring him that for the enjoying her he should never neede to clime farre. *Dorus* to whom time was precious, made no great ceremonies with her, but helping her up to the top of the tree, from whence likewise she could ill come downe without helpe, he muffled her round about the face, so truely that she her selfe could not undoe it. And so he tolde her the manner was, she should hold her mind in continuall devotion to *Apollo*, without making at al any noyse, till at the farthest within twelve howers space, she should heare a voice call her by name three times, & that till the thirde time shee must in no wise aunswere ; & then you shall not need to doubt your cŏming down, for at that time said he, be sure to wish wisely, & in what shape soever he come unto you speake boldly unto him, and your wish shall have as certaine effecte, as I have a desire to enjoy your sweet Loves, in this plight did hee leave *Mopsa*, resolved in her hart, to be the greatest Lady of the world, & never after to feede of worse then furmentie. Thus *Dorus* having delivered his hands of his three tormentors, took speedely the benefit of his devise, and mounting the gracious *Pamela* upon a faire horse he had provided for her he thrust himselfe forthwith into the wildest part of the desarte, where he had left markes to guide him, frŏ place to place to the next sea porte, disguising her very fitly with scarfes although he rested assured, he should meet that way with no body, till he came to his barck, into which hee ment to enter by night. But *Pamela* who al this while, transported with desire & troubled with feare had never free scope of judgemēt to look with perfect consideratiŏ into her own enterprise but evē by the lawes of love, had bequeathed the care of her self upŏ him to whom she had gevē her self. Now that the pang of desire with evident hope was quieted, & most part of the feare passed, reason began to renew his shining in her hart, & make her see her self in her selfe ; & weigh with what wings she flew out of her native contry ; and upon what ground she builte so strange a determinaciõ. But love fortified with her lovers presence kept still his own in her hart. So that as they ridde together with her hand upon her faithfull servants shoulder, sodainly casting her bashfull eies to the ground, and yet bending her self towardes him, (like the clyent that committes the cause of all his worth to a well trusted advocate,) frõ a milde spirit saide unto him these sweetely delivered wordes : Prince *Musidorus*, (for so my assured hope is I may justlie call you, since with no other my harte woulde ever have yeelded to goe ; And if so I doe not rightlie tearme you, all other wordes are as bootelesse, as my deede miserable and I as unfortunate, as you wicked) my Prince *Musidorus* I saye nowe that the vehement shewes of your faithfull Love towardes mee, have brought my minde to answeare it, in so due a proportion, that contrarie to all generall rules of reason, I have layde in you, my estate, my life, my honour : it is your part to double your former care, and make me see your vertue no lesse in preserving then in obtaining : and your faith to bee a faith asmuch in freedome, as bondage. Tender now your owne workemanshippe ; and so governe your love towardes me as I may still remaine worthie to bee loved. Your promise you Remember, which here by the eternall givers of vertue, I conjure you to observe, let me be your owne as I am, but by no unjust conquest ; let not our joyes which ought ever to last, bee stayned in our own consciences, let no shadow of repentaunce steale into the sweet consideration of our mutuall happines. I have yeelded to bee your wife, staye then till the time that I may rightly bee so; let no other defiled name burden my harte. What shoulde I more saye ? If I have chosen well, all doubte is past, since your acounts onely must determine, whether I have done vertuously or shamefully in following you. *Musidorus* that had more aboundaunce of joye in his hart, then *Ulisses* had what time with his owne industrie he stale the fatall *Palladium*, imagined to bee the only relicke of *Troies* safetie, taking *Pamelas* hand, and many times kissing it. What I am said he, the Gods I hope will shortly make your owne eyes Judges ; and of my minde towards you, the meane time shalbe my pledge unto you your contentment is dearer to me then mine owne, & therfore doubt not of his mind, whose thoughts are so thralled unto you, as you are to bend or slack them as it shall seeme best unto you.

You do wrong to your selfe, to make any doubte that a base estate could ever undertake so high an enterprise ; or a spotted minde bee hable to beholde your vertues. Thus much onely I must confesse, I can never doe, to make the worlde see you have chosen worthily, since all the world is not worthy of you. In such delightfull discourses, kept they on their Journye, mayntaining their hartes in that right harmonie of affection, which doth enterchangeably deliver each to other the secret workinges of their soules, till with the unused travaile, the Princesse being weary, they lighted downe in a faire thyck wood, which did entise them with the pleasantnes of it to take their rest there. It was all of Pine trees, whose brodeheades meeting togither, yeelded a perfit shade to the ground, where their bodies gave a spacious and pleasant roome to walke in, they were sett in so perfet an order, that everie waye the eye being full, yet no way was stopped. And even in the middest of them, were there many sweete springes, which did loose themselves upon the face of the earth. Here *Musidorus* drew out such provision of fruites, & other cates, as he had brought for that dayes repaste, and layde it downe upon the faire Carpet of the greene grasse. But *Pamela* had much more pleasure to walke under those trees, making in their barkes prettie knottes, which tyed togither the names of *Musidorus* and *Pamela*, sometimes entermixedly changing there, to *Pammedorus* and *Musimela*, with twentie other flowers of her traviling fancies, which had bounde them selves to a greater restrainte, then they could without much paine well endure, and to one tree more beholdinge to her, then the rest she entrusted the treasure of her thoughtes in these verses:

D O not disdaine, ô streight up raised Pine
That wounding thee, my thoughtes in thee I grave :
Since that my thoughtes, as streight as streightnes thine
No smaller wound, alas ! farr deeper have.

Deeper engrav'd, which salve nor time can save,
Giv'ne to my harte, by my fore wounded eyne :
Thus cruell to my selfe how canst thou crave
My inward hurte should spare thy outward rine ?

Yet still faire tree, lifte up thy stately line,
Live long, and long witnesse my chosen smarte,
Which barde desires, (barde by my selfe) imparte

And in this growing barke growe verses myne.
My harte my worde, my worde hath giv'ne my harte.
The giver giv'n from gifte shall never parte.

Upon a roote of the tree, that the earth had lefte something
barer then the rest, she wrat this couplet :

S*Weete roote say thou, the roote of my desire*
Was vertue cladde in constant loves attire.

Musidorus, seing her fancies drawne up to such pleasaunt
contemplations, accompanied her in them, and made the trees
aswell beare the badges of his passions. As this songe engraved
in them did testifie :

Y*Ou goodly pines, which still with brave assent*
In natures pride your heads to heav'nwarde heave,
Though you besides such graces earth hath lent,
Of some late grace a greater grace receave,

By her who was (O blessed you) content,
With her faire hande, your tender barkes to cleave,
And so by you (O blessed you) hath sent,
Such pearcing wordes as no thoughts els conceave :

Yet yeeld your graunt, a baser hand may leave
His thoughtes in you, where so sweete thoughtes were spent,
For how would you the mistresse thoughts bereave
Of waiting thoughts all to her service ment ?

Nay higher thoughtes (though thralled thoughtes) I call
My thoughtes then hers, who first your ryne did rente.
Then hers, to whom my thoughts a lonely thrall
Rysing from lowe, are to the highest bente;
Where hers, whom worth makes highest over all
Comming from her, cannot but downewarde fall.

While *Pamela* sitting her downe under one of them, and
making a posie of the fayer undergrowinge flowers, filled
Musidorus eares with the heavenly sounde of her musicke,
which before he had never heard, so that it seemed unto him a
new assaulte given to the castle of his hart, alredye conquered,
which to signifie and with all replie to her sweete noates, hee
sang in a kinde of still, but ravishing tune a fewe verses, her
song was this, and his Replie followes :

Pamela.

Ike divers flowers, whose divers beauties serve
To decke the earth with his well-colourde weede,
Though each of them, his private forme preserve,
Yet joyning formes one sight of beautie breede.

Right so my thoughts, where on my hart I feede :
Right so my inwarde partes, and outward glasse,
Though each possesse a divers working kinde,
Yet all well knit to one faire end do passe :
That he to whome, these sondrie giftes I binde
All what I am, still one, his owne, doe finde.

Musidorus.

All what you are still one, his owne to finde,
You that are borne to be the worldes eye,
What were it els, but to make each thing blinde ?
And to the sunne with waxen winges to flie ?

No no, such force with my small force to trye
Is not my skill, or reach of mortall minde.
Call me but yours, my title is most hye :
Holde me most yours, then my longe suite is signde.

You none can clayme but you your selfe aright,
For you do passe your selfe, in vertues might.
So both are yours : I, bound with gaged harte :
You onely yours, too farr beyond desarte.

In this vertuous wantonnes, suffering their mindes to descend to each tender enjoying their united thoughts, *Pamela*, having tasted of the fruites, and growinge extreame sleepie, having ben long kept from it, with the perplexitie of her dangerous attempte, laying her head in his lappe, was invited by him to sleepe with these softly uttered verses:

Ocke up, faire liddes, the treasure of my harte :
Preserve those beames, this ages onely lighte :
To her sweete sence, sweete sleepe some ease imparte,
Her sence too weake to beare her spirits mighte.

And while ô sleepe thou closest up her sight,
(Her sight where love did forge his fayrest darte)
ô harbour all her partes in easefull plighte :
Let no strange dreme make her fayre body starte.

But yet ô dreame, if thou wilt not departe
In this rare subject from the common right:
But wilt thy selfe in such a seate delighte,

Then take my shape, and play a lovers parte:
Kisse her from me, and say unto her spirite,
Till her eyes shine, I live in darkest night.

The sweete *Pamela*, was brought into a sweete sleepe with this songe which gave *Musidorus* opportunity at leasure to beholde her excellent beauties. He thought her faire forehead was a fielde where all his fancies fought; and every haire of her heade semed a strong chain that tied him. Her fairer liddes then hiding her fairer eyes, seemed unto him sweete boxes of mother of pearle, riche in themselves, but contaning in them farre richer Jewells. Her cheekes with their coullour most delicately mixed would have entertained his eyes somewhile, but that the roses of her lippes (whose separating was wont to bee accompanied with most wise speeches) nowe by force drewe his sight to marke how preatily they lay one over the other, uniting their devided beauties: and thorough them the eye of his fancy delivered to his memorie the lying (as in ambush) under her lippes of those armed rankes, all armed in most pure white, and keeping the most precise order of military discipline. And lest this beautie might seeme the picture of some excellent artificer, fourth there stale a softe breath, carying good testimony of her inward sweetnesse: and so stealingly it came out, as it seemed loath to leave his contentfull mansion, but that it hoped to bee drawne in againe to that well cloased paradise, which did so tyrannize over *Musidorus* affectes that hee was compelled to put his face as lowe to hers, as hee coulde, sucking the breath with such joye, that he did determine in himselfe, there had ben no life to a *Camæleons* if he might be suffered to enjoye that foode. But long hee was not suffered being within a while interrupted by the comming of a company of clownish vilaines, armed with divers sortes of weapons, and for the rest both in face and apparell so forewasted that they seemed to beare a great conformity with the savages; who miserable in themselves, taught to encrease their mischieves in other bodies harmes, came with such cries as they both awaked *Pamela*, and made *Musidorus* turne unto them full of a most violent rage, with the looke of a shee *Tigree*, when her whelpes are stolne away.

THE COUNTESSE OF PEMBROKES

But *Zelmane* whome I left in the Cave hardly bestead, having both great wittes and sturring passions to deale with, makes me lend her my penne a while to see with what dexteritie she could put by her daungers. For having in one instant both to resist rage and goe beyond wisedome, being to deale with a Ladie that had her witts awake in every thing, but in helping her owne hurte, she saw now no other remedy in her case, but to qualifie her rage with hope, and to satisfie her witt with plainesse. Yet lest to abrupt falling into it, shoulde yeelde too great advantage unto her, shee thought good to come to it by degrees with this kind of insinuation. Your wise, but very darke speeches, most excellent Lady, are woven up in so intricate a maner, as I know not how to proportiõ mine answere unto thẽ: so are your prayers mixte with threates, and so is the shew of your love hidden with the name of revenge, the natural effect of mortal hatred. You seeme displeased with the opinion you have of my disguising, and yet if bee not disguised, you must needes be much more displeased. Hope then (the only succour of perplexed mindes) being quite cut off, you desire my affection, and yet you your selfe thinke my affection already bestowed. You pretend crueltie, before you have the subjection, and are jealous of keeping that, which as yet you have not gotten. And that which is strangest in your jealousie, is both the unjustice of it, in being loath that should come to your daughter, which you deeme good, and the vaynnesse, since you two are in so divers respects, that there is no necessitie one of you should fall to be a barre to the other. For neyther (if I be such as you fancie) can I mary you, which must needes be the only ende I can aspire to in her: neither neede the maryeng of her keepe me from a gratefull consideracion how much you honor me in the love you vouchsafe to beare me. *Gynæcia*, to whome the fearefull agonies she still lived in made any small reprivall sweete, did quickly finde her words falling to a better way of comfort, and therefore with a minde readie to shewe nothing could make it rebellious against *Zelmane*, but to extreme tyrannie, she thus sayd: Alas too much beloved *Zelmane*, the thoughts are but out-flowings of the minde, and the tongue is but a servant of the thoughtes, therefore marvaile not that my words suffer contrarieties, since my minde doth hourely suffer in it selfe whole armyes of mortall adversaries. But, alas, if I had the use of mine owne reason, then should I not neede, for want of it, to finde my selfe

28

in this desperate mischiefe, but because my reason is vanished, so have I likewise no power to correct my unreasonablenes. Do you therefore accept the protection of my minde, which hath no other resting place, and drive it not, by being unregarded to put it selfe into unknowne extremities. I desire but to have my affection answered, and to have a right reflection of my love in you. That graunted, assure your selfe mine owne love will easily teach me to seeke your contentment: and make me thinke my daughter a very meane price to keepe still in mine eyes the foode of my spirits. But take heede that contempt drive me not into despaire, the most violent cause of that miserable effect. *Zelmane* that alreadie sawe some fruite of her last determined fancie (so farre as came to a mollifyeng of *Gynecias* rage) seeing no other way to satisfye suspicion, which was held open with the continuall prickes of love, resolved now with plainnesse to winne trust, which trust she might after deceyve with a greater subtletie. Therefore looking upon her with a more relenting grace, then ever she had done before, pretending a great bashfulnes before she could come to confesse such a fault, she thus sayde unto her: Most worthye Ladye, I did never thinke, till now, that pittie of another coulde make me betray my selfe, nor that the sounde of wordes could overthrow any wise bodies determinacion. But your words (I thinke) have charmed me, and your grace bewitched me. Your compassion makes me open my hart to you, and leave unharboured mine owne thoughts. For proofe of it, I will disclose my greatest secreate, which well you might suspect, but never knowe, and so have your wandring hope in a more painefull wildernesse, being neither way able to be lodged in a perfect resolucion. I will, I say, unwrappe my hidden estate, and after make you judge of it, perchance director. The truth is, I am a man: nay, I will say further to you, I am borne a Prince. And to make up youre minde in a through understanding of mee, since I came to this place, I may not denye I have had some sprinkling of I knowe not what good liking to my Lady *Philoclea.* For howe coulde I ever imagine, the heavens woulde have rayned downe so much of your favour upon me? and of that side there was a shewe of possible hope, the most comfortable Counsellor of love. The cause of this my chaunged attyre, was a journey two yeares agoe I made among the *Amazons*, where having sought to trye my unfortunate valure, I met not one in all the Countrey but was too harde for me, till in the ende in the presence of their Queene *Marpesia*, I hoping to prevayle agaynst her, challenged an olde woman of fourescore yeares, to fight on horssebacke to the uttermost with me. Who having overthrowne me, for the saving of my life, made me sweare I should goe like an unarmed *Amazon*, till the comming of my beard did, with the discharge of my oath, deliver me of that bondage. Here *Zelmane* ended, not comming to a full conclusion, because she would see what it wrought in *Gynecias* minde, having in her speech sought to winne a beliefe of her, and, if it might be, by disgrace of her selfe to diminish *Gynecias* affection. For the first it had much prevailed. But *Gynecia* whose ende of loving her, was not her fighting, neyther could her love too deepely grounded receive diminishment; and besides she had seene her selfe, sufficient proofes of *Zelmanes* admirable prowesse. Therefore sleightly passing over that poynt of her fayned dishonor, but taking good hold of the confessing her manly sexe, with the shamefaste looke of that suitor, who having already obtayned much, is yet forced by want to demaunde more, put foorth her sorrowfull suite in these words: The gods, sayd she, rewarde thee for thy vertuouse pittie of my overladen soule, who yet hath receyved some breath of comfort, by finding thy confession to maintayne some possibilitie of my languishing hope. But alas! as they who seeke to enrich themselves by minerall industrie, the first labour is to finde the myne, which to their cheerefull comfort being founde, if after any unlookedfor stop, or casuall impediment keepe them from getting the desired ure, they are so much the more greeved, as the late conceaved hope addes torment to their former wante. So falles it out with mee (happie or happlesse woman as it pleaseth you to ordayne) who am now either to receyve some guerdon of my most wofull labours, or to returne into a more wretched darkenes, having had some glimmering of my blisfull Sunne. O *Zelmane*, tread not upon a soule that lyes under your foote: let not the abasing of my selfe make me more base in your eyes, but judge of me according to that I am and have bene, and let my errors be made excusable by the immortall name of love. With that, under a fayned rage, tearing her clothes, she discovered some partes of her fayre body, which if *Zelmanes* harte had not bene so fully possest as there was no place left for any new guest, no doubt it would have yelded to that gallant assault. But *Zelmane* so much the more arming her determination, as she sawe such force threatened, yet still remembring she must wade betwixt constancie and curtesey, embracing *Gynecia*, and once or twise kissing her, Deare Ladie, sayd she, he were a great enemy to himselfe, that would refuse such an offer, in the purchase of which a mans life were blessedly bestowed. Nay, how can I ever yeeld due recompence, for so excessive a favour? but having nothing to geve you but my selfe, take that: I must confesse a small, but a very free gift what other affection soever I have had, shall geve place to as great perfection, working besides uppon the bonde of gratefulnes. The gods forbid I should be so foolish, as not to see, or so wicked as not to remember, how much my small deserts are overballanced by your unspeakeable goodnes. Nay happye may I well accompt my mishap among the *Amazons*, since that dishonor hath bene so true a path to my greatest honor, and the chaunging of my outward rayment, hath clothed my minde in such inwarde contentacion. Take therefore noble Lady as much comfort to youre harte, as the full commandement of me can yeeld you: wipe your faire eyes, and keepe them for nobler services. And nowe I will presume thus much to saye unto you, that you make of your selfe for my sake, that my joyes of my new obtayned riches may be accomplished in you. But let us leave this place, least you be too long missed, and henceforward quiet your minde from any further care, for I will now (to my too much joye) take the charge upon me, within fewe dayes to worke your satisfaction, and my felicitie. Thus much she sayde, and withall led *Gynecia* out of the Cave, for well she sawe the boyling minde of *Gynecia* did easily apprehende the fitnesse of that lonely place. But in deede this direct promise of a short space, joyned with the cumbersome familiar of womankinde, I meane modestie, stayed so *Gynecias* minde, that she tooke thus much at that present for good payment: remayning with a paynefull joye, and a wearysome kinde of comfort, not unlike to the condemned prisoner, whose minde still running uppon the violent arrivall of his cruell death, heares that his pardon is promised, but not yet signed. In this sort they both issued out of that obscure mansion: *Gynecia* already halfe perswaded in her selfe (ô weakenes of humane conceite) that *Zelmanes* affection was turned towards her. For such alas! we are all, in such a mould are we cast, that with the too much love we beare our selves, beeing first our owne flatterers, wee are easily hooked with our owne flattery, we are easily perswaded of others love.

But *Zelmane* who had now to playe her prize, seeing no waye thinges could long remayne in that state, and now finding her promise had tyed her tryall to a small compasse of tyme, began to throwe her thoughtes into each corner of her invention howe shee might atchieve her lives enterprise : for well shee knewe deceite cannot otherwise be mayntayned but by deceite : and how to deceyve such heedfull eyes, and how to satisfye, and yet not satisfye such hopefull desires, it was no small skill. But both their thoughtes were called from themselves, with the sight of *Basilius*, who then lying downe by his daughter *Philoclea*, uppon the fayre, though naturall, bed of greene-grasse, seeing the sunne what speede hee made, to leave our West to doo his office in the other *Hemisphere*, his inwarde Muses made him in his best musicke, sing this Madrigall.

WHy doost thou haste away
　O Titan *faire the giver of the daie?*
Is it to carry newes
To Westerne wightes, what starres in East appeare?
Or doost thou thinke that heare
Is left a Sunne, whose beames thy place may use?
Yet stay and well peruse,
What be her giftes, that make her equall thee,
Bend all thy light to see
In earthly clothes enclosde a heavenly sparke.
Thy running course cannot such beawties marke :
No, no, thy motions bee
Hastened from us with barre of shadow darke,
Because that thou the author of our sight
Disdainst we see thee staind with others light.

And having ended, Deere *Philoclea*, said he, sing something that may diverte my thoughts from the continuall taske of their ruinous harbour : She obedient to him, and not unwilling to disburden her secret passion, made her sweete voice be heard in these words:

O Stealing time the subject of delaie,
　(Delay, the racke of unrefrain'd desire)
What strange dessein hast thou my hopes to staie
My hopes which do but to mine owne aspire?

Mine owne? ô word on whose sweete sound doth pray
My greedy soule, with gripe of inward fire:
Thy title great, I justlie chalenge may,
Since in such phrase his faith he did attire.

O time, become the chariot of my joyes:
As thou drawest on, so let my blisse draw neere.
Each moment lost, part of my hap destroyes:

Thou art the father of occasion deare:
Joyne with thy sonne, to ease my long annoy's.
In speedie helpe, thanke worthie frends appeare.

Philoclea brake off her Song, as soone as her mother with
Zelmane came neere unto them, rising up with a kindly bashfulnes, being not ignorant of the spite her mother bare her, and
stricken with the sight of that person, whose love made all
those troubles, seeme fayre flowers of her deerest garlond, Nay
rather all those troubles, made the love encrease. For as the
arrivall of enemyes, makes a towne so fortifye it selfe, as ever
after it remaynes stronger, so that a man may say, enemyes were
no small cause to the townes strength: So to a minde once
fixed in a well pleased determinacion, who hopes by annoyance
to overthrowe it, doth but teach it to knit together all his best
grounds, and so perchance of a chaunceable purpose, make an
unchangeable resolucion. But no more did *Philoclea* see, the
wonted signes of *Zelmanes* affection towardes her; she thought
she sawe an other light in her eyes, with a bould and carelesse
looke upon her which was wont to be dazeled with her beawtie;
and the framing of her courtesyes rather ceremonious then
affectionate, and that which worst liked her, was, that it proceeded with such quiet setlednes, as it rather threatned a full
purpose, then any sodayne passion. She founde her behaviour
bent altogether to her mother, and presumed in her selfe, she
discerned the well acquainted face of his fancies now turned to
another subjecte. She sawe her mothers worthines, and too
well knewe her affection. These joyning theyr divers working
powers together in her minde, but yet a prentise in the paynefull
misterye of passions, brought *Philoclea* into a newe travers of her
thoughtes, and made her keepe her carefull looke the more
attentive uppon *Zelmanes* behaviour, who in deede (though with
much payne, and condemning her selfe to commit a sacriledge,

33

against the sweete sainɗe that lived in her inmost Temple) yet strengthening her selfe in it, beeing the surest waye to make *Gynecia* bite off her other baytes, did so quite overrule all wonted showes of love to *Philoclea*, and convert them to *Gynecia*, that the parte she played, did worke in both a full and lively perswasion : to *Gynecia*, such excessive comforte, as the beeing preferred to a rivall doth deliver to swelling desire : But to the delicate *Philoclea*, whose calme thoughtes were unable to nourish any strong debate, it gave so stinging a hurt, that fainting under the force of her inwarde torment, she withdrewe her selfe to the Lodge, and there wearye of supporting her owne burden, cast her selfe uppon her bed, suffering her sorrowe to melte it selfe into abundance of teares, at length closing her eyes, as if eache thing she sawe was a piɗure of her mishap, and turning upon her hurtside, which with vehement panting, did summon her to consider her fortune, she thus bemoned her selfe.

Alas *Philoclea*, is this the price of all thy paynes ? Is this the rewarde of thy given awaye libertye ? Hath too much yeelding bred crueltye ? or can too greate acquaintance, make mee helde for a straunger ? Hath the choosing of a companion, made mee lefte alone ? or doth graunting desire, cause the desire to bee negleɗted ? Alas, despised *Philoclea*, why diddest thou not holde thy thoughtes in theyr simple course, and content thy selfe with the love of thy owne vertue, which would never have betrayed thee ? Ah sillie foole, diddest thou looke for truth in him, that with his owne mouth confest his falsehood ? for playne proceeding in him, that still goes disguised ? They say the falsest men will yet beare outward shewes of a pure minde. But he that even outwardly beares the badge of treacherie, what hells of wickednes must needes in the depth be contayned? But ô wicked mouth of mine, how darest thou thus blaspheme the ornament of the earth, the vessel of all vertue ? O wretch that I am that will anger the gods in dispraysing their most excellent worke ! O no, no, there was no fault but in me, that could ever thinke so high eyes would looke so lowe, or so great perfeɗtions would stayne themselves with my unworthines. Alas ! why could I not see ? I was too weake a band to tye so heavenly a hart : I was not fit to limit the infinite course of his wonderfull destenies. Was it ever like that upon only *Philoclea* his thoughtes should rest ? Ah silly soule that couldst please thy selfe with so impossible an imagination! An universall happines is to flowe from him. How was I so inveagled to hope, I might be the marke of such a minde? He did thee no wrong, ô *Philoclea*, he did thee no wrong, it was thy weakenes to fancie the beames of the sonne should give light to no eyes but thine! And yet, ô Prince *Pirocles*, for whome I may well begin to hate my selfe, but can never leave to love thee, what triumph canst thou make of this conquest? what spoiles wilt thou carry away of this my undeserved overthrow? could thy force finde out no fitter field, then the feeble minde of a poore mayde, who at the first sight did wish thee all happines? shall it be sayde the mirrour of mankinde hath bene employed to destroy a hurtlesse gentlewoman? O *Pirocles*, *Pirocles*, let me yet call thee before the judgement of thine owne vertue, let me be accepted for a plaintiffe in a cause which concernes my life: what need hadst thou to arme thy face, with the enchanting mask of thy painted passions? what need hadst thou to fortefy thy excellēcies with so exquisit a cunning, in making our own arts betray us? what needest thou descend so far frō thy incomparable worthines, as to take on the habit of weake womankinde? Was all this to winne the undefended Castle of a friend, which being wonne, thou wouldest after raze? Could so small a cause allure thee? or did not so unjust a cause stop thee? ô me, what say I more, this is my case, my love hates me, vertue deales wickedly with me, and he does me wrong, whose doing I can never accompt wrong. With that the sweet Lady turning her selfe uppon her weary bed, she happly saw a Lute, upon the belly of which *Gynecia* had written this song, what time *Basilius* imputed her jealous motions to proceed of the doubt she had of his untimely loves. Under which vaile she contented to cover her never ceassing anguish, had made the Lute a monument of her minde, which *Philoclea* had never much marked, till now the feare of a competitour more sturred her, then before the care of a mother. The verses were these.

> M*Y Lute which in thy selfe thy tunes enclose,*
> *Thy mistresse song is now a sorrow's crie,*
> *Her hand benumde with fortunes daylie blows,*
> *Her minde amaz'de can neithers helpe applie.*
> *Weare these my words as mourning weede of woes,*
> *Blacke incke becommes the state wherein I dye.*

And though my mones be not in musicke bound,
Of written greefes, yet be the silent ground.

The world doth yeeld such ill consorted shows,
With circkled course, which no wise stay can trye,
That childish stuffe which knowes not frendes from foes,
(Better despisde) bewondre gasing eye.
Thus noble golde, downe to the bottome goes,
When worthlesse corke, aloft doth floting lye.
Thus in thy selfe, least strings are loudest founde,
And lowest stops doo yeeld the hyest sounde.

Philoclea read them, and throwing downe the Lute, is this the legacie you have bequeathed me, O kinde mother of mine said she? did you bestow the light upon me for this? or did you beare me to be the Author of my buriall? A trim purchase you have made of your owne shame; robbed your daughter to ruyne your selfe! The birds unreasonable, yet use so much reason, as to make nestes for their tender young ones; my cruell Mother turnes me out of mine owne harbour; Alas, plaint bootes not, for my case can receave no helpe, for who should geve mee helpe? shall I flye to my parents? they are my murtherers, shall I goe to him who already being woon and lost, must needs have killed all pittie? Alas I can bring no new intercessions, he knows already what I am is his. Shall I come home againe to my self? ô me contemned wretch; I have given away my self. With that the poore soule beate her breast, as if that had bene guilty of her faults, neither thinking of revenge, nor studying for remedy, but sweete creature gave greefe a free dominion, keeping her chamber a few days after, not needing to faine her self sick, feeling even in her soule the pangs of extreeme paine. But little did *Gynecia* reck that, neyther when she sawe her goe awaye from them, neyther when she after found that sicknes made her hide her faire face: so much had fancye prevailed against nature. But ô you that have ever knowen, how tender to every motion love makes the lovers hart, how he measures all his joyes upon her contentment: & doth with respectful eye hang al his behaviour upõ her eyes, judg I praye you now of *Zelmanes* troubled thoughts, when she saw *Philoclea*, with an amazed kinde of sorrow, carrie awaye her sweete presence, and easely founde, (so happie a conjecture unhappie affection hath)

36

that her demeanour was guiltie of that trespasse. There was never foolish softe harted mother, that forced to beate her childe, did weepe first for his paines, and doing that she was loath to do, did repent before she began, did finde halfe that motion in her weake minde, as *Zelmane* did, now that she was forced by reason, to give an outward blowe to her passions, and for the lending of a small time, to seeke the usury of all her desires. The unkindnes she conceaved, *Philoclea* might conceave, did wound her soule, each teare she doubted she spent, drowned all her comforte. Her sicknes was a death unto her. Often woulde shee speake to the image of *Philoclea*, which lived and ruled in the highest of her inwarde parte, and use vehement othes and protestations unto her ; that nothing shoulde ever falsifie the free chosen vowe she had made. Often woulde she desire her that she would looke wel to *Pyrocles* hart, for as for her shee had no more interest in it to bestow it any way : Alas woulde shee saye onely *Philoclea* hast thou not so much feeling of thine owne force, as to knowe no new conquerer can prevaile against thy conquestes ? Was ever any daseled with the moone, that had used his eyes to the beames of the Sunne ? Is hee carried awaye with a greedie desire of Akornes, that hath had his senses ravished with a garden of most delightfull fruites ? O *Philoclea Philoclea*, be thou but as mercifull a Princesse to my minde, as thou arte a trewe possessour, and I shal have as much cause of gladnes as thou hast no cause of misdoubting. O no no, when a mans owne harte is the gage of his debte, when a mans owne thoughts are willing witnesses to his promise, lastly when a man is the gaylour over himselfe : There is little doubte of breaking credit, and lesse doubt of such an escape. In this combat of *Zelmanes* doubtfull imaginations, in the ende reason well backed with the vehement desire, to bring her matters soone to the desired haven, did over rule the boyling of her inward kindnes, though as I say with such a manifest strife, that both *Basilius* and *Gynecias* well wayting eyes, had marked her muses had laboured in deeper subjecte, then ordinarie, which she likewise perceaving they had perceaved, awaking her selfe out of those thoughtes, and principally caring howe to satisfie *Gynecia* (whose judgement and passion shee stood most in regarde of) bowing her head to her attentive eare, Madame saide she, with practise of my thoughts, I have found out a way by which your contentment shall draw on my happines. *Gynecia* delivering in her face as thankfull a joyfulnes, as her harte coulde holde, saide it was then time to retire themselves to their rest, for what, with riding abroade the day before, and late sitting up for Egloges, their bodyes had dearely purchased that nightes quiet. So went they home to their lodge, *Zelmane* framing of both sides bountifull measures of loving countenaunces to eithers joye, and neythers jealousie; to the especiall comforte of *Basilius*, whose weaker bowels were streight full with the least liquour of hope. So that still holding her by the hand, and sometimes tickling it, he went by her with the most gay conceates that ever had entred his braines, growing now so harted in his resolucion, that hee little respected *Gynecias* presence. But with a lustier note then wonted, clearing his voice, and chearing his spirits, looking still upon *Zelmane* (whome now the moone did beautifie with her shining almost at the full) as if her eyes had beene his songe booke, he did the message of his minde in singing these verses:

> WHen two Sunnes do appeare
>   Some say it doth betoken wonders neare
> As Princes losse or change:
> Two gleaming Sunnes of splendour like I see,
> And seeing feele in me
> Of Princes harte quite lost the ruine strange.
>
> But nowe each where doth range
> With ouglie cloke the darke envious night:
> Who full of guiltie spite,
> Such living beames should her black seate assaile,
> Too weake for them our weaker sighte doth vaile.
>
> No saies faire moone, my lighte
> Shall barr that wrong, and though it not prevaile
> Like to my brothers raise, yet those I sende
> Hurte not the face, which nothing can amende.

And by that time being come to the lodge, and visited the sweete *Philoclea*, with much lesse then naturall care of the parents, and much lesse then wonted kindenes of *Zelmane*, each partie full fraught with diversly working fancies, made their pillowes weake proppes of their over loaden heades. Yet of all other were *Zelmanes* braynes most tormoyled, troubled with love both active and passive; and lastely and especially with care, howe to use her shorte limitted time, to the beste purpose, by some wise and happie diverting her two lovers unwelcome desires. *Zelmane* having had the night her onely councellour in the busie enterprise shee was to undertake, and having all that time mused, and yet not fully resolved, howe shee might joyne prevailing with preventing, was offeded with the daies bould entrie into her chamber, as if he had now by custome growne an assured bringer of evill newes. Which she taking a Citterne to her, did laye to *Auroras* chardge with these wel songe verses.

A̲urora *now thou shewst thy blushing light*
(Which oft to hope laies out a guilefull baite,
That trusts in time, to finde the way aright
To ease those paines, which on desire do waite)

Blush on for shame: that still with thee do light
On pensive soules (in steede of restfull baite)
Care upon care (in steede of doing right)
To over pressed brestes, more greevous waight.

As oh! my selfe, whose woes are never lighte
(Tide to the stake of doubt) strange passions baite,
While thy known course, observing natures right
Sturres me to thinke what dangers lye in waite.
  For mischeefes greate, daye after day doth showe:
  Make me still feare, thy faire appearing showe.

Alas saide she, am not I runne into a strange gulfe, that am faine for love to hurt her I love? And because I detest the others, to please them I detest? O onely *Philoclea*, whose beautie is matched with nothing, but with the unspeakeable beautie of thy fayrest minde, if thou didst see upon what a racke my tormented soule is set, little would you thinke I had any scope now, to leape to any new chaunge, with that, with hastie hands she got her selfe up turning her sight to everie thinge, as if chaunge of objecte might helpe her invention. So went she againe to the cave where forthwith it came into her head, that shoulde bee the fittest place to performe her exploite, of which she had now a kinde of confused conceipte, although she had not set downe in her fancie, the meeting with each particularitie that might fall out. But as the painter doth at the first but showe a rude proportion of the thing he imitates, which after with more curious hande, hee drawes to the representing each lineament. So had her thoughts beating about it continually, receaved into them a ground plot of her devise, although she had not in each parte shapte it according to a full determination. But in this sorte having earelie visited the morninges beautie, in those pleasant desartes, she came to the King and Queene and tolde them, that for the performance of certaine her countrie devotions, which onely were to be exercised in solitarines, shee did desire their leave shee might for a fewe daies, lodge her selfe in the Cave, the fresh sweetnes of which did greately delight her, in that hot countrie; and that for that smal space, they would not otherwise trouble themselves in visiting her, but at such times as she would come to waite upon them, which shoulde bee everie daye at certaine houres, neither should it be long, shee would desire his priviledged absence of them. They whose mindes had alredie taken out that lesson, perfectly to yeelde a willing obedience to all her desires, which consenting countenaunce made her soone see her pleasure was a lawe unto them. Both indeede inwardlie glad of it, *Basilius* hoping that her deviding her selfe from them, might yet give him some freer occasion of comming in secrete unto her, whose favourable face, had lately strengthened his fainting courage. But *Gynecia* of all other most joyous, holding her selfe assured that this was but a prologue to the play she had promised her. Thus both flattering them selves, with diversly grounded hopes, they rang a bell which served to call certaine poore women which ever lay in cabins not far off, to do the houshould services of both lodges, and never came to either but being called for: And commaunded them to carry foorthwith *Zelmanes* bed and furniture of her chamber, into the pleasaunt Cave; and to decke it up as finelie, as it was possible for them, That their soules rest might rest her body to her best pleasing maner, that was with all diligence performed of them, and *Zelmane* alredie in possession of her newe chosen lodging, where she like one of *Vestaes* nunnes, entertaind herselfe for a fewe dayes in all showe of streightnes, yet once a day comming to doe her dutie to the King and Queene, in whom the seldomnes of the sight encreased the more unquiet longing, though somwhat qualified, as her countenaunce was decked to either of them with more comforte then wonted. Especially to *Gynecia* who seing her wholy neglecting her

40

daughter *Philoclea*, had now promisd her selfe a full possession of *Zelmanes* harte, still expecting the fruite, of the happie & hoped for invention. But both she and *Basilius* kept such a continuall watch about the Precincts of the Cave, that either of them was a bar to the other from having any secret, commoning with *Zelmane*. While in the meane time the sweete *Philoclea* forgotten of her father, despised of her mother, and in apparance lefte of *Zelmane* had yeelded up her soule to be a pray to sorow and unkindnes, not with raging conceite of revenge as had passed thorow the stout and wise harte of her mother, but with a kindly meeknes taking upon her the weight of her owne woes, and suffering them to have so full a course as it did exceedinglie weaken the estate of her bodie, aswell for which cause as for that, shee could not see *Zelmane*, without expressing (more then shee woulde) how farr now her love, was imprisoned in extremitie of sorrow, she bound her selfe first to the limits of her own chamber, and after, (griefe breeding sicknes) of her bed. But *Zelmane* having now a full libertie to cast about every way, how to bring her conceaved attempt to a desired successe, was ofte so perplexed with the manifould difficultie of it, that sometimes she would resolve by force to take her away, though it were with the death of her parents, somtimes to go away her self with *Musidorus* and bring both their forces, so to winne her. But lastly even the same day that *Musidorus* by feeding the humor of his three loathsome gardiens, had stolne awaye the Princes *Pamela* (whether it were that love ment to match them everie waie, or that her friendes example had holpen her invention, or that indeede *Zelmane* forbare to practise her devise till she found her friend had passed through his.) The same daye, I saye, shee resolved on a way to rid out of the lodge her two combersome lovers, and in the night to carrie away *Philoclea* : where unto shee was assured her owne love, no lesse then her sisters, woulde easely winne her consent. Hoping that although their abrupt parting had not suffered her to demaund of *Musidorus* which way he ment to direct his jorney) yet either they should by some good fortune, finde him : or if that course fayled, yet they might well recover some towne of the *Helotes*, neere the frontieres of *Arcadia*, who being newly againe up in armes against the Nobilitie, shee knew would bee as glad of her presence, as she of their protection. Therefore having taken order for all

thinges requisite for their going, and first put on a sleight undersute of mans apparel, which before for such purposes she had
provided, she curiously trimmed her self to the beautifiing of
her beauties, that being now at her last triall, she might come
unto it in her bravest armour. And so putting on that kinde of
milde countenaunce, which doth encourage the looker on to hope
for a gentle answere, according to her late receaved maner, she
lefte the pleasant darkenes of her melancholy cave, to goe take
her dinner of the King and Queene, and give unto them both
a pleasant foode of seing the owner of their desires. But even
as the *Persians* were aunciently wont, to leave no rising Sun
unsaluted, but as his faire beames appeared clearer unto thẽ wold
they more hartely rejoyce, laying upõ them a great fortoken, of
their following fortunes: So was ther no time that *Zelmane*
encoũtred their cies, with her beloved presence, but that it bred
a kind of burning devotiõ in thẽ, yet so much the more glading
their gredy soules, as her coũtenance were cleared with more
favour unto thẽ, which now being determinatly framed to the
greatest descẽt of kindnesse, it took such hold of her infortunate
lovers, that like children aboute a tender father, from a long
voyage returned, with lovely childishnes hange about him, and
yet with simple feare measure by his countenance, how farr he
acceptes their boldnes : So were these now throwne into so
serviceable an affeċtion, that the turning of *Zelmanes* eye, was a
strong sterne enough to all their motions, wending no way, but
as the inchaunting force of it ; guided them. But having made
a light repaste of the pleasunt, fruites of that countrye, enter-
larding their foode with such manner of generall discourses, as
lovers are woont to cover their passions in, when respeċte of a
thirde person keepes them from plaine particulars, at the earnest
entreatie of *Basilius*, *Zelmane*, first saluting the muses with a
base voyal hong hard by her, sent this ambassade in versified
musicke, to both her ill requited lovers.

> *BEautie hath force to catche the humane sight.*
> *Sight doth bewitch, the fancie evill awaked.*
> *Fancie we feele, encludes all passions mighte,*
> *Passion rebelde, oft reasons strength hath shaked.*
>
> *No wondre then, though sighte my sighte did tainte,*
> *And though thereby my fancie was infeċted,*

Though (yoked so) my minde with sicknes fainte,
Had reasons weight for passions ease rejeƈted.

But now the fitt is past : and time hath giv'ne
Leasure to weigh what due deserte requireth.
All thoughts so spronge, are from their dwelling driv'n,
And wisdome to his wonted seate aspireth.
  Crying in me : eye hopes deceitefull prove.
Thinges rightelie prizde, love is the bande of love.

And after her songe with an affeƈted modestie, shee threwe
downe her eye, as if the conscience of a secret graunt her inward
minde made, had sodainely cast a bashfull vaile over her. Which
Basilius finding, and thinking now was the time, to urge his
painefull petition, beseeching his wife with more carefull eye to
accompanie his sickly daughter *Philoclea*, being rid for that time
of her, who was content to graunt him any scope, that she might
after have the like freedome, with a gesture governed by the
force of his passions, making his knees his best supporters hee
thus saide unto her.

Yf either, said he, O Ladie of my life, my deadly pangues
coulde beare delaye or that this were the first time the same were
manifested unto you, I woulde nowe but maintaine still the remembraunce of my misfortune, without urging any further
reward, then time and pittie might procure for me. But, alas,
since my martirdome is no lesse painefull, then manifest, and
that I no more feele the miserable daunger, then you know the
assured trueth thereof : why shoulde my tonge deny his service
to my harte? Why should I feare the breath of my words who
daylie feele the flame of your workes? Embrace in sweete consideration I beseech you, the miserie of my Case, acknowledge
your selfe to bee the cause, and thinke it is reason for you to
redresse the effeƈtes. Alas let not certaine imaginatife rules,
whose trueth standes but upon opinion, keepe so wise a mind
from gratefulnes and mercie, whose never fayling laws nature
hath planted in us. I plainly lay my death unto you, the death
of him that loves you, the death of him whose life you maye save,
say your absolute determination, for hope it selfe is a paine, while
it is over mastered with feare, and if you do resolve to be cruel,
yet is the speediest condemnation, as in evills, most welcome.
Zelmane who had fully set to her selfe the traine she would keepe,

yet knowing that who soonest meanes to yeelde doth well to make the bravest parley, keeping countenaunce alofte. Noble prince said she, your wordes are to well couched, to come out of a restlesse minde, and thanked be the Gods your face threatens no daunger of death. These are but those swelling speeches, which give the uttermost name to everie trifle, which all were worth nothinge, if they were not enammeled with the goodly outside of love. Truely love were verie unlovely, if it were halfe so deadly, as your lovers (still living) tearme it I thinke well it may have a certaine childish vehemencie, which for the time to one desire will engage al the soule, so long as it lasteth. But with what impacience you your selfe showe, who confesse the hope of it a paine, and thinke your owne desire so unworthy, as you would faine bee ridd of it, and so with overmuch love sue hard for a hastie refusall. A refusall! (cried out *Basilius*, amazed with al, but perced with the last) Now assure your self, when soever you use that word diffinitively, it will be the un-doubted dome of my approching death. And then shall your owne experience knowe in mee, how soone the spirites dryed up with anguish, leave the performaunce of their ministerie, where-upon our life depĕdeth. But alas what a crueltie is this, not only to tormĕt but to think the tormĕt slighte? The terriblest tirants would say by no man they killed, he dyed not, nor by no man they punished, that he escaped free, for of all other, ther is least hope of mercie where there is no acknowledging of the paine: and with like crueltie, are my wordes breathed out from a flamy harte, accompted as messingers of a quiet mind. If I speake nothing, I choake my selfe, and am in no way of reliefe: if simplye neglected: if confusedly not understoode: if by the bending together all my inwarde powers, they bring forth any lively expressing of that they truly feele, that is a token, forsooth, the thoughts are at too much leasure. Thus is silence desperate, follie punished, and witt suspected. But indeed it is vaine to say any more, for wordes can bind no beliefe. Lady, I say, deter-mine of me, I must confesse I cannot beare this battell in my minde, and therefore let me soone know what I may accompt of my selfe, for it is a hell of dolours, when the mind still in doubt for want of resolution, can make no resistaunce.

In deed aunswered *Zelmane*, if I should graunt to your request, I should shew, an example in my selfe that I esteeme the holy bande of chastitie to bee but an Imaginatife rule, as you tearmed it: and not the truest observaunce of nature the moste noble commaundement that mankinde can have over themselves, as indeede both learning teacheth, and inward feeling assureth. But first shal *Zelmanes* grave, become her marriage bedd, before my soule shall consent to his owne shame, before I will leave a marke in my self of an unredemable trespasse. And yet must I confesse that if ever my hart were sturred, it hath ben with the manifest & manifold shewes of the misery you live in for me. For in trueth so it is, nature gives not to us her degenerate children, any more general precepte, then one to helpe the other, one to feele a true compassion of the others mishappe. But yet if I were never so contented to speake with you, (for further never ô *Basilius* looke for at my hands) I know not howe you can avoyde your wives jealous attendaunce, but that her suspicion shall bring my honour into question. *Basilius* whose small sailes the leaste winde did fill, was forth with as farre gonne into a large promising him selfe his desire, as before hee was striken downe with a threatned devill. And therefore bending his browes as though he were not a man to take the matter as he had done, what saide hee, shall my wife become my misteris? Thinke you not that thus much time hath taught mee to rule her? I will mewe the gentlewoman till she have cast all her feathers, if she rouse her selfe against me. And with that he walked up and downe, nodding his head, as though they mistooke him much that thought he was not his wives maister. But *Zelmane* now seeing it was time to conclude, of your wisdome and manhood sayd she, I doubt not, but that sufficeth not me, for both they can hardly tame a malicious toong, and impossibly barre the freedom of thought, which be the things that must be only witnesses, of honor, or judges of dishonor. But that you may see I doo not set light your affection, if to night after your wife be assuredly asleepe, whereof by your love I conjure you, to have a most precise care, you will steale handsomely to the cave unto me, there do I graunt you as great proportion as you will take of free conference with me, ever remembring you seeke no more, for so shall you but deceyve your selfe, and for ever loose me. *Basilius* that was olde inough to know, that women are not wont to appoint secreat night meetings for the purchasing of land, holding himselfe alreadye an undoubted possessour of his desires, kissing her hand, and lifting up his eyes to heaven, as if the greatnes of the benefit did goe beyonde all measure of thankes, sayde no more, least sturring of more words, might bring forth some perhaps contrarye matter. In which traunce of joye, *Zelmane* went from him, sayeng she would leave him to the remembrance of their appoyntment, and for her she would goe visite the Ladie *Philoclea*, into whose chamber being come, keeping still her late taken on gravitie, and asking her how she did, rather in the way of dutifull honour, then any speciall affection, with extreeme inward anguish to them both, she turned from her, and taking the Queene *Ginæcia*, ledde her into a baye windowe of the same Chamber, determining in her selfe, not to utter to so excellent a wit as *Gynæcia* had, the uttermost poynt of her pretended devise, but to keepe the clause of it for the last instant, when the shortnes of the time should not geve her spirits leasure to looke into all those doubts, that easily enter to an open invention. But with smiling eyes, and with a delivered over grace, fayning as much love to her, as she did counterfeit love to *Philoclea*, she began with more credible then eloquent speech to tell her, that with much consideracion of a matter so neerely importing her owne fancie, and *Gynæcias* honour, she had nowe concluded that the night following should be the fittest time for the joyning together their severall desires, what time sleepe should perfectly do his office upon the King her husband, and that the one should come to the other into the Cave. Which place, as it was the fyrst receipt of their promised love, so it might have the fyrst honour of the due performance. That the cause why those fewe dayes past, she had not sought the lyke, was, least the newe chaunge of her lodging, might make the Duke more apte to marke anye sodayne event: which nowe the use of it would take out of his minde. And therefore nowe, most excellent Ladie sayde she, there resteth nothing but that quicklie after supper, you trayne up the King to visit his daughter *Philoclea*, and then fayning your selfe not well at ease, by your going to bedde, drawe him not long to be after you. In the meane time I will be gone home to my lodging, where I will attend you, with no lesse devocion, but as I hope with better fortune, then *Thisbe* did the toomuch loving and toomuch loved *Piramus*. The blood that quicklie came into *Ginecias* fayre face, was the only answeare she made, but that one might easily see, contentment and consent were both to the full in her; which she did testifie with the wringing *Zelmane* fast by the hand, cloasing her eyes, & letting her head fall, as if she would geve her to knowe, she was not ignorant of her fault, although she were transported with the violence of her evill. But in this triple agreement did the daye seeme tedious of all sides, till his never erring course, had given place to the nightes succession: And the supper by eache hande hasted, was with no lesse speede ended, when *Gynecia* presenting a heavie sleepines in her countenance, brought up both *Basilius* and *Zelmane* to see *Philoclea* still keeping her bedde, and farre more sicke in minde then bodye, and more greeved then comforted with any such visitacion. Thence *Zelmane* wishing easefull rest to *Philoclea*, did seeme to take that nightes leave of this princely crewe, when *Gynecia* likewise seeming somewhat deseased, desired *Basilius* to stay a while with her daughter, while she recommended her sicknes to her beds comfort, in deede desirous to determine agayne of the manner of her stealing away; to no lesse comfort to *Basilius*, who the sooner she was asleepe, the sooner hoped to come by his long pursued praye. Thus both were bent to deceave each other, and to take the advantage of either others disadvantage. But *Gynæcia* having taken *Zelmane* into her bed-chamber, to speake a little with her of their sweete determinacion: *Zelmane* upon a sodaine (as though she had never thought of it before) Now the Gods forbid, sayde she, so great a Lady as you are should come to me: or that I should leave it to the handes of fortune, if by eyther the ill governing of your passion, or your husbands sodayne waking, any daunger might happen unto you. No, if there be any superioritie in the poyntes of true love, it shall be yours: if there be any daunger, since my selfe am the author of this devise, it is reason it should be mine. Therefore doo you but leave with me the keyes of the gate, and upon your selfe take my upper garment, that if any of *Damætas* house see you, they may thinke you to be my selfe, and I will presently lye downe in your place, so muffled for your supposed sicknes, as the King shall nothing knowe me. And then as soone as he is a sleepe, will I (as it much better becommes me) waite upon you. But if the uttermost of mischiefes should happen, I can assure you the Kings life shall sooner pay for it, then your honour. And with the ending of her words, she threwe off her gowne, not geving *Gynæcia* any space to take the full image of this newe chaunge into her fancie. But seeing no readye objection against it in her heart, and knowing that there was no time then to stand long disputing; besides, remembring the gever was to order the maner of his gift, yeelded quickly to this conceit, in deede not among the smallest causes, tickled thereunto by a certayne wanton desire, that her husbands deceipt might be the more notable. In this sort did *Zelmane,* nimbly disarayeng her selfe, possesse *Gynæcias* place, hiding her head in such a close manner, as grievous and overwatched sicknesse is wont to invite to itselfe the solace of sleepe. And of the other side the Queene putting on *Zelmanes* utmost apparell, went fyrst into her closet, there quickly to beawtifie her selfe, with the best and sweetest night deckings. But there, casting an hastie eye over her precious things, which ever since *Zelmanes* comming, her head otherwise occupied had left unseene, she hapned to see a bottle of golde, upon which downe along were graved these verses:

> *Let him drinke this, whome long in armes to folde*
> *Thou doest desire, and with free power to holde.*

She remembred the bottle, for it had bene kept of long time by the Kings of *Cyprus,* as a thing of rare vertue, and given to her by her mother, when she being very young maried to her husband of much greater age, her mother perswaded it was of propertie to force love, with love effects, had made a precious present of it to this her beloved child, though it had bene received rather by tradition to have such a qualitie, then by any approved experiment. This *Gynæcia,* (according to the common disposition, not only (though especiallie) of wives, but of all other kindes of people, not to esteeme much ones owne, but to thinke the labor lost employed about it) had never cared to geve to her husband, but suffred his affection to runne according to his owne scope. But now that love of her particular choyse had awaked her spirits, and perchance the very unlawfulnes of it had a litle blowne the coale: among her other ornaments with glad minde she tooke most part of this liquor, putting it into a faire cup, all set with diamonds: for what dares not love undertake armed with the night, and provoked with lust? And thus downe she went to the Cave-ward, guyded only by the Moones faire shining, suffering no other thought to have any familiaritie with her

48

braines, but that which did present unto her a picture of her approching contentment. She that had long disdayned this solitary life her husband had entred into, now wished it much more solitary, so she might only obtaine the private presence of *Zelmane*. She that before would not have gone so farre, especially by night, and to so darke a place, now tooke a pride in the same courage, and framed in her minde a pleasure out of the payne it selfe. Thus with thicke doubled paces she went to the Cave, receyving to her selfe, for her first contentment, the only lying where *Zelmane* had done : whose pillow she kist a thousand times, for having borne the print of that beloved head. And so keeping, with panting heart, her travelling fancies so attentive, that the winde could stirre nothing, but that she stirred her selfe, as if it had bene the pace of the longed-for *Zelmane*, she kept her side of the bed ; defending only and cherishing the other side with her arme, till after a while wayting, counting with her selfe how many steps were betwixt the Lodge and the Cave, and oft accusing *Zelmane* of more curious stay then needed, she was visited with an unexpected guest.

For *Basilius*, after his wife was departed to her fayned repose, as long as he remayned with his daughter, to geve his wife time of unreadying her selfe, it was easily seene it was a very thorny abode he made there : and the discourses with which he entertayned his daughter, not unlike to those of earnest players, when, in the middest of their game, trifling questions be put unto them, his eyes still looking about, and himselfe still changing places, beginne to speake of a thing, and breake it off before it were halfe done. To any speach *Philoclea* ministred unto him, with a sodayne starting, and casting up his head, make an answere farre out of all Grammer: a certayne deepe musing, and by and by out of it: uncertayne motions, unstayed graces. Having borne out the limit of a reasonable time with as much payne as might be, he came darkeling into his chamber, forcing himselfe to treade as softly as he coulde. But the more curious he was, the more he thought every thing creaked under him : and his minde being out of the way with another thought, and his eyes not serving his turne in that darke place, each Coffer or Cupbord he met, one saluted his shinnes, another his elbowes: sometimes ready in revenge to strike them agayne with his face. Till at length, fearing his wife were not fully asleepe, he came lifting up the cloathes, as gently as (I thinke) poore *Pan* did, when, in stead of *Ioles* bedde, he came into the rough imbracings of *Hercules:* and laying himselfe downe, as tenderly as a new Bride, rested a while with a very open eare, to marke each breath of his supposed wife. And sometimes he himselfe would yeeld a long fetched sigh, as though that had bene a musike to drawe one another to sleepe, till within a very little while, with the other parties well counterfeyt sleepe (who was as willing to be rid of him, as he was to be gone thence) assuring himselfe he left all safe there, in the same order stale out agayne, and putting on his night gowne, with much groping and scrambling, he gate himselfe out of the little house, and then did the Moone-light serve to guide his feete. Thus with a greate deale of payne, did *Basilius* goe to her whome he fledde, and with much cunning left the person for whome he had employed all his cunning. But when *Basilius* was once gotten (as he thought) into a cleare coast what joye he then made, how each thing seemed vile in his sight, in comparison of his fortune, how farre already he deemed himselfe in the chiefe tower of his desires, it were tedious to tell: once his heart could not choose but yeeld this song, as a fayring of his contentment.

> *G*Et *hence foule Griefe, the canker of the minde:*
>   *Farewell Complaint, the misers only pleasure:*
> *Away vayne Cares, by which fewe men do finde*
>   *Their sought-for treasure.*
>
> *Ye helplesse Sighes, blowe out your breath to nought,*
> *Teares, drowne your selves, for woe (your cause) is wasted,*
> *Thought, thinke to ende, too long the frute of thought*
>   *My minde hath tasted.*
>
> *But thou, sure Hope, tickle my leaping heart.*
> *Comfort, step thou in place of wonted sadnes.*
> *Fore-felt Desire, begin to savour parts*
>   *Of comming gladnes.*
>
> *Let voice of Sighes into cleare musike runne,*
> *Eyes, let your Teares with gazing now be mended,*
> *In stede of Thought, true pleasure be begunne,*
>   *And never ended.*

Thus imagining as then with himselfe, his joyes so held him

up, that he never touched ground. And, like a right olde beaten souldiour, that knewe well enough the greatest Captaynes do never use long Orations, when it commes to the very point of execution, as soone as he was gotten into the Cave, and to the joyfull (though silent) expectation of *Gynæcia*, come close to the bed, never recking his promise to looke for nothing but conference, he lept into that side reserved for a more welcome guest. And layeng his lovingest hold upon *Gynæcia*: O *Zelmane*, sayd he, embrace in your favor this humble servant of yours: hold within me my heart, which pantes to leave his maister to come unto you. In what case poore *Gynæcia* was, when she knewe the voyce, and felt the bodie of her husband, faire Ladies, it is better to knowe by imagination then experience. For straight was her minde assaulted, partly with the being deprived of her unquenched desire, but principallie with the doubt that *Zelmane* had betrayed her to her husband, besides the renewed sting of jealosie, what in the meane time might befall her daughter. But of the other side, her love, with a fixed perswasion she had, taught her to seeke all reason of hopes. And therein thought best before discovering of her selfe, to marke the behaviour of her husband; who, both in deedes and wordes still using her, as taking her to be *Zelmane*, made *Gynæcia* hope that this might be *Basilius* owne enterprise, which *Zelmane* had not stayed, least she should discover the matter which might be perfourmed at another time. Which hope accompanyed with *Basilius* maner of dealing, (he being at that time fuller of livelier fancies, then many yeares before he had bene) besides the remembrance of her daughters sicknesse, and late strange countenance betwixt her & *Zelmane*, all comming together into her mind, which was loth to condemne it selfe of an utter overthrow, made her frame her selfe, not truly with a sugred joye, but with a determinate patience to let her husband thinke he had found a very gentle and supple-minded *Zelmane*; which he good man making full reckening of, did melt in as much gladnesse as she was oppressed with divers ungratefull burthens.

But *Pyrocles* who had at this present no more to play the part of *Zelmane*, having so naturally measured the maner of his breathing, that *Basilius* made no doubt of his sounde sleeping, and layne a preatie while with a quiet unquietnes to perfourme his entended enterprise, as soone as by the debate betwixt *Basilius* shinnes and the unregarding fourmes he perceived that he had fully left the Lodge: after him went he with stealing steps, having his sword under his arme (still doubting least some mischance might turne *Basilius* backe againe) downe to the gate of the Lodge. Which not content to locke fast, he barred and fortified with as many devises, as his wit and haste would suffer him, that so he might have full time both for making readye *Philoclea*, and conveying her to her horse, before any might come in to finde them missing. For further endes of those endes, and what might ensue of this action, his love and courage well matched never looked after, houlding for an assured grounde, that whosoever in great things will thinke to prevent all objections, must lye still, and doo nothing. This determination thus wayed, the first part thus perfourmed, up to *Philocleas* chamber dore went *Pyrocles*, rapt from himselfe with the excessive fore-feeling of his (as he assured himselfe) neere comming contentment. Whatever paynes he had taken, what daungers he had runne into, and especially those sawcy pages of love, doubts, griefes, languishing hopes, and threatning despayres, came all now to his minde, in one ranke to beawtifye his expected blisfulnesse, and to serve for a most fit sawce, whose sourenesse might give a kinde of life to the delightfull cheare his imagination fed upon. All the great estate of his father, all his owne glorie, seemed unto him but a trifling pompe, whose good stands in other mens conceit, in cõparison of the true comfort he found in the depth of his mind, and the knowledge of any miserie that might ensue this joyous adventure, was recked of but as a slight purchase of possessing the top of happines, for so farre were his thoughts past through all perils, that alreadie he conceyved himselfe safelie arrived with his Ladie at the stately pallace of *Pella*, among the exceeding joyes of his father, and infinite congratulacions of his frends, geving order for the royall entertayning of *Philoclea*, and for sumptuous shewes and triumphes against their mariage. In the thought wherof as he found extremity of joy, so well found he that extremitie is not without a certayne joyfull paine, by extending the heart beyond his wonted limits, and by so forcible a holding all the senses to one object, that it confounds their mutuall working, not without a charming kinde of ravishing them, from the free use of their owne function. Thus grieved only with too much gladnes, being come to the doore, which should be the entrie to his happines, he was met with the latter end of a song, which *Philoclea* like a solitarie Nightingale, bewayling her guiltlesse punishment, and helplesse misfortune, had newly delivered over, meaning none should be judge of her passiõ, but her owne conscience. The song having bene accorded to a sweetly playde on Lute, conteyned these verses, which she had lately with some arte curiously written, to enwrap her secret and resolute woes.

V[1]Ertue, beawtie[2], and speach[3], did strike[1], wound[2], charme[3],
My harte[1], eyes[2], eares[3], with wonder[1], love[2], delight[3]:
First[1], second[2], last[3], did binde[1], enforce[2], and arme[3],
His workes[1], showes[2], suites[3], with wit[1], grace[2], and vow's[3] might.

Thus honour[1], liking[2], trust[3], much[1], farre[2], and deepe[3],
Held[1], pearst[2], possest[3], my judgement[1], sence[2], and will[3],
Till wrong[1], contempt[2], deceipt[3], did growe[1], steale[2], creepe[3],
Bandes[1], favour[2], faith[3], to breake[1], defile[2], and kill[3].

Then greefe[1], unkindnes[2], proofe[3], tooke[1], kindled[2], tought[3],
Well grounded[1], noble[2], due[3], spite[1], rage[2], disdaine[3],
But ah[1], alas[2]! (In vayne) my minde[1], sight[2], thought[3],
Doth him[1], his face[2], his words[3], leave[1], shunne[2], refraine[3],
For no thing[1], time[2], nor place[3], can loose[1], quench[2], ease[3],
Mine owne[1], embraced[2], sought[3], knot[1], fire[2], desease[3].

The force of love to those poore folke that feele it, is many wayes very strange, but no way stranger, then that it doth so enchaine the lovers judgement upon her that holdes the raines of his minde, that what soever she doth is ever in his eyes best. And that best, being by the continuall motion of our changing life, turned by her to any other thing, that thing againe becommeth best. So that nature in each kinde suffring but one superlative, the lover only admits no positive. If she sit still, that is best, for so is the conspiracie of her severall graces held best together to make one perfect figure of beawtie. If she walke, no doubt that is best, for besides the making happie the more places by her steps, the very sturring addes a pleasing life to her native perfectiõs. If she be silent, that without comparison is best, since by that meanes the untroubled eye, most freely may devoure the sweetnes of his object. But if she speake, he will take it upon his death that is best, the quintessence of each worde, beeing distilled downe into his affected soule. Example of this was well to be seene in the given over *Pyrocles*, who with panting breath, and somtime sighes, not such as sorrowe restrayning the inwarde partes doth make them glad to deliver, but such as the impacience of delay, with the unsuretie of never so sure hope, is wont to breath out nowe being at the doore, of the one side, hearing her voice, which hee thought if the Philosophers said true of the heavenly seven sphered harmony, was by her not only represented, but farre surmounted, and of the other having his eyes overfilled with her beautie, (for the King at his parting had left the chamber open, and she at that time laye, as the heate of that countrie did wel suffer, upon the toppe of her bedd, having her beauties eclipsed with nothing but with a faire smock, wrought al in flames of ash-coullour silke and golde, lying so upõ her right side, that the left thigh downe to the foote, yeelded his delightfull proportion to the full vew which was seene by the helpe of a ritche lampe, which thorowe the curtaines a little drawne caste forth a light upon her, as the moone doth when it shines into a thinne wood) *Pyrocles* I saye was stopped with the violence of so many dartes, cast by *Cupid* altogether upon him, that quite forgetting him selfe, and thinking therein alreadie he was in the best degree of felicitie, he would have lost much of his time, and with too much love omitted the enterprise undertaken for his love, had not *Philocleas* pittifull accusing of him forced him to bring his spirites againe, to a newe bias, for shee laying her hand under her faire cheek, upon which there did privilie tickle the sweet droppes of her delightfull though sorrowfull teares, made these wordes waite upon her monefull songe. And hath that cruell *Pyrocles* saide shee, deserved thus much of me, that I should for his sake lift up my voice in my best tunes, and to him continually, with powring out my plainte, make a disdayned oblacion? Shall my soule still doe this honour to his unmercyfull tirranie, by my lamenting his losse, to show his worthines and my weakenes?

He heares thee not simple *Philoclea*, he heares thee not ; and if he did, some hartes grow the harder, the more they find their advantage. Alas what a miserable constitution of minde have I ! I disdaine my fortune, and yet reverence him that disdaines me. I accuse his ungratefulnes, and have his vertue in admiration. O yee deafe heavens, I would either his injury could blot out myne affection, or my affection could forget his injury. With that geving a pittiful but sweet shriche, shee tooke againe the lute, and beganne to sing this sonnet which might serve as an explaining to the other :

> THe love which is imprinted in my soule
>   *With beauties seale, and vertue faire disguis'de,*
> *With inward cries putts up a bitter role*
> *Of huge complaintes, that now it is despis'de.*
>
> *Thus thus the more I love, the wronge the more*
> *Monstrous appeares, long trueth receaved late,*
> *Wrong sturres remorsed greefe, griefes deadly sore*
> *Unkindnes breedes, unkindnes fostreth hath.*
>
> *But ah the more I hate, the more I thinke*
> *Whome I doe hate, the more I thinke on him,*
> *The more his matchlesse giftes do deepely sinck*
> *Into my breste, and loves renewed swimme.*
> *What medicin then, can such desease remove*
> *Where love draws hate, and hate engendreth love ?*

But *Pyrocles* that had heard his name accused, & cõdemned by the mouth which of all the world, and more then all the world, he most loved : had then cause enough to call his minde to his home, and with the most haste he could (for true love feares the accident of an instant) to match the excusing of his faulte, with declaration of his arrand thither. And therefore blowne up & downe with as many contrary passions, as *Æolus* sent out windes upon the trojan reliques, guided upon the sea by the valiant *Æneas*, hee went into her chamber with such a pace as reverent feare doth teach, where kneeling downe, and having prepared a long discourse for her, his eies were so filled with her sight that as if they woulde have robbed all their fellowes of their services, both his hart fainted, and his toung fayled in such sorte, that he could not bring forth one word, but referred her understanding to his eyes language. But she in extremitie amazed to see him there, at so undue a season, & ashamed that her beautifull body made so naked a prospeɕt, drawing in her delicate lims into the weake guard of the bedd, and presenting in her face to him such a kinde of pittifull anger, as might shew, this was only a fault, therfore because she had a former grudge unto him, turning away her face from him she thus said unto him : O *Zelmane* or *Pyrocles*, (for whether name I use it much skils not, by the one I was first deceived, & by the other now betrayed) what strange motion is the guide of thy cruel mind hither ? Dost thou not thinke the day torments thou hast given me sufficient, but that thou doest envie me the nights quiet ? Wilt thou give my sorrowes no truce, but by making me see before mine eyes how much I have lost, offer me due cause of cōfirming my plainte ? Or is thy hart so full of rancour, that thou dost desire to feede thine eyes with the wretched speɕtacle of thine overthrowen enemie, and so to satisfie the full measure of thy undeserved rage, with the receving into thy sight the unrelevable ruines of my desolate life ? O *Pyrocles, Pyrocles* for thine own vertues sake, let miseries be no musique unto thee, & be content to take to thy selfe some coloure of excuse, that thou didest not knowe to what extremitie thy inconstancie, or rather falshood hath brought me. *Pyrocles* to whom every sillable she pronounced, was a thunderboult to his hart, equally distraught betwixt amasement & sorow, abashed to se such a stop of his desires, greved with her paine, but tormēted to find himself the author of it, with quaking lips, & pale cheere, alas divine Lady said he, your displeasure is so contrary to my deserte, & your words so farre beyond all expec-tatiõs, that I have least abilitie now I have most need, to speake in the cause upõ which my life dependeth. For my troth is so undoubtedly cōstāt unto you, my hart is so assured a witnes to it self, of his unspotted faith, that having no one thing in me, wherout any such sacriledg might arise, I have likewise nothing in so direɕt a thing to say for my selfe, but sincere & vehemēt protestatiõs, for in truth, there may most words be spent, where there is some probabilitie, to breed of both sids cōjeɕtural allegatiõs. But so perfeɕt a thing as my love is of you, as it suffers no questiõ, so it semes to receive injurie by additiõ of any words unto it. Yf my soule could have ben polluted with treachery, it woulde likewise have provided for itself, due furniture of coullourable answeres, but as it should upõ the naked cõscience of his untouched dutie, so I must cõfes it is altogether unarmed against so unjust a violẽce as you lay upõ me, alas ! let not the paines I have takẽ to serve you, be now accoũted injurious unto you, let not the dãgerous cũning I have used to pleasure you be demed a treasõ against you, since I have deceved thẽ whom you feare for your sake, doe not you destroye mee for their sake what can I without you further doe ? Or to what more forwardnes can any counsell bring our desired happines ? I have provided whatsoever is needfull for our going, I have rid them both out of the lodge, so that there is none here to bee hinderers or knowers of our departure, but only the almightie powers, whom I invoke as triers of mine innocencie and witnesses of my wel meaning. And if ever my thoughts did receive so much as a fainting in their affeċtions : if they have not continually with more and more ardoure, from time to time pursued the possession of your sweetest favour ; if ever in that possession they receaved either spott, or falshoode: Then let their most horrible plagues fall upon me, let mine eyes be deprived of the light which did abase the heavenly beames that strake them, let my falsified toung serve to no use but to bee more mine owne wretchednes, let my harte empoysoned with detestable treason, be the seate of infernall sorrowe, let my soule with the endles anguish of his conscience become his owne tormentor. O false mankind cried out the sweete *Philoclea.* How can an impostumed heart, but yeelde forth evill matter by his mouth? Are oathes there to be believed, where vowes are broken ? No no, who doth wounde the eternall justice of the Gods, cares little for abusing their names : and who in doing wickedly doth not feare due recompencing plagues, doth little feare that invoking of plagues, will make them come ever a whit the sooner. But alas what ayleth this new conversation, have you yet another sleight to playe, or doe you think to deceave me in *Pyrocles* forme, as you have done in *Zelmanes* ? Or rather now you have betrayed me in both, is some third sex left you, into which you can transforme your selfe to inveigle my simplicitie? Enjoye, enjoye the conquest you have already wone: and assure your selfe you are come to the farthest pointe of your cunning. For my parte unkinde *Pyrocles*, my only defence shalbe beleefe of nothing, my comforte my faithfull innocencie, and the punishment I desire of you shalbe your owne conscience. *Philocleas* hard persevering in this unjust condemnation of him, did so overthrowe all the might of *Pyrocles* minde (who saw that time woulde not serve to prove by deedes, and that the better wordes he used, the more they were suspected of deceiptfull cunning.) That voide of all counsell, and deprived of all comforte, finding best desertes punished, and nearest hopes prevented, hee did abandon the succour of himselfe, and suffered griefe so to close his harte, that his breath fayling him, with a deathfull shutting off his eyes hee fell downe at her bedside, having had time to say no more, but oh whom doest thou kil *Philoclea*? She that litle looked for such an extreame event of her doinges, starte out of her bedd, like *Venus* rising from her mother the sea, not so much striken downe with amazement, and griefe of her faulte, as lifted up with the force of love and desire to helpe, she laide her faire body over his brest, and throwing no other water in his face, but the streame of her teares nor giving him other blowes but the kissing of her welformed mouth, her onely cries were these lamentations : O unfortunate suspicion, saide shee, the very meane to loose that we most suspect to loose. O unkind kindnesse of mine, which returnes an imagined wrong with an effectuall injury. O foole to make quarell my supplication or to use hate as the mediator of love, childish *Philoclea*, had thou throwne away the Jewell wherein all thy pride consisted? Hast thou with too much hast overrun thy selfe? Then would she renew her kisses : O yet not finding the life retourne, redouble her plaintes in this manner : O divine soule, saide she, whose vertue can possesse no lesse then the highest place in heaven, if for mine eternall plague, thou haste utterly lefte this most sweet mansion, before I follow thee with *Thisbes* punishment for my rashe unwarinesse, heare this protestation of mine : That as the wrong I have done thee proceeded of a most sincere, but unresistable affection : so led with this pittifull example it shall ende in the mortall hate of my selfe, and (if it may be) I will make my soule a tombe of thy memory. At that worde with anguish of minde and weakenes of body encreased one by the other, and both augmented by this feareful accident, she had falne downe in a sounde : but that *Pyrocles* then first severing his eye liddes, and quickly apprehending her daunger, to him more then death, beyond all powers striving to recover the commaundement of al his powers, staied her from falling : and then, lifting the sweet burthen of her body in his armes, laid her againe in her bedd. So that she, but then the Physition, was nowe become the pacient : & he, to whom her weaknesse had bene serviceable, was now enforced to do service to her weaknesse, which performed by him with that hartie care, which the most carefull love on the best loved subject in greatest extremitie could employ, prevailed so farre, that ere long shee was able (though in strength exceedingly dejected) to call home her wandering senses, to yeelde attention to that her beloved *Pyrocles* had to deliver. But he lying downe on the bed by her, holding her hand in his, with so kind an accusing her of unkindnes, as in accusing her he condemned himself, began from pointe to pointe to discover unto her all that had passed betwene his loathed lovers & him. How he had entertained, & by entertaining deceived, both *Basilius* & *Gynecia* : & that with such a kind of deceipt, as either might see the cause in the other but neither espie the effect in themselves. That al his favors to thē had tended only to make them strangers to this his actiō : & al his strangnes to her to the final obtaining of her long promised, & now to be perfourmed favour. Which devise seing it had so well succeeded to the removing all other hinderances, that only her resolutiō remained for the taking their happy journie, he conjured her by al the love she had ever borne him, shee would make no longer delay to partake with him whatsoever honors the noble kingdöe of *Macedon*, & al other *Euarchus* dominiōs might yeeld him, especially since in this enterprise he had now waded so farr, as he could not possibly retire himself back, without being overwhelmed with daūger & dishōour. He neded not have used further arguments of perswasiō : for that only conjuratiō had so forcibly bound all her spirits, that could her body have secōded her mind, or her mind have strengthened her body, without respect of any worldly thing, but only feare to be againe unkind to *Pyrocles*, she had condiscended to goe with him. But raising her selfe a litle in her bed, & finding her own unabilitie in any sorte to endure the aire: My *Pyrocles* said she (with tearefull eyes & a pittifull coūtenance, such as well witnessed she had no will to deny any thing she had power to performe) if you can convey me hence in such plight as you see me ; I am most willing to make my extreamest daûger a testimonie, that I esteme no daûger in regard of your vertuous satisfaction. But if shee fainted so faste, that she was not able to utter the rest of her conceived speech : which also turned *Pyrocles* thoughts from expecting further answere, to the necessary care of reviving her, in whose fainting himself was more thê overthrown. And that having effected with al the sweet meãs his wits could devise, though his highest hopes were by this unexpected downfall sunke deeper thê any degree of dispaire : yet lest the appearãce of his inward grief might occasiô her further discômfort, having racked his face to a more côfortable semblãce, he sought some shew of reason, to shew shee had no reason, either for him, or for her selfe so to be aflicted. Which in the sweete minded *Philoclea*, whose consideration was limited by his wordes, and whose conceite pearced no deeper then his outwarde countenaunce, wrought within a while such quietnesse of mind, and that quietnesse againe such repose of bodie, that slepe by his harbingers weakenesse, wearines, and watchfulnes, had quickly taken up his lodging in all her senses. Then indeed had *Pyrocles* leasure to sit in judgement on himselfe, and to heare his reason accuse his rashnes, who, without forecaste of doubte, without knowledge of his friende, without acquainting *Philoclea* with his purpose or being made acquainted with her present estate, had falne headlong into that attempt, the successe whereof hee had long since set downe to himselfe as the measure of all his other fortunes. But callirg to minde howe weakely they do that rather finde faulte with what cannot be amended, then seek to amend wherein they have beene faultie : he soone turned him from remembring what might have beene done to considering what was now to be done, and when that consideration fayled what was now to be expected. Wherein having runne over all the thoughts, his reason called to the strictest accountes could bring before him, at length he lighted on this : That as long as *Gynecia* bewraied not the matter (which he thought she woulde not doe, aswell for her owne honour and safetie, as for the hope she might stil have of him, which is loth to die in a lovers hart) all the rest might turne to a preatie meryment, and enflame his lover *Basilius*, againe to cast aboute for the missed favour. And as naturally the harte stuffed up with wofulnes is glad greedelie to sucke the thinnest aire of comforte: so did hee, at the first, embrace this conceite as offeringe great hope, if not assurance of well doing. Till looking more neerely into it, and not able to answere the doubts and difficulties he sawe therein more and more arising the night being also farre spent, his thoughtes even wearie of their owne burthens, fell to a straying kind of uncertaintie : and his minde standing onely upon the nature of inward intelligences lefte his bodie to give a sleeping respite to his vitall spirites, which he, according to the qualitie of Sorrow, received with greater greedines then ever in his life before. According to the nature of sorrow, I say, which is past cares remedie. For care sturring the braines, and making thinne the spirites breaketh rest: but those griefes wherein one is determined there is no preventing, do brede a dull heavinesse which easely clothes it selfe in sleepe. So as laid downe so neare the beautie of the worlde *Philoclea*, that their neckes were subject each to others chaste embracements, it seemed love had come thither to laye a plott in that picture of death how gladly, if death came, their soules would goe together.

The thirde Egloges.

THyrsis not with many painted words nor falsified promises, had wone the consent of his beloved *Kala*, but with a true & simple making her know he loved her not forcing himselfe beyond his reach to buy her affection, but giving her such preatie presentes, as neither coulde wearie him with the giving, nor shame her for the taking. Thus the first Strawberies he could find, were ever in a cleane washt dish sent to *Kala* thus poesies of the spring flowers were wrapt up in a litle grene silke and dedicated to *Kalas* brestes, thus somtimes his sweetest Creame, sometimes the best Cakebread his mother made, were reserved for *Kalas* taste. Neither would hee stick to kil a lamb when she would be content to come over the way unto him. But thẽ lo, how the house was swept & rather no fire thẽ any smoke lefte to trouble her. Then love songes were not daintie, when she would heare them, and as much manerlie silence when shee would not: in going to Church great worship to *Kala*. So that all the parish said, never a maide they knew so well wayted on: and when dauncing was about the Maypole, no body taken out

but she, and he after a leape or two to shewe her his owne
activitie, woulde frame all the rest of his dauncing, onely to
grace her. As for her fathers sheepe, he had no lesse care of
them then his owne : so that she might play her as she would,
warranted with honest *Thyrsis* carefulnes. But if he spied *Kala*
favourd any one of the flocke more then his fellowes, then that
was cherished ; shearing him so (when shorne he must be) as
might most become him : but while the wole was on, wrapping
within it some verses, wherin *Thyrsis* had a speciall gifte, and
making the innocent beast his unweting messinger. Thus con-
stantly continuing, though he were none of the fayrest, at length
he wanne *Kalas* harte, the honestest wenche in all those quarters.
And so with consent of both parents (without which nether
Thyrsis would aske, nor *Kala* grant) their marring day was
appointed, which because it fell out in this time, I thinke it
shall not be impertinent, to remember a little our shepheards,
while the other greater persons, are either sleeping or otherwise
troubled. *Thyrsis* mariage time once knowne, there needed no
inviting of the neighbours in that valley, for so well was *Thyrsis*
beloved, that they were already to doe him credit, neither yet
came they like Harpies to devoure him : but on bought a fat
pigge, the other a tender kidd, the thirde a great goose : as for
chese, milke, & butter, were the gossips presents. Thither came
of strange shepheards onely the melancholy *Philisides*, for the
vertuous *Coridon* had long since left off al his joyful solemnities.
And as for *Strephon* and *Klaius*, they had lost their mistresse,
which put them into such extreme sorrowes as they could
scarcely abide the light of the daye, much lesse the eyes of
men. But of the *Arcadian* borne shepheardes, thither came good
olde *Geron*, young *Histor*, though unwilling, and upright *Dicus*,
mery *Pass* and jolly *Nico*. As for *Damætas* they durst not presume (his pride was such) to invite him : and *Dorus* they founde
might not bee spared. And there under a bower was made of
bowes (for *Thyrsis* house was not able to receave them) every
one placed according to his age. The women (for such was the
maner of the country) kept together to make good cheare among
themselves, from which otherwise a certaine painefull modestie
restraines them, and there might the sadder matrones give good
counsel to *Kala* : who poore soule wept for feare of that she
desired. But among the shepheards was al honest libertie, no

62

feare of daungerous tel-tales, who hunt greater prayes, nor indeede mindes in them to give tell-tales any occasion ; but one questioning with another of the manuring his ground, and governing his flock, the highest pointe they reached to was to talke of the holines of mariage, to which purpose assoone as their sober dynner was ended, *Dycus* insteede of thankes, sange this songe with a cleare voice and cheerfull countenaunce.

LEt mother earth now decke her selfe in flowers,
To see her ofspring seeke a good increase,
Where justest love doth vanquish Cupids *powers*
And ware of thoughts is swallow'd up in peace
  Which never may decrease
  But like the turtells faire
  Live one in two, a well united paire,
  Which that no chaunce may staine,
  O Himen *long their coupled joyes maintaine.*

O heav'n awake shewe forth thy stately face,
Let not these slumbring clowds thy beawties hide,
But with thy cheerefull presence helpe to grace
The honest Bridegroome, and the bashfull Bride,
  Whose loves may ever bide,
  Like to the Elme and Vyne,
  With mutuall embracements them to twyne :
  In which delightfull paine,
  O Himen *long their coupled joyes maintaine.*

Yee Muses all which chaste affects allow,
And have to Thyrsis *shewd your secret skill,*
To this chaste love your sacred favours bow,
And so to him and her your giftes distill,
  That they all vice may kill :
  And like to lillies pure
  May please all eyes, and spotlesse may endure.
  Where that all blisse may raigne,
  O Himen *long their coupled joyes maintaine.*

Yee Nymphes which in the waters empire have,
Since Thyrsis *musick oft doth yeeld you praise,*
Graunt to the thing which we for Thyrsis *crave.*
Let one time (but long first) close up their daies,
  One grave their bodies seaze :

And like two rivers sweete,
When they though divers do together meete :
One streame both streames containe,
O Himen *long their coupled joyes maintaine.*

Pan, *father* Pan, *the god of silly sheepe,*
Whose care is cause that they in number growe,
Have much more care of them that them do keepe,
Since from these good the others good doth flowe,
    And make their issue showe
    In number like the hearde
    Of yonglings, which thy selfe with love hast rearde.
    Or like the drops of raine.
    O Himen *long their coupled joyes maintaine.*

Vertue (if not a God) yet Gods chiefe parte,
Be thou the knot of this their open vowe,
That still he be her head, she be his harte,
He leane to her, she unto him do bow :
    Each other still allow :
    Like Oke and Mistletoe.
    Her strength from him, his praise from her do growe.
    In which most lovely traine,
    O Himen *long their coupled joyes maintaine.*

But thou foule Cupid *syre to lawlesse lust,*
Be thou farre hence with thy empoyson'd darte,
Which though of glittring golde, shall heere take rust
Where simple love, which chastnesse doth imparte,
    Avoydes thy hurtfull arte,
    Not needing charming skill,
    Such mindes with sweet affections for to fill,
    Which being pure and plaine,
    O Himen *long their coupled joyes maintaine.*

All churlish wordes, shrewd answeres, crabbed lookes,
All privatenes, selfe-seeking, inward spite,
All waywardnes, which nothing kindly brookes,
All strife for toyes, and clayming masters right :
    Be hence aye put to flight,
    All sturring husbands hate
    Gainst neighbors good for womanish debate
    Be fled as things most vaine,
    O Himen *long their coupled joyes maintaine.*

All peacock pride, and fruites of peacocks pride
Longing to be with losse of substance gay
With retchlesnes what may thy house betide,
So that you may on hyer slippers stay
  For ever hence awaye:
  Yet let not sluttery,
  The sinke of filth, be counted huswifery:
  But keeping holesome meane,
  O Himen *long their coupled joyes maintaine.*

But above all away vile jealousie,
The evill of evils just cause to be unjust,
(How can he love suspecting treacherie?
How can she love where love cannot win trust?)
  Goe snake hide thee in dust,
  Ne dare once shew thy face,
  Where open hartes do holde so constant place,
  That they thy sting restraine,
  O Himen *long their coupled joyes maintaine.*

The earth is deckt with flowers, the heav'ns displaid,
Muses graunt guiftes, Nymphes long and joyned life,
Pan *store of babes, vertue their thoughts well staid,*
Cupids *lust gone, and gone is bitter strife,*
  Happy man, happy wife.
  No pride shall them oppresse,
  Nor yet shall yeeld to loathsome sluttishnes,
  And jealousie is slaine:
  For Himen *will their coupled joyes maintaine.*

Truly *Dicus,* sayd *Nico,* although thou didst not graunt me the price the last day, when undoubtedly I wan it, yet must I needes say, thou for thy parte hast soong well and thriftelie. *Pas* straight desired all the companie they would beare witnes, that *Nico* had once in his life spoken wisely; for sayde he, I will tell it his father, who will be a glad man when he heares such newes. Very true, sayd *Nico,* but indeede so would not thine in like case, for he would looke thou shouldest live but one houre longer, that a discreate word wandred out of thy mouth. And I pray thee (sayd *Pas*) gentle *Nico,* tell me what mischaunce it was that brought thee to taste so fine a meate?

THE COUNTESSE OF PEMBROKES

Mary goodman blockhead sayde *Nico*, because hee speakes against jealousie, the filthie traytor to true affection, and yet disguising it selfe in the rayment of love. Sentences, Sentences, cried *Pas*. Alas howe ripe witted these young folkes be now adayes! But well counselled shall that husband be, when this man commes to exhort him not to be jealous. And so shall he, aunswered *Nico*, for I have seene a fresh example, though it be not very fit to be knowen. Come, come, sayde *Pas*, be not so squeamish, I knowe thou longest more to tell it, then we to heare it. But for all his wordes *Nico* would not bestowe his voyce till he was generally entreated of all the rest. And then with a merry marriage looke, he sang this following discourse, for with a better grace he could sing then tell.

A Neighbor mine not long agoe there was,
(But namelesse he, for blamelesse he shall be)
That married had a trick and bonny lasse
As in a sommer day a man might see:
 But he himselfe a foule unhansome groome,
 And farre unfit to hold so good a roome.

Now whether mov'd with selfe unworthines,
Or with her beawtie fit to make a pray,
Fell jealousie did so his braine oppresse,
That if he absent were but halfe a day,
 He gest the worst (you wot what is the worst)
 And in himselfe new doubting causes nurst.

While thus he fear'd the silly innocent,
Who yet was good, because she knewe none ill,
Unto his house a jollie shepeheard went,
To whome our prince did beare a great good will,
 Because in wrestling and in pastorall
 He farre did passe the rest of Shepheards all.

And therefore he a courtier was benamed,
And as a courtier was with cheere receaved,
(For they have toongs to make a poore man blamed.
If he to them his dutie misconceaved)
 And for this Courtier should well like his table,
 The goodman bad his wife be serviceable.

And so she was, and all with good intent,
But fewe dayes past while she good maner us'de,
But that her husband thought her service bent
To such an end as he might be abus'de.
　　Yet like a coward fearing strångers pride,
　　He made the simple wench his wrath abide.

With chumpish lookes, hard words, and secret nips,
Grumbling at her when she his kindnes sought,
Asking her how she tasted Courtiers lips,
He forst her thinke that which she never thought.
　　In fine he made her gesse, there was some sweet
　　In that which he so fear'd that she should meet.

When once this entred was, in womans hart,
And that it had enflam'd a new desire,
There rested then, to play a womans part,
Fuell to seeke and not to quench the fire :
　　But (for his jealous eye she well did finde)
　　She studied cunning how the same to blinde.

And thus she did. One day to him she came,
And (though against his will) on him she leand,
And out gan cry, ah well away for shame,
If you helpe not our wedlocke will be staind,
　　The goodman starting, askt what did her move ?
　　She sigh'd and sayd, the bad guest sought her love.

He little looking that she should complaine
Of that, whereto he feard she was enclinde,
Bussing her oft, and in his hart full faine,
He did demaunde what remedy to finde ;
　　How they might get that guest, from them to wend,
　　And yet the prince (that lov'd him) not offend.

Husband, quoth she, go to him by and by,
And tell him you do finde I doo him love,
And therefore pray him that of courtesie
He will absent himselfe, least he should move
　　A young girles hart, to that were shame for both,
　　Whereto you knowe, his honest harte were loath.

THE COUNTESSE OF PEMBROKES

Thus shall you show that him you do not doubt,
And as for me (sweete husband) I must beare.
Glad was the man when he had heard her out,
And did the same, although with mickle feare.
　For feare he did, least he the young man might
　In choller put, with whom he would not fight.

The Courtlie shepheard much agast at this,
Not seeing earst such token in the wife,
Though full of scorne, would not his duty misse,
Knowing that evill becommes a houshold strife,
　Did goe his way, but sojourn'd neere thereby,
　That yet the ground hereof he might espie.

The wife thus having settled husbands braine,
Who would have sworne his spowse Diana was,
Watched when she a furder point might gaine,
Which little time did fitlie bring to passe.
　For to the Courte her man was calld by name,
　Whither he needes must goe for feare of blame.

Three dayes before that he must sure depart,
She written had (but in a hand disguisde)
A letter such which might from either part
Seeme to proceede, so well it was devisde.
　She seald it first, then she the sealing brake,
　And to her jealous husband did it take.

With weeping eyes (her eyes she taught to weepe)
She told him that the Courtier had it sent:
Alas, quoth she, thus womens shame doth creepe.
The goodman read on both sides the content,
　It title had, Unto my only love,
　Subscription was, Yours most, if you will prove.

The pistle selfe, such kinde of wordes it had,
My sweetest joy, the comfort of my sprite,
So may thy flockes encrease thy deere hart glad,
So may each thing, even as thou wishest lighte,
　As thou wilt deigne to reade and gentlie reede
　This mourning inck, in which my hart doth bleede.

Long have I lov'd, (alas thou worthy arte)
Long have I lov'd, (alas love craveth love)
Long have I lov'd thy selfe, alas my harte
Doth breake, now toong unto thy name doth move,
  And thinke not that thy answere answere is,
  But that it is my doome of bale or blisse.

The jealous wretch must now to Courte be gone:
Ne can he faile, for prince hath for him sent:
Now is the time we may be here alone,
And geve a long desire a sweet content.
  Thus shall you both reward a lover true,
  And eke revenge his wrong suspecting you.

And this was all, and this the husband read
With chafe enough, till she him pacified:
Desiring, that no griefe in him he bread
Now that he had her words so truely tried:
  But that he would, to him the letter show
  That with his fault he might her goodnes know.

That streight was done with many a boistrous threat,
That to the King, he would his sinne declare,
But now the Courtier gan to smell the feate,
And with some words which shewed little care,
  He stayd untill the goodman was departed,
  Then gave he him the blow which never smarted.

Thus may you see, the jealous wretch was made
The Pandare of the thing, he most did feare,
Take heed therefore, how you ensue that trade,
Least the same markes of jealousie you beare.
  For sure, no jealousie can that prevent,
  Whereto two parties once be full content.

Behold, sayd *Pas*, a whole dicker of wit: he hath pickt out such a tale with intention to keepe a husband from jealosie, which were enough to make a sanctified husband jealous, to see subtleties so much in the feminine gender. But, sayd he, I will strike *Nico* dead, with the wise words shall flowe out of my gorge. And without further entreatie thus sang.

WHo doth desire that chaste his wife should be,
    First be he true, for truth doth truth deserve :
Then such be he, as she his worth may see,
And one man still credit with her preserve.

Not toying kinde, nor causlesly unkinde,
Not sturring thoughts, nor yet denying right
Not spying faults, nor in plaine errors blinde,
Never hard hand, nor ever raines too light.

As farre from want, as farre from vaine expence,
(The one doth force, the later doth entise)
Allow good company, but kepe from thence
Al filthy mouth's that glory in their vice.
    This done, thou hast no more, but leave the rest
    To vertue, fortune, time & womans brest.

Wel cõcluded said *Nico*, When he hath done al, he leaves the
matter to his wives discretion. Now whensoever thou mariest,
let her discretion decke thy head with *Actæons* ornament, *Pas*
was so angrie with his wish, being in deede towards mariage,
that they might perchaunce have falne to buffets, but that *Dicus*
desired *Philisides* (who as a stranger sate among them, revolving
in his mind al the tempests of evil fortunes hee had passed) that
he woulde doe so much grace to the companie, as to sing one of
his country songes. *Philisides* knowing it no good maners to be
squemish of his comming, having put himself in their company,
without further studie began to utter that, wherewith his
thoughtes were then (as alwaies) most busied : and to shew what
a straunger he was to himselfe, spake of himselfe as of a thirde
person, in this sorte.

THe ladd Philisides
    Lay by a rivers side,
In flowry fielde a gladder eye to please :
His pipe was at his foote
His lambs were him besides,
A widow turtle neere on bared rootes
Sate wailing without bootes.
Each thing both sweet & sadd
Did draw his boyling braine
To thinke, & thinke with paine
Of Miras *beames eclipst by absence bad.*

And thus, with eyes made dimme
With teares, he saide, or sorrow said for him.
O earth, once answere give,
So may thy stately grace
By north, or south still rich adorned live:
So Mira *Long may be*
On thy then blessed face,
Whose foote doth set a heav'n on cursed thee,
I aske, now answere me.
If th' author of thy blisse
Phœbus, *that shepheard high*
Do turne from thee his eye,
Doth not thy selfe, when he long absent is,
Like Rogue, all ragged goe,
And pine away with daily wasting woe?
Tell me you wanton brooke,
So may your sliding race
Shunn lothed-loving bankes with conning crooke:
So in you ever new
Mira *may looke her face,*
And make you faire with shadow of her hue:
So when to pay your due
To mother sea you come,
She chide you not for stay,
Nor beat you for your play,
Tell me if your diverted springs become
Absented quite from you,
Are you not dried? Can you your selves renew?
Tell me you flowers faire
Cowslipp & Columbine,
So may your Make this wholsome springtime aire
With you embraced lie,
And lately thence untwine:
But with dew dropps engendre children by:
So may you never dy,
But pulld by Miras *hande*
Dresse bosome hers or hedd,
Or scatter on her bedd,
Tell me, if husband springtime leave your lande,
When he from you is sent,

Whither not you, languisht with discontent?
Tell me my seely pipe,
So may thee still betide
A clenly cloth thy moistnes for to wipe:
So may the cheries redd
Of Miras *lipps divide*
Their sugred selves to kisse thy happy bedd:
So may her eares be ledd,
Her eares where Musique *lives,*
To heare, &. not despise
The liribliring cries,
Tell, if that breath, which thee thy sounding gives,
Be absent farre from thee,
Absent alone canst thou then piping be?
Tell me my lamb of gold,
So maist thou long abide
The day well fed; the night in faithfull folde:
So grow thy wooll of note,
In time that richly di'de
It may be part of Miras *peticoate,*
Tell me, if wolves the throte
Have cought of thy deare damme,
Or she from thee be staide,
Or thou from her be straide,
Canst thou, poore lamme, become anothers lamme?
Or rather till thou die
Still for thy Dam with bea-waymenting crie?
Tell me ô Turtle true,
So may no fortune breed
To make thee nor thy better-loved rue:
So may thy blessings swarme
That Mira *may thee feede*
With hand & mouth, with lapp & brest keepe warme,
Tell me if greedy arme,
Do fondly take away
With traitor lime the one,
The other left alone,
Tell me poore wretch, parted from wretched pray
Disdaine not you the greene,
Wayling till death shun you not to be seene?

Earth, brooke, flowr's, pipe, lambe, Dove
Say all, & I with them,
Absence is death, or worse, to them that love.
So I unlucky lad
Whome hills from her do hemme,
What fitts me now but teares, & sighings sadd?
O fortune too too badd,
I rather would my sheepe
Thad'st killed with a stroke,
Burnt Caban *lost my cloke,*
When want one hower those eyes which my joyes keepe.
Oh! what doth wailing winne?
Speeche without ende were better not begin.
My song clime thou the winde
Which holland sweet now gently sendeth in,
That on his wings the leavell thou maist finde
To hit, but Kissing hit
Her ear's the weights of wit.
If thou know not for whome thy Master dies,
These markes shall make thee wise:
She is the heardesse faire that shines in darke
And gives her kidds no food, but willow's barke.
This said, at length he ended,
His oft sigh-broken dittie,
Then raise, but raise on leggs: which faintnes bended,
With skinne in sorrow died,
With face the plot of pittie,
With thoughts which thoughts their owne tormentors tried,
He rase, & streight espied
His Ramme, who to recover
The Ewe another loved,
With him proud battell proved.
He envied such a death in sight of lover,
And alwaies westward eying
More envied Phœbus *for his westerne flyinge.*

The whole company would gladly have taken this occasion of requesting *Philisides* in plainer sorte to discover unto them his estate. Which he willing to prevent (as knowing the relation thereof more fit for funeralles than the time of a mariage) began

73

to sing this song he had learned before he had ever subjected his thoughts to acknowledge no Master, but a Mistresse.

A S I my little flocke on Ister banke
 (A little flocke; but well my pipe the couthe)
Did piping leade, the Sunne already sanke
Beyond our worlde, and ere I got my boothe
Each thing with mantle black the night doth scothe;
 Saving the glowe worme, which would curteous be
 Of that small light oft watching shepheards see.

The welkin had full niggardly enclosed
In cofer of dimme clowdes his silver groates,
Icleped starres; each thing to rest disposed:
The caves were full, the mountaines voide of goates:
The birds eyes closd closed their chirping notes.
 As for the Nightingale woodmusiques King,
 It August was, he daynde not then to sing.

Amid my sheepe, though I sawe nought to feare
Yet (for I nothing sawe) I feared sore;
Then founde I which thing is a charge to beare
As for my sheepe I dradded mickle more
Then ever for my selfe since I was bore.
 I sate me downe: for see to goe ne could,
 And sange unto my sheepe lest stray they should.

The songe I sange old Lanquet had me taught,
Lanquet, the shepheard best swift Ister knewe,
For clerkly reed, and hating what is naught,
For faithfull hart, cleane hands, and mouth as true:
With his sweet skill my skillesse youth he drewe,
 To have a feeling tast of him that sitts
 Beyond the heaven, far more beyond your witts.

He said, the Musique best thilke powers pleasd
Was jumpe concorde betweene our wit and will:
Where highest notes to godlines are raisd,
And lowest sinke not downe to jote of ill:
With old true tales: he woont mine eares to fill,
 How sheepheards did of yore, how now they thrive,
 Spoiling their flock, or while twixt them they strive.

He liked me, but pitied lustfull youth:
His good strong staffe my slippry yeares upbore:
He still hop'd well, because he loved truth;
Till forste to parte, with harte and eyes even sore,
To worthy Coriden *he gave me ore,*
 But thus in okes true shade recounted he
 Which now in nights deepe shade sheep heard of me.

Such maner time there was (what time I n'ot)
When all this Earth, this damme or mould of ours
Was onely won'd with such as beastes begot:
Unknowne as then were they that builded towers:
The cattell wild, or tame, in natures bowers
 Might freely rome, or rest, as seemed them:
 Man was not man their dwellings into hem.

The beastes had sure some beastly pollicie:
For nothing can endure where order n'is.
For once the Lion by the Lambe did lie;
The fearefull Hinde the Leopard did kisse:
Hurtles was Tygers pawe and Serpents hisse.
 This thinke I well, the beasts with courage clad
 Like Senators a harmeles empire had.

At which whether the others did repine,
(For envie harbreth most in feeblest hartes)
Or that they all to chaunging did encline,
(As even in beasts their dammes leave chaunging partes)
The multitude to Jove *a suite empartes,*
 With neighing, blaying, braying, and barking,
 Roring, and howling for to have a King.

A King, in language theirs they said they would:
(For then their language was a perfect speech)
The birdes likewise with chirpes, and puing could
Cackling, and chattering, that of Jove *beseech.*
Onely the owle still warnde them not to seech
 So hastily that which they would repent:
 But sawe they would, and he to deserts went.

Jove *wisely said (for wisedome wisely sayes)*
O beasts, take heed what you of me desire.
Rulers will thinke all things made them to please,

And soone forget the swincke due to their hire,
But since you will, part of my heav'nly fire
   I will you lende ; the rest your selves must give,
   That it both seene and felte may with you live.

Full glad they were and tooke the naked sprite,
Which streight the Earth yclothed in his claye :
The Lion, harte ; the Ounce gave active might ;
The Horse, good shape ; the Sparrow, lust to playe ;
Nightingale, voice, entising songes to saye.
   Elephant gave a perfect memorie :
   And Parot, ready tongue, that to applie.

The Foxe gave crafte ; the Dog gave flatterie ;
Asse, pacience ; the Mole, a working thought ;
Eagle, high looke ; Wolfe secrete crueltie :
Monkie, sweet breath ; the Cow, her faire eyes brought ;
The Ermion, whitest skinne, spotted with nought ;
   The sheep, mild-seeming face ; climing, the Beare ;
   The Stagge did give the harme eschewing feare.

The Hare, her sleights ; the Cat, his melancholie ;
Ante, industrie ; and Connie, skill to builde ;
Cranes, order ; Storkes, to be appearing holie ;
Camæleon, ease to chaunge ; Ducke, ease to yelde ;
Crocodile, teares, which might be falsely spilde :
   Ape great thing gave, though he did mowing stand,
   The instrument of instruments, the hand.

Ech other beast likewise his present brings :
And (but they drad their Prince they ought should want)
They all consented were to give him wings :
And aye more awe towards him for to plant,
To their owne worke this priviledge they graunt,
   That from thenceforth to all eternitie,
   No beast should freely speake, but onely he.

Thus Man was made ; thus Man their Lord became :
Who at the first, wanting, or hiding pride,
He did to beastes best use his cunning frame ;
With water drinke, herbes meate, and naked hide,
And fellow-like let his dominion slide ;
   Not in his sayings saying I, but we :
   As if he meant his lordship common be.

But when his seate so rooted he had found,
That they now skilld not, how from him to wend ;
Then gan in guiltlesse earth full many a wound,
Iron to seeke, which gainst it selfe should bend,
To teare the bowels, that good corne should send.
   But yet the common Damme none did bemone ;
   Because (though hurt) they never heard her grone.

Then gan the factions in the beastes to breed ;
Where helping weaker sort, the nobler beastes,
(As Tygers, Leopards, Beares, and Lions seed)
Disdaind with this, in deserts sought their restes ;
Where famine ravine taught their hungrie chestes,
   That craftily he forst them to do ill,
   Which being done he afterwards would kill.

For murthers done, which never erst was seene,
By those great beastes, as for the weakers good,
He chose themselves his guarders for to bene,
Gainst those of might, of whom in feare they stood,
As horse and dogge, not great, but gentle blood :
   Blith were the commons cattell of the fielde,
   Tho when they saw their foen of greatnes kilde.

But they or spent, or made of slender might,
Then quickly did the meaner cattell finde,
The great beames gone, the house on shoulders light :
For by and by the horse faire bitts did binde :
The dogge was in a coller taught his kinde.
   As for the gentle birds like case might rewe
   When falcon they, and gossehauke saw in mewe.

Worst fell to smallest birds, and meanest heard,
Whom now his owne, full like his owne he used.
Yet first but wooll, or fethers off he teard :
And when they were well us'de to be abused,
For hungrie teeth their flesh with teeth he brused :
   At length for glutton taste he did them kill :
   At last for sport their sillie lives did spill.

But yet ô man, rage not beyond thy neede :
Deeme it no glorie to swell in tyrannie.
Thou art of blood ; joy not to see things bleede :

Thou fearest death; thinke they are lothe to die.
A plaint of guiltlesse hurt doth pierce the skie.
And you poore beastes, in patience bide your hell,
Or know your strengths, and then you shall do well.

Thus did I sing, and pipe eight sullen houres
To sheepe, whom love, not knowledge, made to heare,
Now fancies fits, now fortunes balefull flowers:
But then I homewards call'd my lambkins deare:
For to my dimmed eyes began t' appeare
The night growne old, her blacke head waxen gray,
Sure shepherds signe, that morne should soone fetch day.

ACcording to the nature of diverse eares, diverse judgements streight followed: some praising his voice, others his words fit to frame a pastorall stile, others the strangenes of the tale, and scanning what he should meane by it. But old *Geron* (who had borne him a grudge ever since in one of their Eclogues he had taken him up over-bitterly) tooke hold of this occasion to make his revenge, and sayd, He never saw thing worse proportioned, then to bring in a tale of he knewe not what beastes at such a sport-meeting, when rather some song of love, or matter for joyfull melody was to be brought forth. But, said he, This is the right conceipt of young men, who thinke, then they speake wiseliest, when they cannot understand themselves. But little did the melancholike shepherd regard either his dispraises, or the others praises, who had set the foundation of his honour there; where he was most despised. And therefore he returning againe to the traine of his desolate pensivenesse, *Geron* invited *Histor* to answere him in Eclogue-wise; who indeed having bene long in love with the faire *Kala*, and now by *Lalus* overgone; was growne into a detestation of mariage. But thus it was.

Geron. Histor.

Geron.   IN *faith, good* Histor, *long is your delay,*
  From holy marriage sweete and surest meane:
Our foolish lust in honest rules to stay.
  I pray thee doo to Lalus *sample leane:*
Thou seest, how friske, and jolly now he is,
That last day seem'd, he could not chew a beane.

Beleeve me man, there is no greater blisse,
Then is the quiet joy of loving wife;
Which who so wants, halfe of himselfe doth misse.
 Friend without change, playfellow without strife,
Foode without fulnes, counsaile without pride,
Is this sweet doubling of our single life.

Histor. *No doubt to whom so good chance did betide,*
As for to finde a pasture strawed with golde,
He were a foole, if there he did not bide.
 Who would not have a Phœnix *if he could?*
The humming Waspe, if it had not a sting,
Before all flies the Waspe accept I would.
 But this bad world, few golden fieldes doth bring,
Phœnix *but one, of Crowes we millions have:*
The Waspe seemes gay, but is a combrous thing.
 If many Kalaes *our* Arcadia *gave,*
Lalus *example I would soone ensue,*
And thinke, I did my selfe from sorrow save.
 But of such wives we finde a slender crew;
Shrewdnes so stirres, pride so puffes up the hart,
They seldome ponder what to them is due.
 With meager lookes, as if they still did smart;
Puiling, and whimpring, or else scolding flat,
Make home more paine then following of the cart.
 Either dull silence, or eternall chat;
Still contrarie to what her husband sayes;
If he do praise the dog, she likes the cat.
 Austere she is, when he would honest playes;
And gamesome then, when he thinkes on his sheepe;
She bids him goe, and yet from jorney stayes.
 She warre doth ever with his kinsfolke keepe,
And makes them fremb'd, who friends by nature are,
Envying shallow toyes with malice deepe.
 And if forsooth there come some new found ware,
The little coine his sweating browes have got,
Must goe for that, if for her lowres he care:
 Or els; Nay faith, mine is the lucklest lot,
That ever fell to honest woman yet:
No wife but I hath such a man, God wot.

Such is their speech, who be of sober wit;
But who doo let their tongues shew well their rage,
Lord, what bywords they speake, what spite they spit?

The house is made a very lothsome cage,
Wherein the birde doth never sing but cry;
With such a will as nothing can asswage.

Dearely the servants doo their wages buy,
Revil'd for ech small fault, sometimes for none:
They better live that in a gaile doo lie.

Let other fowler spots away be blowne;
For I seeke not their shame, but still me thinkes,
A better life it is to lye alone.

Geron.　　*Who for ech fickle feare from vertue shrinkes,*
Shall in his life embrace no worthy thing:
No mortall man the cuppe of suretie drinkes.

The heav'ns doo not good haps in handfuls bring,
But let us pike our good from out much bad:
That still our little world may know his king.

But certainly so long we may be glad,
While that we doo what nature doth require,
And for th'event we never ought be sad.

Man oft is plag'de with aire, is burnt with fire,
In water drownd, in earth his buriall is;
And shall we not therefore their use desire?

Nature above all things requireth this,
That we our kind doo labour to maintaine;
Which drawne-out line doth hold all humane blisse.

Thy father justly may of thee complaine,
If thou doo not repay his deeds for thee,
In granting unto him a grandsires gaine.

Thy common-wealth may rightly grieved be,
Which must by this immortall be preserved,
If thus thou murther thy posteritie.

His very being he hath not deserved,
Who for a selfe-conceipt will that forbeare,
Whereby that being aye must be conserved.

And God forbid, women such cattell were,
As you paint them: but well in you I finde,
No man doth speake aright, who speakes in feare.

Who onely sees the ill is worse then blind.
These fiftie winters maried have I beene;
And yet finde no such faults in womankind.
 I have a wife worthie to be a Queene,
So well she can command, and yet obay;
In ruling of a house so well shee's seene.
 And yet in all this time betwixt us tway,
We beare our double yoke with such consent,
 That never past foule word, I dare well say.
 But these be your love-toyes, which still are spent
In lawlesse games, and love not as you should,
But with much studie learne late to repent.
 How well last day before our Prince you could
Blinde Cupids *workes with wonder testifie?*
Yet now the roote of him abase you would.
 Goe to, goe to, and Cupid *now applie*
To that where thou thy Cupid *maist avowe,*
And thou shalt finde, in women vertues lie.
 Sweete supple mindes which soone to wisdome bowe
Where they by wisdomes rule directed are,
And are not forst fonde thraldome to allow.
 As we to get are fram'd, so they to spare:
We made for paine, our paines they made to cherish:
We care abroad, and they of home have care.
 O Histor, *seeke within thy selfe to flourish:*
Thy house by thee must live, or els be gone:
And then who shall the name of Histor *nourish?*
 Riches of children passe a Princes throne;
Which touch the fathers hart with secret joy,
When without shame he saith, these be mine owne.
 Marrie therefore; for marriage will destroy
Those passions which to youthfull head doo clime,
Mothers and Nurses of all vaine annoy.

He spake these wordes with such affection, as a curious eye
might easilie have perceyved he liked *Thyrsis* fortune better then
he loved his person. But then in deede did all arise, and went to
the women, where spending all the day, and good part of the
night in dauncing, carolling, and wassalling. Lastly, they left

Thyrsis, where he long desired to be left, and with many unfayned thankes returned everie man to his home. But some of
them having to crosse the way of the two Lodges, might see a
Ladie making dolefull lamentations over a bodie which seemed
dead unto them. But me thinkes *Damætas* cries unto me, if I
come not the sooner to comfort him, he will leave off his golden
worke that hath alreadie cost him so much labour and longing.

The ende of the third Booke.

THE FOURTH BOOKE
OF THE COUNTESSE OF
PEMBROKES ARCADIA.

THE almightie wisedome evermore delighting to shewe the
world, that by unlikeliest meanes greatest matters may come
to conclusion: that humane reason may be the more humbled,
and more willinglie geve place to divine providence: as at the first
it brought in *Damætas* to play a part in this royall pageant, so
having continued him still an actor, now that all things were
growne ripe for an end, made his folly the instrument of revealing that, which far greater cunning had sought to conceale. For
so it fell out that *Damætas* having spent the whole day in breaking up the cumbersome worke of the pastor *Dorus*, and feeling in
all his labour no paine so much, as that his hungrie hopes received
any stay, having with the price of much sweate and wearinesse
gotten up the huge stone, which he thought should have such a
golden lining, the good man in the great bed that stone had made,
founde nothing but these two verses, written upon a broad piece
of velume:

> *Who hath his hire, hath well his labour plast:*
> *Earth thou didst seeke, and store of earth thou hast.*

What an inward discountenance it was to maister *Damætas*,
to finde his hope of wealth turned to poore verses, for which he
never cared much, nothing can describe, but either the feeling in
ones selfe the state of such a minde *Damætas* had, or at least the
bethinking what was *Midas* fancie, when after the great pride he
conceived to be made Judge betweene Gods, he was rewarded
with the ornament of an Asses eares. Yet the deepe apprehen-
sion he had received of such riches, could not so sodainlie loose
the coullor that had so throughlie died his thicke braine, but that
he turned and tossed the poore bowels of the innocent earth, till
the comming on of the night, and the tediousnes of his frutelesse
labor made him content rather to exercise his discontentation at
home then there. But forced he was (his horse being otherwise

83

burthened with digging instruments) to returne, as he came, most part of the way on foote: with such grudging lamentations as a nobler minde would (but more noblie) make for the losse of his mistresse. For so farre had he fed his foolish soule with the expectation of that which he reputed felicitie, that he no lesse accompted himselfe miserable, then if he had falne from such an estate his fancie had embraced. So then home againe went *Damœtas*, punished in conceite, as in conceite he had erred, till he founde himselfe there from a fancied losse falne to essentiall miserie. For entring into his house three houres within night, in steede of the lightsome countenance of *Pamela*, which gave such an inwarde decking to that lodge, as prowdest pallaces might have cause to envie it; and of the gratefull conversation of *Dorus*, whose wittie behaviour made that lonelines to seeme ful of good company: in steed of the loude scolding of *Miso*, and the busie rumbling up and downe of *Mopsa*, which though they were so shorte, as quite contrarie to the others praise-worthines, yet were they farre before them in filling of a house: he founde nothing but a solitarie darkenesse; which as naturally it breedes a kinde of irksome gastfulnes, so it was to him a most present terror, remembring the charge he had left behinde, which hee well knew imported no lesse then his life unto him. Therefore lighting a candle, there was no place a mouse could have dwelled in, but that he with quaking diligence sought into. But when he saw hee could see nothing of that hee most cared for, then became hee the right patterne of a wretch dejected with feare: for crying and howling, knockinge his head to the wall hee began to make pittifull complaintes where no body coulde heare him: and with too much dread he should not recover her, leave all consideration how to recover her. But at length looking like a she goate, when she casts her kidd, for verie sorrow he tooke in his owne behalfe, out of the lodge hee went running as hard as he could; having now received the verie forme of hanging into his consideration. Thus running as a man would gladly have runne from himselfe, it was his foolish fortune to espie, by the glim'ring light of the moone did then yeelde him, one standing aloft among the bowes of a faire ashe. He that would have asked counsell at that time of a dogg, cast up his face, as if his tooth had bene drawing: and with much bending his sight perceived it was mistres *Mopsa*, fitly seated there for wit and dignitie: There

(I wil not say with joye, for how could he tast of joy, whose imagination was falne from a pallace, to a gallowes?) But yet with some refreshing of comfort, in hope he should learne better tidings: of her, he began to crie out: O *Mopsa* my beloved chicken, here am I thine owne father *Damœtas*, never in such a towardnes of hanging, if thou canst not helpe me. But never a word coulde his eloquence procure of *Mopsa*, who indeed was there attending for greater matters. This was yet a newe burthen to poore *Damœtas*, who thought all the worlde was conspired against him: and therefore with a seely choler he began another tune. Thou vile *Mopsa*, saide he, now the vengeance of my fatherly curse light overthwart thee, if thou doe not streight answere me. But neither blessing nor cursing coulde prevaile *Mopsa*, who was now great with childe, with the expectation of her may-game hopes, and did long to be delivered with the thirde time being named. Which by and by followed. For *Damœtas* rubbing his elbowe, stamping and whining, seing neither of these take place, began to throwe stones at her, and withall to conjure her by the name of hellish *Mopsa*. But when he had named her the third time, no chime can more sodainly follow the striking of a Clocke, then shee, verily thinking it was the God, that used her fathers voice, throwing our armes abroade, and not considering she was muffled upon so high a tree, came fluttering down, like a hooded hawke; like enough to have broken her neck, but that the tree full of bowes tossed her from one bow to another, and lastly well brused brought her to receive an unfrindly salutation of the earth. *Damœtas*, as soone as she was downe, came running to her: and finding her so close wrapt, pulled of the scarlet cloake: in good time for her, for with the sorenesse of the fall, if she had not had breath given her, she had delivered a foolish soule to *Pluto*. But then *Damœtas* began a fresh to desire his daughter not to forget the paines he had taken for her in her childhoode (which he was sure she could not remember) and to tell him where *Pamela* was. O good *Apollo*, saide *Mopsa*, if ever thou didest beare love to *Phaethons* mother, let me have a King to my husband. Alas, what speakest thou of *Phaethon*? Saide *Damœtas*: If by thy circumspect meanes I finde not out *Pamela*, thy father will be hanged to morow. It is no matter though he be hanged, answered *Mopsa*: doe but thou make *Dorus* a King, and let him bee my husband, good *Apollo*: for my courage doth much pricke mee towarde him. Ah *Mopsa*, cryed out *Damætas*, where is thy witt? Doest thou not know thy father? How hast thou forgotten thy selfe? I do not aske witt of thee mine owne God, said shee: but I see thou wouldest have me remember my father, and indeede forget my selfe. No, no, a good husband, thou shalt have thy fill of husbandes saide *Damætas*, and doe but answere me my question. O I thanke thee saide *Mopsa*, withall my harte hartely: but let them bee all Kinges. *Damætas* seing no other way prevaile fel downe on his knees, *Mopsa Mopsa*, saide he, doe not thus cruelly torment me: I am already wretched enough, alas either helpe me or tell me thou canst not. She that woulde not bee behinde *Apollo* in curtesie, kneeled downe on thother side, I wil never leave tormenting thee said *Mopsa*, untill thou hast satisfied my longing, but I will proclaime thee a promise breaker, that even *Jupiter* shall heare it. Now by the fostring thou hast receaved in this place save my life saide *Damætas*, now by the faire Ash aunswered *Mopsa*, where thou didest receave so great a good turne, graunt post haste to my burning fancie. O where is *Pamela* saide *Damætas*? O a lustie husband, saide *Mopsa*; *Damætas* that nowe verely assured himselfe, his daughter was madd, beganne utterly to dispaire of his life, and therefore amazedly catching her in his armes, to see whether hee coulde bring her to her selfe, hee might feele the weight of a greate cudgell light upon his shoulders, and for the first greeting hee knew his wife *Misos* voice, by the calling him ribaulde villaine, & asking him whether she coulde not serve his turne as well as *Charita*? For *Miso* having according to *Dorus* counsaile, gone to *Mantinea*, and there harboured her selfe in an olde acquaintaunce house of hers, as soone as tenne of the clocke was striken (where shee had remayned closely all that while, I thinke with such an amiable cheare, as when jealous *Juno* sate crosse-legged, to hinder the child-birth of her husbands love) with open mouth shee went to the Magistrate appointed over such matters, and there with the most scolding invective, her rage rather then eloquence could bring forth, she required his ayde to take *Damætas*, who had lefte his dutie to the Kinge and his daughter, to cõmit adultery in the house of *Charitas* uncle, in the Ondemian streete. But neither was the name of *Charita* remembred, nor any such streete knowne. Yet such was the generall mislike all men had of *Damætas* unworthy advancement, that every man was glad to

make himselfe a minister of that, which might redounde to his
shame, and therfore with *Panike* cries and laughters, there was
no suspected place in all the cittie but was searched for under the
title of *Damætas*; *Miso* ever formost encowraging them with all
the shamefull blasings of his demeanoure, encreasing the sporte
of hunting her husband, with her diligent barking, till at length
having already done both him and her selfe, as much infamous
shame, as such a tonge in such an action might performe, in the
end not being, able to find a thing that was not, to her mare
again she wēt having neither suspition nor rage any thing mitigated. But (leaving behinde her a sufficient comedie of her
tragicall fancies) away homewarde she came, imputing the not
finding her husband, to any chaunce, rather then to his innocencie.
For her harte being apt to receave and nourish a bitter thought
it had so swallowed up a determinate condemnation, that in the
verie anotomie of her spirits one should have found nothing but
divelish disdaine, and hatefull jealousie. In this sorte grunting
out her mischevous spite, shee came by the tree, even as *Damætas*
was making that ill understoode intercession, to his foolish *Mopsa*.
As soone as she harde her husbands voice, she verily thought she
had her playe: and therefore stealing from her mare as softely as
she coulde, shee came creeping and halting behinde him, even as
he thinking his daughters little witts had quite lefte her great
nowle; beganne to take her in his armes; thinking perchaunce
her feeling sence might call her mind partes unto her. But
Miso who sawe nothing but thorowe the coulloure of revengefull anger, established upon the fore-judgement of his trespasse,
undoubtedly resolving that *Mopsa* was *Charita*, *Dorus* had tolde
her of, mumping out her hoarse chafe, she gave him the wooden
salutation you hearde of. *Damætas* that was not so sensible in
any thing as in blows, turned up his blubbred face like a great
lowt newe whipte: Alas thou woman, said hee, what hath thy
poore husband deserved to have his owne ill lucke loaden with
thy displeasure? *Pamela* is lost, *Pamela* is lost. *Miso* still holding
on the course of her former fancie, what tellest thou mee naughtie
varlet of *Pamela*, doest thou thinke that doth aunsweare me, for
abusing the lawes of marriage? Have I brought thee children,
have I bene a true wife unto thee, to bee dispised in mine olde
age? And ever among shee would sawce her speeches with such
Bastonados, that poore *Damætas* beganne now to thinke, that

either a generall madding was falne, or else that all this was but
a vision. But as for visions the smarte of the cudgell put out of
his fancie: and therefore againe turning to his wife, not knowing
in the world what she ment, *Miso* said hee, hereafter thou maiest
examine me, doe but now tell me what is become of *Pamela*.
I will first examine this drabbe said she, and withall let fall her
stafe as hard as she could upon *Mopsa*, still taking her for *Charita*.
But *Mopsa* that was alredy angry, thinking that she had hindred
her from *Apollo*, lepte up and caught her by the throte, like to have
strangled her, but that *Damætas* from a condemned man was faine
to become a judge and part this fraye, such a picture of a rude
discord, where each was out with the other two. And then
getting the opportunitie of their falling out, to holde himselfe in
suretie, who was indeede, the veriest coward of the three, he renewed his earnest demaund of them. But it was a sporte to see,
how the former conceites *Dorus* had printed in their imaginations,
kept still such dominion in them, that *Miso* though now shee
founde and felte it was her daughter *Mopsa*, yet did *Charita*
côtinually passe through her thoughts which she uttered with
such crabbed questions to *Damætas*, that hee not possiblie con-
ceaving any parte of her doubt, remained astonished, and the
astonishment encreased her doubt. And as for *Mopsa*, as first she
did assuredly take him to be *Apollo* and thought her mothers
comming did marre the bargaine: So now much talkinge to and
fro, had delivered so much light, into the mistie mould of her capacitie, as to know him to be her father: Yet remayned there such
foote-steppes of the foretaken opinion, that shee thought verily her
father and mother were hasted thether to gett the first wishe. And
therefore to whatsoever they asked of her, she would never answere, but embracing the tree, as if she feared it had bene running
awaye, nay sayes shee I will have the first wish for I was here
first; which they understoode no more, then *Damætas* did what
Miso ment by *Charita*: till at length with much urging them,
being indeede better able to perswade both, then to meete hande
to hand with either, he prevailed so much with them, as to bring
them into the lodge to see what losse their necligence had
suffered. Then indeed the nere neighborhood they bare to themselves, made them leave other toyes, and look into what dangerous
plight they were all faln, assone as the King should know his
daughters escape. And as for the wemen they beganne a fresh

to enter into their brawling, whether were in the faulte. But
Damætas who did feare that among his other evils, the thunder-
bolt of that storme would fall upon his shoulders, slipte away
from them, but with so maigre a cheare as might much sooner
engender laughter then pittie. O true *Arcadia* would he say
(tearinge his haire and bearde, & somtime for too much woe,
making unweldie somersaults) how darest thou beare upon thee
such a felonious traytor as I am? And you false harted trees,
why woulde you make no noyse, to make her ungratious departure known? Ah *Pamela Pamela*, how often whẽ I brought
thee in fine posies of all coulored flowers wouldest thou clappe
me on the cheek, and say thou wouldst be on day even with
me? Was this thy meaning to bring me to an evẽ paire of
gallows? Ah il taught *Dorus* that camest hither to learne good
maners of me? Did I ever teach thee to make thy maister sweate
out his hart for nothing, & in the meane time to run away with
thy mistres? O my dun cow, I did think sõe evil was towards
me, ever since the last day thou didst run away from me, & held
up thy taile so pitifully: did not I se an eagle kil a Cuckoe,
which was a plain fore token unto me *Pamela* should be my
destruꝰtiõ? O wife *Miso* (if I durst say it to thy face) why didst
thou suspeꝰt thy husbãd, that loveth a peece of chese better then
a womã? And thou litle *Mopsa* that shalt inherite the shame
of thy fathers death, was it time for thee to clime trees, which
should so shortly be my best buriall? ô that I could live without
death, or die before I were aware. O hart why hast thou no
hands at commaundement to dispatch thee? O hands why want
you a hart to kill this villanie? In this sorte did he invey against
every thing, sometimes thinking to have away, while it was yet
night: but he that had included all the world within his shepe-
cote, thought that worse thẽ any death sometime for dread of
hanging hee ment to hange himselfe: finding as in deede it is,
that feare is farre more paynfull to cowardise, then death to a true
courage. But his fingers were nothing nimble in that aꝰtion; &
any thing was let inough thereto, he being a true lover of himselfe
without any ryvall. But lastly guided by a farre greater con-
stellacion then his owne, he remembred to search the other lodge
where it might be *Pamela* that night had retired her selfe. So
thether with trembling hammes hee carried himselfe, but em-
ployinge his double keye which the Kinge for speciall credit had

unworthylie bestowed upon him, hee found all the gates so
barred, that his key could not prevaile, saving onely one trapt
doore which went down into a vault by the seller which as it
was unknowen of *Pyrocles* so had he lefte it unregarded. But
Damætas that ever knew the buttery better then any other place,
got in that way and pasing softly to *Philocleas* chamber, where he
thought most likely to finde *Pamela*, the doore being left open hee
entred in, and by the light of the lampe, he might discerne on
in bed with her : which he although hee tooke to bee *Pamela*, yet
thinking no suretie enough in a matter touchinge his necke, hee
went heard to the bedside of these unfortunate lovers, whoe at
that time being not much before the breake of day (whether it
were they were so divinely surprised, to bring this whole matter
to be destinied conclusion, or that the unresistable force of their
sorrowes, had overthrowne the wakefull use of their senses) were
as then possessed, with a mutuall sleep) yet not forgetting with
viny embracements, to give any eye a perfect modell of affection.
But *Damætas* looking with the lampe in his hande but neither
with such a face nor mind) upon these excellent creatures, as
Psyche did upon her unknowen lover, and giving every way freedome to his fearefull eyes, did not onely perceave it was *Zelmane*
and therefore much different from the Lady hee sought : but
that this same *Zelmane* did more differ from the *Zelmane* hee and
others had ever taken her for, wherein the chaunge of her apparell
chiefely confirmed his opinion satisfied with that, and not thinking
it good to awake the sleeping Lyon, he went downe againe,
taking with him *Pyrocles* sworde, (wherewith upon his sleight
undersute *Pyrocles* came onely apparelled thether) being sure to
leave no weapon in the chamber, and so making the doore as
fast as hee coulde on the outside, hopinge with the revealing of
this, (as hee thought greater fault) to make his owne the lesse,
or at least that this injurie would so fill the Kinges head, that
he should not have leysure to chastice his necligence (like a fool
not considering that the more rage breeds the crueller punishment) he went first into the Kings chamber, and not finding
him there, he ranne downe crying with open mouth, the Kinge
was betrayde, and that *Zelmane* did abuse his daughter. The
noise he made being a man of no few wordes joyned to the
yelping sound of *Miso*, and his unpleasant enheritrix brought
together some number of the shepheards, to whom he without

any regard of reserving it for the Kinges knowledge spattered out the bottom of his stomacke, swearing by him he never knew that *Zelmane* whom they had taken all that while to be a woman, was as arrant a man as himselfe was, whereof hee had seene sufficient signes and tokens; and that hee was as close as a butterflie with the Ladie *Philoclea*, the poore men jealous of their Princes honour, were readie with weapons to have entred the lodge; standing yet in some pause, whether it were not best, first to heare some newes from the King himselfe, when by the sodaine comming of other shepheards which with astonished lookes ranne from one crie to the other their griefes were surcharged, with the evil tydings of the Kings death. Turning therefore all their minds and eyes that way, they ranne to the Cave where they said he lay dead, the Sunne beginning now to send some promise of comming light, making hast I thinke to bee spectator of the folowing tragedies. For *Basilius* having past over the night more happie in contemplation then action, having had his spirits sublymed with the sweete imagination of embrasing the most desired *Zelmane*, doubting least the Caves darknes might deceave him in the dayes approch, thought it nowe season to returne to his wedlocke bed, remembring the promise he had made *Zelmane*, to observe due orders towards *Gynecia*. Therefore departing but not departing without bequeathing by a will of wordes, sealed with many kisses, a full guifte of all his love and life to his misconceaved bedfellowe, he went to the mouth of the Cave, there to apparel himselfe, in which doing the motion of his joye coulde not bee bridled from uttering such like wordes. Blessed be thou O night said he, that hast with thy sweete winges shrowded mee in the vale of blisse it is thou that art the first gotten childe of time, the day hath bene but an usurper upon thy delightfull inheritaunce, thou invitest all living thinges to comfortable rest, thou arte the stop of strife and the necessarie truce of aproching battels. And therewith hee sange these verses, to confirme his former prayses:

O *Night the ease of care the pledge of pleasure,*
Desires best meane, harnest of hartes affected,
The seate of peace, the throne which is erected
Of humane life to be the quiet measure,

Be victor still of Phœbus *golden treasure:*
Who hath our sight with too much sight infected,
Whose light is cause we have our lives neglected
Turning all natures course to selfe displeasure.

These stately starrs in their now shining faces,
With sinlesse sleepe, and silence wisdomes mother,
Witnesse his wrong which by thy helpe is eased:

Thou arte therefore of these our desart places
The sure refuge, by thee and by no other
My soule is bliste, sence joyde, and fortune raysed.

And yet farther would his joyes needes breake foorth. O
Basilius, sayde he, the rest of thy time, hath bene but a dreame
unto thee: it is now onely thou beginnest to live, now onely
thou hast entred into the way of blisfulnes. Should fancie of
marriage keepe me from this paradise ? Or opinion of I know
not what promise binde me from paying the right duties to
nature and affection ? O who woulde have thought there could
have been such difference betwixt women? Bee jealous no more
O *Gynecia,* but yeelde to the preheminence of more excellent
guiftes, supporte thy selfe with such marble pillers as she doth,
decke thy brest with those alablaster boules that *Zelmane* doth:
then accompanied with such a tittle, perhapes thou maist recover
the possession of my otherwise enclined love. But alas *Gynecia*
thou canst not shew such evidence ; therefore thy plea is vaine.
Gynecia hearde all this hee saide who had cast about her *Zelmanes*
garment, wherein she came thether, and had followed *Basilius*
to the Caves entrie; full of inward vexation, betwixt the deadly
accusation of her own guiltines, and the spitefull doubt shee had
Zelmane had abused her. But because of the one side (finding
the King did thinke her to be *Zelmane* she had libertie to imagine
it might rather be the Kings owne unbridled enterprise, which
had barred *Zelmane,* then *Zelmanes* cunning deceiving of her, and
that of the other if shee shoulde heddilie seeke a violent revenge
her owne honour might bee as much interessed, as *Zelmane* endaungered: she fell to this determination. First with fine handling
of the King to settle in him a perfect good opinion of her, and
then as shee shoulde learne, how things had passed, to take into
her selfe new devised counsaile, but this beinge her first action,

having geven unlooked for attendaunce to the King, she heard with
what partiality he did prefer her to her self, she saw in him how
much fancy doth not onely darken reasō but beguile sence shee
foūd opinion Mistres of the lovers judgement, which serving as a
good lesson to her good conceite, she went out to *Basilius*, setting
her selfe in a grave behaviour and stately silence before him : untill
he, (who at the first thinking her by so much˙ shadow as he
could see to bee *Zelmane*, was beginning his loving ceremonies)
did now being helped by the peeping light, wherewith the
morning did overcome the nights darkenes, knowe her face and
his error, which acknowledging in himself with starting back
from her, she thus with a modest bitternes spake unto him : Alas
my Lorde, well did your wordes discipher your minde, and well be
those wordes confyrmed with this gesture. Verie loathsome must
that woman be, from whome a man hath cause to goe backe ;
and little better liked is that wife, before whome the husband
preferrs them hee never knewe. Alas, hath my faithfull observing
my parte of duety made you thinke your selfe ever a whit the
more exempted ? Hath that which should claime gratefulnes,
bene a cause of contempt ? Is the being the mother of *Pamela*,
become an odious name unto you ? If my life hetherto ledde
have not avoyded suspicion ? If my violated truth to you be
deseruing of any punishment, I refuse not to be chastised with
the most cruell torment of your displeasure, I refuse not misery,
purchased by mine owne merite. Hard I must needes saye,
(although till now I never thought I should have had cause to saye)
is the destinie of womankinde, the tryall of whose vertue must
stande upon the loving of them, that employe all theyr industrie
not to be beloved. If *Zelmanes* young yeares had not had so much
gravitie hidden under a youthfull face, as your graye heares
have bene but the visar of unfitting youthfulnes, your vicious
minde had brought some fruites of repentance, and *Gynæcia* might
then have bene with much more right so basely despised.

    Basilius that was more ashamed to see himselfe so overtaken,
then *Vulcan* was, when with much cunning hee proved himselfe
a Cuckolde, beganne to make certayne extravagant excuses : but
the matter in it selfe hardly brooking any purgacion, with the
suddainnes of the time, which barred any good conjoyned invention, made him sometimes alledge one thing, to which by
and by he would bring in a contrarye, one time with flat denyall,

another time with mitigating the fault, now brave, then humble, use such a stammering defensive, that *Gynæcia*, the violence of whose sore in deede ranne another waye, was content thus to fasten up the last stitch of her anger. Well, well my Lorde, sayde she, it shall well become you so to governe your selfe, as you may be fit rather to direct me, then to be judged of me; and rather to be a wise maister of me, then an unskilfull pleader before me. Remember the wrong you have done is not onely to me, but to your children, whome you had of mee : to your countrey, when they shall finde they are commaunded by him, that can not commaund his owne undecent appetites : lastly to your selfe, since with these paynes you do but build up a house of shame to dwell in : if from those moveable goods of nature (wherewith, in my fyrst youth my royall parents bestowed me uppon you) bearing you children, and encrease of yeares have withdrawen me, consider I pray you, that as you are cause of the one, so in the other, time hath not left to worke his never-fayling effectes in you. Truly, truly Sir, very untimely are these fyres in you : it is time for us both to let reason enjoye his due soveraigntie. Let us not plant anewe those weedes, which by natures course are content to fade.

Basilius that would rather then his life the matter had bene ended, the best rethorike he had, was flat demanding pardon of her, swearing it was the very force of *Apollos* destenye which had caryed him thus from his owne bias ; but that nowe like as farre travellers were taught to love their owne countrie, he had such a lesson without booke, of affection unto her, as he would repay the debt of this error with the interest of a great deale more true honour then ever before he had done her : neyther am I to geve pardon to you my Lord, sayd she, nor you to beare honour to me. I have taken this boldnes for the unfayned love I owe unto you, to deliver my sorrowe unto you ; much more for the care I have of your well doing, then for any other selfe fancie. For well I knowe that by your good estate my life is mayntayned, neyther, if I would, can I separate my selfe from your fortune. For my parte therefore I clayme nothing but that which may be safest for your selfe ; my life, will, honor, and what soever else, shall be but a shadow of that bodie. How much *Basilius* owne shame had found him culpable, and had alreadie even in soule read his owne condemnacion, so much did this

unexpected mildnes of *Gynæcia* captive his harte unto her, which
otherwise perchaunce would have growne to a desperat carelesnes. Therefore embracing her, and confessing that her vertue
shined in his vice, he did even with a true resolved minde vowe
unto her, that as long as he unworthie of her did live, she should
be the furthest and onlie limit of his affection. He thanked the
destenies, that had wrought her honour out of his shame, and
that had made his owne striving to goe amisse, to be the best
meane ever after to hold him in the right pathe. Thus reconciled
to *Basilius* great contentacion, who began something to marke
himselfe in his owne doings, his hard hap guided his eye to the
cuppe of golde, wherein *Gynæcia* had put the lickourment for
Zelmane, and having fayled of that guest, was now carrying it
home agayne. But he whome perchaunce sorrowe, perchaunce
some long disaccustomed paynes, had made extremely thirstie,
tooke it out of her handes, although she directly tolde him, both
of whome she had it, what the effect· of it was, and the little
proofe she had seene thereof; hiding nothing from him, but
that she ment to minister it to another pacient. But the Duke
whose belly had no eares, and much drouthe kept from the
desiring a taster, finding it not unpleasant to his pallate, dranke
it almost off, leaving very little to cover the cuppes bottome.
But within a while that from his stomacke the drincke had
delivered to his principall vaynes his noysome vapours, first with
a painefull stretching, and forced yawning, then with a darke
yellownes dyeng his skinne, and a colde deadlie sweate principally about his temples, his bodie by naturall course longing to
deliver his heavie burden to his earthly damme, wanting force
in his knees, which utterly abandoned him, with heavie fall gave
some proofe whether the operation of that unknowne potion
tended. For with pang-like grones, and gastly turning of his
eyes, immediatlie all his limmes stiffened, and his eyes fixed, he
having had time to declare his case only in these wordes. O
Gynæcia I dye. Have care : of what or how much further he
would have spoken, no man can tell. For *Gynæcia* having well
perceyved the changing of his cullour, and those other evill
signes, yet had not looked for such a sodaine overthrowe, but
rather had bethought her selfe what was best for him, when she
sodainely sawe the matter come to that periode, comming to
him, and neyther with any cryes getting a worde of him, nor

with any other possible meanes, able to bring any living action from him, the height of all ouglie sorrowes did so horriblie appeare before her amazed minde, that at the first, it did not only distract all power of speech from her, but almost wit to consider, remayning as it were quicke buried in a grave of miseries. Her paynefull memorie had streight filled her with the true shapes of all the fore-past mischiefes, her reason began to crye out against the filthye rebellion of sinfull sense, and to teare it selfe with anguish, for having made so weake a resistance, her conscience a terrible witnes of the inwarde wickednes, still nourishing this debatefull fyre; her complaynte nowe not having an ende to be directed unto something to disburden sorrowe, but a necessary downefall of inwarde wretchednes. She sawe the rigour of the lawes was like to lay a shamefull death upon her, which being for that action undeserved, made it the more insupportable, and yet in deapth of her soule most deserved, made it more miserable. At length letting her tong goe as her dolorous thoughts guided it, she thus with lamentable demeanour spake.

O bottomles pit of sorrowe, in which I cannot conteyne my selfe, having the fyrebrands of all furyes within me, still falling, and yet by the infinitenes of it never falne. Neyther can I ridde myselfe, being fettred with the everlasting consideracion of it. For whether should I recommend the protection of my dishonored fall ? to the earth ? it hath no life, and waites to be encreased by the reliques of my shamed carcasse : to men ? who are alwayes cruell in their neighboures faultes, and make others overthrowe become the badge of their ill masked vertue? to the heavens? ô unspeakeable torment of conscience, which dare not looke unto them. No sinne can enter there, oh there is no receipt for polluted mindes. Whether then wilt thou leade this captive of thine, ô snakye despayre ? Alas, alas, was this the free-holding power that accursed poyson had graunted unto me, that to be held the surer it should deprive life ? was this the folding in mine armes promised, that I should fould nothing but a dead body ? O mother of mine, what a deathfull sucke have you geven me ? O *Philoclea, Philoclea*, well hath my mother revenged uppon me my unmotherly hating of thee. O *Zelmane*, to whome yet (least any miserye should fayle me) remayne some sparkes of my detestable love, if thou hast (as now alas! now my minde assures me thou hast) deceaved me, there is a fayre stage prepared for thee, to see the tragicall ende of thy hated loves. With that worde there flowed out two rivers of teares out of her fayre eyes, which before were drye, the remembraunce of her other mischiefes being dryed up in a furious fyre of selfe detestation, love only according to the temper of it melting it selfe into those briny tokens of passion. Then turning her eyes agayne upon the body, she remembred a dreame she had had some nights before, wherein thinking herselfe called by *Zelmane*, passing a troublesome passage, she found a dead body which tolde her there should be her only rest. This no sooner caught holde of her remembraunce, then that she determining with her selfe, it was a directe vision of her fore-appoynted ende, tooke a certayne resolucion to embrace death, assoone as it. should be offred unto her, and no way to seeke the prolonging of her annoyed life. And therefore kissing the cold face of *Basilius*; And even so will I rest sayd she, and joyne this faultye soule of mine to thee, if so much the angry gods will graunt mee.

As shee was in this plight, the Sunne nowe climing over our Horizon, the first Shepherds came by, who seeing the King in that case, and hearing the noyse *Damætas* made of the Lady *Philoclea*, ranne with the dolefull tidings of *Basilius* death unto him, who presently with all his company came to the Caves entrye where the Kings body lay. *Damætas* for his parte more glad for the hope he had of his private escape, then sorye for the publike losse his Countrie receaved for a Prince not to be misliked. But in *Gynæcia* nature prevayled above judgement ; and the shame shee conceaved to be taken in that order, overcame for that instant the former resolucion, so that assoone as she sawe the formost of the pastorall troupe, the wretched Princesse ranne to have hid her face in the next woods, but with such a minde, that she knewe not almost her selfe what she could wish to be the grounde of her safetie. *Damætas* that sawe her runne awaye in *Zelmanes* upper rayment, and judging her to be so, thought certaynely all the spirits in hell were come to play a Tragedie in these woods, such strange change he sawe every way. The King dead at the Caves mouth ; the Queene as hee thought absent; *Pamela* fledde away with *Dorus*; his wife and *Mopsa* in divers franzies. But of all other things *Zelmane* conquered his

97

capacitie, sodainly from a woman growne to a man; and from a lockt chamber gotten before him into the fieldes, which hee gave the rest quicklie to understande; for in steede of doing any thing as the exigent required, he beganne to make circles, and all those fantasticall defences that hee had ever hearde were fortifications against Divells. But the other Shepheards who had both better wittes, and more faith, forthwith devided themselves, some of them running after *Gynecia*, and esteeming her running away, a great condemnation of her owne guiltinesse; others going to their Prince, to see what service was left for them eyther in recoverie of his life, or honoring his death. They that went after the Queene, had soone overtaken her, in whome nowe the fyrst feares were stayde, and the resolucion to dye had repossessed his place in her minde. But when they sawe it was the Queene, to whome besides the obedient dutie they ow'de to her state, they had alwayes carried a singuler love, for her courteous liberalities, and other wise and vertuous partes, which had filled all that people with affection and admiracion. They were all sodainely stopped, beginning to aske pardon for their followinge her in that sorte, and desiring her to be their good Ladie, as she had ever bene. But the Queene who nowe thirsted to be ridde of her selfe, whome she hated above all thinges with such an assured countenance as they have, who alreadie have dispensed with shame, and digested the sorrowes of death, she thus sayde unto them. Continue, continue, my friends: your doing is better then your excusing, the one argues assured faith, the other want of assurance. If you loved your Prince, when he was able and willing to doo you much good, which you could not then re-quite to him ; doo you now publish your gratefulnes, when it shall be seene to the world, there are no hopes left to leade you unto it. Remember, remember you have lost *Basilius* a Prince to defend you, a Father to care for you, a companyon in your joyes, a friend in your wants. And if you loved him, shew you hate the author of his losse. It is I, faithfull *Arcadians*, that have spoyled the Countrie of their protector. I, none but I, was the minister of his unnaturall end. Cary therfore my blood in your hãds, to testifie your own innocencie, neither spare for my titles sake, but consider it was he that so entituled me. And if you think of any benefits by my meanes, thinke with it that I was but the instrumēt and he the spring. What stay ye

Shepheards whose great Shepheard is gone? you neede not feare a woman, reverence your Lords murtherer, nor have pittie of her, who hath not pittie of herself. With this she presented her faire neck; some by name, others by signes, desired them to do justice to the world, dutie to their good king, honor to themselves, and favour to her. The poore men looked one upon the other, unused to be arbiters in Princes matters, and being now falne into a great perplexitie, betwixt a Prince dead and a Princesse alive. But once for them she might have gone whether she would, thinking it a sacriledge to touch her person, when she finding she was not a sufficiēt oratour to perswade her own death by their hāds, well, said she, it is but so much more time of miserie, for my part I will not geve my life so much pleasure from hence forward as to yeeld to his desire of his own choise of death; since all the rest is taken away, yet let me excell in miserie. Leade me therfore whether you will; only happy, because I can not be more wretched. But neyther so much would the honest Shepheards do, but rather with many teares bemoned this encrease of their former losse, till she was faine to leade them, with a very strange spectacle, either that a Princesse should be in the hands of Shepheards, or a prisoner should direct her gardiens: lastly, before either witnes or accuser, a Lady condemne her selfe to death. But in such monefull march they went towards the other Shepheards, who in the meane time had left nothing unassaied to revive the King, but all was bootles; and their sorrowes encreased the more they had suffred any hopes vainly to arise. Among other trialls they made to know at least the cause of his end, having espied the unhappy cup, they gave the little liquor that was left to a dogge of *Damætas*, in which within a short time it wrought the like effect; although *Damætas* did so much to recover him, that for very love of his life he dasht out his braines. But now all together and having *Gynæcia* among them, who to make her selfe the more odious, did continuallie record to their mindes the excesse of their losse, they yelded themselves over to all those formes of lamentacion that dolefull images do imprint in the honest but over tender hartes; especially when they thinke the rebound of the evill falls to their owne smart. Therefore after the auncient greeke maner, some of them remembring the nobilitie of his birth, continued by being like his Auncestors:

others his shape, which though not excellent, yet favour and pittie drew all things now to the highest point; others his peaceable government, the thing which most pleaseth men resolved to live of their owne; others his liberalitie, which though it cannot light upon all men, yet men naturallie hoping it may be, they make it a most amiable vertue. Some calling in question the greatnes of his power, which encreased the compassion to see the present change, (having a dolefull memorie how he had tempered it with such familier curtesie among them, that they did more feele the fruites, then see the pompes of his greatnes) all with one consent geving him the sacred titles of good, just, mercifull, the father of the people, the life of his Countrie, they ranne about his body, tearing their beards and garments; some sending their cryes to heaven, other inventing perticular howling musicke; manie vowing to kill themselves at the day of his funeralls, generallie geving a true testimonye, that men are loving creatures when injuries put them not from their naturall course: and howe easily a thing it is for a Prince by succession, deeplie to sinke into the soules of his subjects, a more lively monument then *Mausolus* Tombe. But as with such hartie lamentacion, they dispersed among those woods their resounding shrikes, the Sunne the perfectest marke of time, having now gotten up two howres journey in his dayly changing Circle, their voice helped with the only answering Echo, came to the eares of the faithfull and worthy Gentleman *Philanax*: who at that time was comming to visite the King, accompanyed with divers of the worthie *Arcadian* Lords, who with him had visited the places adjoyning for the more assurance of *Basilius* solitarines, a thing after the late mutinie he had usually done, and since the Princesses returne more diligentlie continued, which having nowe likewise performed, thinking it as well his duty to see the King as of good purpose, being so neare, to receyve his further direction: accompanied as above sayd he was this morning comming unto him, when these unpleasant voices gave his minde an uncertaine presage of his neere approching sorow. For by and by he saw the bodie of his dearely esteemed Prince, and heard *Gynecias* lamenting: not such as the turtle-like love is wont to make for the ever over-soone losse of her only loved make, but with cursings of her life, detesting her owne wickednes, seeming only therefore not to desire death, because she would not shew a love of any thing. The Shepheards, especially *Damætas*, knowing him to be the second person in Aucthoritie, gave forthwith relacion unto him, what they knewe and had proved of this dolorous spectacle, besides the other accidents of his children. But he principally touched with his maisters losse, lighting from his horse with a heavie cheare, came and kneeled downe by him, where finding he could do no more then the Shepheards had for his recoverie, the constancie of his minde, surprised before he might call together his best rules, could not refraine such like words. Ah deere maister, sayd he, what change it hath pleased the Almightie Justice to worke in this place? How soone (not to your losse, who having lived long to nature, and to time longer by your well deserved glorie, but longest of all in the eternall mansion you now possesse) But how soone I say to our ruine, have you left the fraile barke of your estate? O that the words in most faithfull dutie delivered unto you, when you first entred this solitarie course, might have wrought as much perswasion in you, as they sprang from truth in me perchaunce your servaunt, *Philanax* should not nowe have cause in your losse, to bewayle his owne overthrowe. And therewith taking himselfe; and in deede evill fitteth it me, sayde he, to let goe my harte to womanish complaints, since my Prince being undoubtedly well, it rather shewes love of my selfe, which makes me bewaile mine owne losse. No, the true love must be proved in the honor of your memorie, and that must be shewed with seeking just revenge upon your unjust and unnaturall enemies; and farre more honorable it will be for your Tombe, to have the blood of your murderers sprinkled upon it, then the teares of your friendes. And if your soule looke downe uppon this miserable earth, I doubt not it had much rather your death were accompanyed with well deserved punishment of the causers of it, then with the heaping on it more sorrowes with the ende of them, to whome you vouchsafed your affection, let them lament that have woven the webbe of lamentacion; let theyr owne deathes make them crye out for your death that were the authors of it. Therewith carying manfull sorowe and vindicatife resolucion in his face, he rose up, so looking on the poore guiltlesse princesse transported with an unjust justice, that his eyes were sufficient herauldes for him, to denounce a mortall hatred. She, (whome furies of love, firebrands of her conscience, shame of the

world, with the miserable losse of her husband, towardes whome
nowe the disdaine of her selfe bred more love; with the remembrance of her vision, wherewith she resolved assuredly the Gods
had appointed that shamefull end to be her resting place, had set
her mind to no other way but to death) used such like speeches
to *Philanax*, as she had before to the Shepheards; willing him not
to looke upon her as a woman, but a monster; not as a princesse,
but a traytor to his prince; not as *Basilius* wife, but as *Basilius*
murtherer. She tolde him howe the worlde required at his handes,
the just demonstration of his friendship, if hee nowe forgot his
Prince, hee shoulde shewe hee had never loved but hys fortune:
like those vermine that sucke of the living bloud, and leave the
body assoone as it is dead, poore Princesse needelesly seeking to
kindle him, who did most deadly detest her, which he uttered
in this bitter answere. Madame saide he, you do well to hate
your selfe, for you cannot hate a worse creature; and though we
feele enough your hellish disposition, yet we neede not doubt
you are of counsell to your selfe of much worse then we know.
But now feare not, you shall not long be combred with being
guided by so evell a soule, therefore prepare your selfe that if it
be possible you may deliver up your spirit so much purer, as you
more wash your wickednes with repentaunce. Then having
presently given order for the bringing from *Mantinea*, a great
number of tents, for the receipt of the principall *Arcadians* :
the maner of that countrie being, that where the Prince died,
ther should be orders taken for the countries government, and
in the place any murther was committed, the judgement should
be given ther, before the body was buried, both concurring in
this matter, and alredy great parte of the Nobilitie being arived,
he delivered the Princes to a gentleman of greate trust, and as
for *Damætas* taking from him the keyes of both the lodges, calling
him the moth of his Princes estate, and onely spot of his judgement, he caused him with his wife and daughter, to bee fettered
up in as manye chaines and clogges, as they coulde beare, and
every thirde howre to bee cruelly whipt, till the determinate
judgement should be given of all these matters. That done
having sent alredy at his comming, to all the quarters of the
countrie to seeke *Pamela*, although with smal hope of overtaking
them, he himself went wel accompanied to the lodge where the
two unfortunate lovers were attending a cruell conclusion, of

their long painefull, and late most painefull affection, *Damætas*
clownish eyes, having ben the onely discoverers of *Pyrocles*
stratagem, had no sooner taken a full vewe of them (which in
some sightes would rather have bred any thing, then an accusing
minde) and looked the doore upon these two yong folkes, now
made prisoners for love, as before they had bene prisoners to
love; But that imediatly upon his going downe, (whether with
noyse *Damætas* made, or with the creeping in of the light, or
rather that as extreame griefe had procured his sleepe, so extreame
care had measured his sleepe, givinge his sences a very early
salüe to come to themselves) *Pyrocles* awaked; And being up the
first evill hansell he had of the ill case wherein he was, was the
seeing himselfe deprived of his sworde, from which he had never
seperated himselfe in any occasion, and even that night first by
the Kinges bedd, and then there had laid it, as he thought safe:
putting great parte of the trust of his well doing in his owne
cowrage so armed. For indeed the confidence in ones self is the
chiefe nurse of magnanimitie, which confidence notwithstanding
doth not leave the care of necessarie furnitures, for it : and
therefore of all the Grecians *Homere* doth ever make *Achilles* the
best armed. But that, as I say, was the first ill token : but by
and by he perceaved he was a prisoner before any arest, for the
doore which he had lefte open was made so fast of the outside,
that for all the force he could employe unto it he could not undo
Damætas doing, then went he to the windowes, to see if that
waye, there were any escape for him and his deare Lady, but
as vaine hee founde all his employment there not having might
to breake out but onely one barre, wherin notwithstanding he
strained his sinewes to the uttermost. And that he rather took
out to use for other service, then for any possibilitie he had to
escape, for even then it was, that *Damætas* having gathered together the first comming sheepheards, did blabber out what hee
had founde in the Ladye *Philocleas* chamber, *Pyrocles* markingly
harkned to all that *Damætas* said, whose voice and minde,
acquaintance had taught him sufficiently to know. But when
he assuredly perceaved that his being with the Lady *Philoclea*
was fullie discovered; & by the follie or malice, or rather
malicious follie of *Damætas* her honour therein touched in the
hiest degree ; remembring withal the crueltie of the *Arcadian*
lawes which without exception did condemn al to death, who

were foũd (as *Damætas* reported of them) in acte of mariage
without solemnitie of mariage; assuring himselfe besides the law,
the King & the Queene, woulde use so much more hate against
their daughter, as they had found themselves sotted by him, in
the pursute of their love; Lastly seing they were not only in
the way of death, but fittly encaged for death, looking with a
hartie griefe upon the honour of love, the fellowes *Philoclea*,
(whose innocent soule now enjoying his owne goodnes did little
knowe the daunger of his ever faire then sleeping harbour) his
excellent wit strengthened with vertue but guided by love, had
soone described to himselfe a perfect vision of their present con-
dition, wherein having presently cast a resolute reckoning of his
owne parte of the misery, not only the chiefe but sole burthen
of his anguish consisted in the unworthy case, which was like
to fall upon the best deserving *Philoclea*. He saw the misfortune
not the mismeaning of his worke, was like to bring that creature
to end, in whom the worlde as he thought did begin to receave
honour hee saw the weake judgement of man, woulde condemne
that as death deserving voice in her, which had in troth never
broken the bonds of a true living vertue, & how often his eye
turned to his attractive adamant: so often did an unspeakable
horror strike his noble hart: to cõsider so unripe yeares, so
fautles a beautie, the mansion of so pure goodnes, should have
her youth so untimely cut off, her naturall perfections un-
naturallie cõsumed, her vertue rewarded with shame, somtimes
he would accuse himselfe of necligence, that had not more
curiously looked to al the house entries, & yet coulde hee not
imagine the way *Damætas* was gotten in, & to call backe what
might have ben to a mã of wisdom & courage, caries but a
vaine shadow of discourse somtimes he could not chose but with
a dissolutiõ of his inward might lamentably consider with what
face he might looke upon his (till then) joy *Philoclea*, when the
next light waking should deliver unto her, should perchaunce
be the last of her hurtles life. And that the first time she should
bend her excellent eyes upon him, shee should see the accursed
aucthor of her dreadfull end, & even this consideration more
then any other, did so set it selfe in his well disposed minde,
that dispersing his thoughts to all the wayes that might be of
her safetie, finding a verye small discourse in so narrowe lymits
of time and place, at length in many difficulties he saw none

beare any likelyhood for her life, but his death. For thē he thought it would fal out that when they foūd his body dead, having no accuser but *Damætas* as by his speach he found there was not, it might justly appeare that either *Philoclea* in defending her honour, or els he himself in dispaire of atchieving, had left his carcase profe of his intent but witnes of her clearenes, having a small while staied upon the greatnes of his resolution and loked to the furthest of it, be it so said the valiant *Pyrocles* : never life for better cause, nor to better end was bestowed, for if death be to follow this doing, which no death of mine could make me leave undon, who is to die so justly as my self ? And if I must die, who can be so fit executioners as mine owne hands ? Which as they were accessaries to the doing, so in killing me they shall suffer their owne punishment. But then arose ther a new impediment, for *Damætas* having caried away any thing, which he thought might hurt as tender a man as himselfe, hee coulde finde no fit instrument which might geve him a finall dispatch, at length makinge the more haste, leaste his Lady should awake, taking the Iron barre, (which being sharper something at the one end, then the other, he hoped joynd to his willing strength, might breake of the former threed of mortallitie, truely said he, fortune thou hast well persevered mine enemie, that wilt graunt me no fortune, to be unfortunate, nor let me have an easie passage now I am to troubl thee no more. But said he O bar blessed in that thou hast done service to the chamber of the paragon of life, since thou couldest not help me to make a perfitter escape, yet serve my turne I pray thee, that I may escape from my selfe, there withall yet once looking to fetch the last repast of his eyes and newe againe transported with the pittifull case hee lefte her in, kneeling downe he thus prayed. O great maker and great ruler of this worlde, saide hee, to thee do I sacrifice this bloud of mine, and suffer Lorde the errors of my youth, to passe away therein, and let not the soule by thee made, and ever bending unto thee, be now rejected of thee, neither be offended that I do abandon this body, to the government of which thou hadst placed me, without thy leave, since how cā I know but that thy unsearchable minde is, I should so doe, since thou hast taken from me all meanes longer to abide in it ? And since the difference stāds but in a short time of dying, thou that hast framed my soule enclyned to do good, howe can I in this smal

space of mine, benefit so much all the humane kinde, as in preserving thy perfittest workmanship, their chiefest honour ? O
justice it selfe, howsoever thou determinest of me, let this excellent innocency not bee oppressed ! Let my life pay her losse, O
Lord geve me some signe that I may die with this comfort. (And
pawsing a little as if he had hoped for some token) and when
soever to the eternall darknes of the earth she doth followe me,
let our spirits possesse one place, and let them bee more happie
in that uniting. With that word striking the barre upon his
harte side, withall the force he had, and falling withall upon to
give it the thorower passage, the barre in troth was to blunt to do
theffect, although it pearced his skinne and brused his ribbes very
sore, so that his breath was almost past him. But the noyse of
his fall, drave away sleepe from the quiet sences of the deere
Philoclea, whose sweete soule had an earely salutation of a deadly
spectacle unto her, with so much more astonishment, as the falling a sleepe but a litle before she had retired her selfe from the
uttermost pointe of wofulnes, and sawe now againe before her
eyes the most cruell enterprise that humane nature can undertake without discerning any cause therof. But the lively printe
of her affection had soone taught her not to stay long upon di-
liberation, in so urgent a necessitie, therefore getting with speede
her weake though well accorded limmes out of her sweetned
bedd, as when Juells are hastely pulled out of some riche coffer,
she spared not the nakednes of her tender feete, but I thincke
borne as fast with desire as feare carried *Daphne*, she came running to *Pyrocles*, and finding his spirits somthing troubled with
the fall ; she put by the barre that lay close to him, and strayning
him in her most beloved embracement, my comforte, my joye,
my life saide shee, what haste have you to kill your *Philoclea*
with the most cruell torment that ever Lady suffred ? Do you
not yet perswade your selfe that any hurte of yours is a death
unto me ? And that your death shoulde bee my hell ? Alas, if any
sodaine mislike of mee (for other cause I see none) have caused
you to loath your selfe, if any fault or defect of mine hath bred
this terriblest rage in you, rather let mee suffer the bitternes of
it, for so shal the deserver be punished, mankind preserved
from such a ruine, & I for my part shall have that comforte, that
I dye by the noblest hande that ever drew sword. *Pyrocles*
greved with his fortune that he had not in one instant cut of all

such deliberation, thinking his life onely reserved to be bound to bee the unhappie newes teller: Alas said he, my onely Starre, why doe you this wrong to God, your selfe and me, to speake of faultes in you, no, no, most faultlesse, most perfet Lady, it is your excellencie that makes me hasten my desired end, it is the right I owe to the generall nature, that (though against private nature) makes me seek the preservation of all that she hath done in this age, let me, let me dye. There is no way to save your life most worthy to be conserved, then that my death be your clearing, then did he with farre more paine and backward loathnes, then the so neere killing himselfe was (but yet driven with necessitie to make her yeeld, to that hee thought was her safetie) make her a short but pithie discourse, what he had heard by *Damætas* speeches, confirming the rest with a plaine demonstratiõ of their imprisonment. And then sought he new meanes of stopping his breath, but that by *Philocleas* labour, above her force, he was stayed to heare her. In whom a man might perceve, what smal difference in the working there is, betwixt a simple voidnes of evill, & a judiciall habit of vertue. For she, not with an unshaked magnanimitie, wherewith *Pyrocles* wayed and dispised death, but with an innocent guiltlessnes, not knowing why she should feare to deliver her unstayned soule to God, helped with the true loving of *Pyrocles*, which made her think no life without him, did almost bring her minde to as quiet attending all accidents, as the unmastred vertu of *Pyrocles*. Yet having with a pretty palenes (which did leave milken lines, upon her rosie cheekes) payd a little dutie to humane feare, taking the Prince by the hand, and kissing the wound he had given himselfe; O the only life of my life, and (if it fall out so) the comforte of my death, saide shee, farre farre from you, be the doing me such wronge, as to thinke I will receave my life as a purchase of your death, but well may you make my death so much more miserable, as it shall any thinge be delayed after my onely felicitie. Doe you thincke I can accompte of the moment of death, like the unspeakeable afflictions my soule shoulde suffer, so ofte as I call *Pyrocles* to my minde, which should be as ofte as I breathed? Should these eyes guide my steppes, that had seene your murder? should these hands feede me that had not hindred such a mischiefe? Should this harte remaine within me, at every pant to count the continuall clock of my miseries? O no, if die we must, let us thanke death, he hath not devided so true an union! And truely my *Pyrocles*, I have heard my father, and other wise men say that the killing ones selfe is but a false coulloure, of true courage; proceeding rather of feare of a further evil, either of torment or shame. For if it were a not respecting the harme, that woulde likewise make him not respect what might be done unto him : and hope, being of al other, the most contrary thing to feare · this being an utter banishment of hope, it seemes to receave his ground in feare. Whatsoever (would they say) comes out of despaire, cannot beare the title of valure, which should bee lifted up to such a hight, that holding al things under it selfe, it should be able to maintaine his greatnes even in the middest of miseries. Lastly they would saye, God had appointed us Captaines of these our boddylie fortes, which without treason to that Majestie, were never to be delivered over till they were redemaunded. *Pyrocles*, who had that for a lawe unto him, not to leave *Philoclea* in any thing unsatisfied, although hee still remained in his former purpose, and knew that time would grow short for it, yet hearing no noyse (the shepheardes being as then run to *Basilius*) with setled and humbled countenaunce, as a man that should have spoken of a thing that did not concerne himself, bearing evẽ in his eyes sufficient showes, that it was nothing but *Philocleas* danger, which did any thinge burden his harte, farre stronger then fortune, having with vehement embracinges of her, got yet some fruite of his delayed end, he thus aunswered the wise innocency of *Philoclea*. Lady most worthy not only of life, but to be the verie life of al things the more notable demonstrations you make of the love, so farre beyond my deserte, with which it pleaseth you to overcome fortune, in making mee happye; the more am I even in course of humanitie (to leave that loves force, which I neither can nor will leave) bound, to seeke requitals witnes, that I am not ungratefull, to do which the infinitnes of your goodnes being such as it cãnot reach unto it, yet doing al I can and paying my life, which is all I have, though it be farre (without measure) shorte of your desarte, yet shall I not die in debt, to mine owne dutie. And truly the more excellent arguments you made, to keep me from this passage, imagined farre more terrible then it is; the more plainely it makes mee see what reason I have, to prevent the losse not only of *Arcadia*, but all the face of the earth should receave, if such a tree (which even in his first spring, doth not onely beare most beautifull blossomes, but most rare fruites) should be so untimely cut off. Therefore, ô most truely beloved Lady, to whom I desire for both our goods, that these may bee my last wordes, geve me your consent even out of that wisedome which must needes see, that (besids your unmatched betternesse, which perchaunce you will not see) it is fitter one die the both. And since you have sufficiently showed you love me, let me claime by that love, you wil be content rather to let me die contentedly, then wretchedly : rather with a cleare and joyfull conscience, then with desperate condemnation in my selfe, that I accursed villaine, shoulde bee the meane of banishing from the sight of men the true example of vertue. And because there is nothing lefte me to be imagined, which I so much desire, as that the memory of *Pyrocles*, may ever have an allowed place in your wise judgement, I am content to drawe so much breath longer, as by aunswearing the sweete objections you alledged, maye bequath (as I thinke) a right conceate unto you, that this my doinge is out of judgement, and not sprong of passion. Your father you say, was wont to say, that this like action doth more proceed of feare, of furder evil or shame, then of a true courage, Truly first, they put a very gessing case, speaking of them who can ever after come to tell, with what minde they did it. And as for my parte, I call them imortall truth to witnes, that no feare of torment can apall me : who know it is but diverse manners of apparelling death : and have long learned, to set bodely paine but in the second fourme of my being. And as for shame, how can I be ashamed of that, for which my well meaning conscience wil answeare for me to God, and your unresistable beautie to the world ? But to take that argument in his owne force, and graunt it done for avoyding of further paine or dishonour, (for as for the name of feare, it is but an odious title of a passion, given to that which true judgement performeth) graunt, I say, it is, to shun a worse case, & truly I do not see, but that true fortitude, loking into al humaine things with a persisting resoluti[on], carried away neither with wonder of pleasing things, nor astonishment of the unpleasaunt, doth not yet deprive it selfe, of the discerning the difference of evill, but rather is the onely vertue, which with an assured tranquillitye shunnes the greater by the valiant entring into the lesse. Thus for his countries safety he wil spend his life, for the saving of a lym, he will not niggardly spare his goods; for the saving of all his body, hee will not spare the cutting of a lym, where indeed the weake harted man will rather dye, then see the face of a surgeon: who might with as good reason saye, that the constant man abides the painefull surgery, for feare of a further evill: but he is content to waite for death it selfe, but neither is true; for neither hath the one any feare, but a well choosing judgement, nor the other hath any contentment, but onely feare; and not having a harte actively to performe a matter of paine, is forced passively to abide a greater damage. For to doe, requires a whole harte; to suffer falleth easeliest in the broken minds. And if in bodely torment thus, much more in shame; wherein since vallure is a vertue, and vertue is ever limited, we must not runne so infinitely, as to thinke the valiant man is willinglie to suffer any thing, since the very suffering of some things is a certaine proofe of want of courage. And if any thing unwillinglie among the chiefest may shame goe: for if honour be to be held deere, his contrarye is to be abhorred, and that not for feare, but of a true election. For which is the lesse inconvenient, either the losse of some yeares more or lesse (for once we knowe our lives be not immortall) or the submitting our selves to each unworthy misery, which the foolish world may lay upon us? As for their reason, that feare is contrary to hope, neither do I defend feare, nor much yeeld to the aucthoritye of hope; to eyther of which great enclining shewes but a feeble reason, which must be guided by his servaunts; and who builds not uppon hope, shall feare no earthquake of despaire. There last alleadging of the heavenly powers, as it beares the greatest name, so it is the only thing, that at all bred any combate in my minde. And yet I do not see, but that if God hath made us maisters of any thing, it is of our owne lives; out of which without doing wrong to any body, we are to issue at our owne pleasure. And the same Argument would asmuch prevayle to say we should for no necessitie lay away from us, any of our joyntes, since they being made of him, without his warrant we should not depart from them; or if that may be, for a greater cause we may passe to a greater degree. And if we be Lieutenants of God, in this little Castle, do you not thinke we must take warning of him to geve over our charge when he leaves us unprovided, of good meanes to tarrye in it? No certainelie do I not answered the sorrowfull *Philoclea*, since it is not for us to appoint that mightie Majestie, what time he will helpe us: the uttermost instant is scope enough for him, to revoke every thing to ones owne desire. And therefore to prejudicate his determinacion, is but a doubt of goodnes in him, who is nothing but goodnes. But when in deede he doth either by sicknes, or outward force lay death upon us, then are we to take knowledge, that such is his pleasure, and to knowe that all is well that he doth. That we should be maisters of our selves, we can shewe at all no title, nor clayme; since neyther we made our selves, nor bought our selves, we can stand upon no other right but his guift, which he must limit as it pleaseth him. Neyther is there any proporcion, betwixt the losse of any other limme and that, since the one bends to the preserving all, the other to the destruction of all; the one takes not away the minde from the actions for which it is placed in the world, the other cuts off all possibilitie of his working. And truly my most deere *Pyrocles*, I must needes protest unto you, that I can not thinke your defence even in rules of vertue sufficient. Sufficient and excellent it were, if the question were of two outward things, wherein a man might by natures freedome determine, whether he would preferre shame to payne; present smaller torment, to greater following, or no. But to this (besides the comparison of the matters vallewes) there is added of the one part a direct evill doing, which maketh the ballance of that side too much unequall. Since a vertuous man without any respect, whether the griefe be lesse or more, is never to do that which he can not assure himselfe is allowable before the everliving rightfulnes. But rather is to thinke honoures or shames, which stande in other mens true or false judgements, paynes or not paynes, which yet never approach our soules, to be nothing in regarde of an unspotted conscience. And these reasons do I remember, I have heard good men bring in, that since it hath not his ground in an assured vertue, it proceedes rather of some other disguised passion. *Pyrocles* was not so much perswaded as delighted, by her well conceaved and sweetely pronounced speaches; but when she had cloased her pittifull discourse, and as it were sealed up her delightfull lippes, with the moistnes of her teares, which followed still one another like a precious rope of pearle, now thinking it hye time. Be it as you saye (sayde hee most vertuous beawtye) in all the rest, but never can

III

God himselfe perswade me, that *Pyrocles* life is not well lost, for to preserve the most admirable *Philoclea*. Let that be if it be possible written on my Tombe, and I will not envye *Codrus* honour. With that he would agayne have used the barre, meaning if that failde, to leave his braynes uppon the wall. When *Philoclea* now brought to that she most feared, kneeled downe unto him, and embracing so his legges, that without hurting her, (which for nothing he would have done) he could not ridde himselfe from her, she did with all the conjuring wordes, which the authoritye of love may laye, beseeche him, he would not nowe so cruelly abandon her, he woulde not leave her comfortlesse in that miserye, to which he had brought her. That then in deede she woulde even in her soule accuse him, to have most fouly betrayed her; that then she should have cause, to curse the time that ever the name of *Pyrocles* came to her eares, which otherwise no death could make her do. Will you leave me, sayde she, not onely dishonoured as supposed unchaste with you, but as a murderer of you? Will you geve mine eyes such a picture of hell, before my neere approaching death, as to see the murdred bodie of him, I love more then all the lives that nature can geve? With that she sware by the hyest cause of all devocions, that if he did persever in that cruell resolucion, she would (though untruly) not onely confesse to her father, that with her cösent this acte had bene committed, but if that would not serve (after she had puld out her owne eyes, made accursed by such a sight) she would geve her selfe so terrible a death, as she might think the paine of it would countervaile the never dying paine of her minde. Now therefore kill your selfe, to crowne this vertuous action with infamy: kill your selfe to make me (whome you say you love) as long as I after live, change my loving admiracion of you, to a detestable abhorring your name. And so indeede you shall have the ende you shoote at, for in steede of one death, you shall geve me a thousand, and yet in the meane time, deprive me of the helpe God may sende me. *Pyrocles* even overwayed with her so wisely uttred affection, finding her determinacion so fixed, that his ende should but deprive them both of a present contentment, and not avoyde a comming evill (as a man that ranne not unto it, by a sodayne qualme of passion, but by a true use of reason, preferring her life to his owne) nowe that wisedome did manifest unto him, that waye woulde not prevayle, he retired himselfe, with as much tranquillitie from it, as before he had gone unto it. Like a man, that had set the keeping or leaving of the bodye, as a thing without himselfe, and so had thereof a freed and untroubled consideracion. Therefore throwing away the barre from him, and taking her up from the place, where he thought the consummating of all beawties, very unworthely lay, suffring all his sences to devoure up their chiefest foode, which he assured himselfe they should shortly after for ever be deprived of: well, said he, most deere Lady, whose contentment I preferre before mine own, and judgement esteeme more then mine owne, I yeeld unto your pleasure. The gods send you have not woon your owne losse. For my part they are my witnesses, that I thinke I do more at your commaundement, in delayeng my death, then another would in bestowing his life. But now, sayd he, as thus farre I have yeelded unto you, so graunt me in recompence thus much againe, that I may finde your love in graunting, as you have found your authorrye in obteyning. My humble suite is, you will say I came in by force into your Chamber, for so am I resolved now to affirme, and that will be the best for us both; but in no case name my name, that whatsoever come of me my house be not dishonored. *Philoclea* fearing least refusall would turne him backe againe, to his violent refuge, gave him a certayne countenance, that might shewe she did yeeld to his request, the latter part whereof indeed she meant for his sake to performe. Neyther could they spend more wordes together, for *Philanax*, with twentie of the noblest personages of *Arcadia* after him, were come into the Lodge, *Philanax* making the rest stay belowe, for the reverence he bare to womanhood, as stillie as he could came to the dore, and opening it, drewe the eyes of these two dolefull lovers upon him. *Philoclea* cloasing againe for modestie sake, within her bed the ritchesse of her beawties, but *Pyrocles* tooke holde of his barre, minding at least to dye, before the excellent *Philoclea* should receyve any outrage. But *Philanax* rested awhile uppon himselfe, stricken with admiracion at the goodlie shape of *Pyrocles*, whome before he had never seene, and withall remembring besides others the notable acte he had done (when with his courage and eloquence, he had saved *Basilius*, perchaunce the whole state from utter ruyne) he felte a kinde of relenting minde towardes him. But when that same thought, came waighted on, with the remembraunce of his maisters death, which he by all probabilities thought he had bene of Councell unto with the Queene, compassion turned to hatefull passion, and lefte in *Philanax* a straunge medley, betwixt pittie and revenge, betwixt lyking and abhorring. O Lorde, sayde hee to himselfe, what wonders doth nature in our tyme, to set wickednesse so beawtifully garnished? and that which is straungest, out of one spring to make wonderfull effectes both of vertue and vice to issue? *Pyrocles* seeing him in such a muse, neyther knowing the man, nor the cause of his comming, but assuring himselfe, it was for no good, yet thought best to begin with him in this sort. Gentleman sayde hee, what is the cause of your comming to my Lady *Philoclea* chamber? is it to defende her from such violence, as I might goe about to offer unto her? if it be so, truly your comming is vayne, for her owne vertue hath bene a sufficient resistaunce, there needes no strength to be added to so inviolate chastetie, the excellencie of her mind, makes her bodie impregnable. Which for mine own part I had soone yelded to confesse, with going out of this place (where I found but little comfort being so disdainefully received) had I not bene, I know not by whom presently upon my cõming hether, so locked into this chamber, that I could never escape hence: where I was fettred in the most gilty shame, that ever mã was, seing what a paradice of unspotted goodnes, my filthy thoughts sought to defile. If for that therfore you come, alredy I assure you, your arrãt is performed; but if it be to bring me to any punishmẽt whatsoever, for having undertaken so unexcusable presumption. Truly I beare such an accuser about me of mine own conscience, that I willingly submit my selfe unto it. Only this much let me demaund of you, that you will be a witnesse unto the King what you heare me say, & oppose your selfe, that neither his sodaine fury, nor any other occasion may offer any hurt to this Lady; in whome you see nature hath accomplished so much, that I am faine to lay mine owne faultines, as a foile of her purest excellency. I can say no more, but looke uppon her beawtie, remember her bloud, consider her yeares, and judge rightly of her vertues, and I doubt not a gentlemans mind, will then be a sufficient enstructer unto you, in this I may tearme it miserable chaunce, happened unto her by my unbridled audacitie. *Philanax* was content to heare him out, not for any favour he owed him, but to see whether he would reveale any thing of the originall cause, and purpose of the kings death. But finding it so farre from that, that he named *Basilius* unto him, as supposing him alive, thinking it rather cunning then ignorance: Yong man, said he, whome I have cause to hate before I have meane to know, you use but a point of skill, by confessing the manifest smaller fault, to be beleeved hereafter in the deniall of the greater. But for that matter, all passeth to one end, and hereafter we shal have leisure by torments to seke the truth, if the love of truth it selfe will not bring you unto it. As for my Lady *Philoclea*, if it so fall out as you say, it shall be the more fit for her yeares, & comely for the great house she is come of, that an ill governed beawtie hath not cancelled the rules of vertue. But howsoever it be, it is not for you to teach an *Arcadian*, what reverent duty we owe to any of that progeny. But, said he, come you with me without resistance, for the one cannot availe, and the other may procure pitie. Pitie? said *Pyrocles* with a bitter smiling, disdained, with so currish an answere: no, no, *Arcadian*, I can quickly have pitie of my selfe, and I would think my life most miserable, which should be a gift of thine. Only I demaund this innocent Ladies securitie, which untill thou hast côfirmed unto me by an oath, assure thy selfe, the first that layes hands upô her, shall leave his life for a testimony of his sacriledge. *Philanax* with an inward storme, thinking it most manifest they were both, he at least, of counsell with the kings death : well, said he, you speake much to me of the king: I do here sweare unto you, by the love I have ever borne him, she shal have no worse, howsoever it fal out, then her own parents. And upon that word of yours I yeld, said the poore *Pyrocles*, deceived by him that ment not to deceive him. Then did *Philanax* deliver him into the hands of a noble man in the company, every one desirous to have him in his charge, so much did his goodly presence (wherin true valure shined) breede a delightfull admiration in all the beholders. *Philanax* himselfe stayed with *Philoclea*, to see whether of her he might learne some disclosing of this former conclusion. But the sweet Lady whom first a kindly shamefastnes had separated from *Pyrocles*, (having bene left in a more open view then her modesty would well beare) then the attending her fathers comming, and studying how to behave her selfe towards him for both their safeties, had called her spirits all within her: now that upon a sodaine *Pyrocles* was delivered out of the chamber from her, at the first she was so surprized with the extreame strok[e of] the wofull sight, that, like those that in their dreames are taken with some ougly vision, they would fain cry for help, but have no force, so remained she awhile quite deprived not only of speach, but almost of any other lively actiŏ. But whĕ indeed *Pyrocles* was quite drawne frŏ her eys, & that her vital strĕgth begã to return unto her, now not knowing what they did to *Pyrocles*, but (according to the nature of love) fearing the worst, wringing her hands, and letting abundance of teares be the first part of her eloquence, bending her Amber-crowned head over her bed side to the hard-hearted *Philanax* : O *Philanax, Philanax,* sayd she, I knowe how much authoritye you have with my father : there is no man whose wisedome he so much esteemes, nor whose faith so much he reposeth upon. Remember how oft you have promised your service unto me, how oft you have geven me occasion to beleeve that there was no Lady in whose favor you more desired to remayne : and, if the remembrance be not unpleasant to your mind, or the rehearsall unfitting for my fortune, remember there was a time when I could deserve it. Now my chaunce is turned, let not your truth turne. I present my selfe unto you, the most humble and miserable suppliant living, neither shall my desire be great : I seeke for no more life then I shall be found worthy of. If my bloud may wash away the dishonor of *Arcadia,* spare it not, although through me it hath in deede never bene dishonored. My only sute is you wil be a meane for me, that while I am suffered to enjoy this life, I may not be separated from him, to whom the Gods have joyned me, and that you determine nothing of him more cruelly then you do of me. If you rightly judge of what hath past, wherein the Gods (that should have bene of our mariage) are witnesses of our innocencies : then procure, we may live together. But if my father will not so conceive of us, as the fault (if any were) was united, so let the punishmĕt be united also. There was no man that ever loved either his Prince, or any thing pertaining to him with a truer zeale then *Philanax* did. This made him even to the depth of his heart receive a most vehemĕt griefe, to see his master made as it were more miserable after death. And for himselfe, calling to mind in what sort his life had bene preserved by *Philoclea,* what time taken by *Amphialus* he was like to suffer

116

a cruell death, there was nothing could have kept him from falling to all tender pittie, but the perfect perswasion he had, that all this was joyned to the packe of his maisters death, which the misconceived speech of marriage made him the more beleeve. Therefore first muttering to himselfe such like words: The violence the gentleman spake of, is now turned to mariage : he alledged *Mars*, but she speakes of *Venus*. O unfortunate maister. This hath bene that faire divell *Gynæcia :* sent away one of her daughters, prostituted the other, empoysoned thee, to overthrowe the diademe of *Arcadia*. But at length thus unto her selfe he sayde: If your father, Madame, were now to speake unto, truly there should no body be found a more ready advocate for you, then my selfe. For I would suffer this fault, though very great to be blotted out of my minde, by your former led life, your benefit towards my selfe, and being daughter to such a father. But since among your selves you have taken him away, in whome was the only power to have mercy, you must now be clothed in your owne working : and looke for none other, then that which dead pittilesse lawes may allot unto you. For my part, I loved you for your vertue, but now where is that ? I loved you in respect of a private benefit, what is that in comparison of the publike losse ? I loved you for your father, unhappy folks you have robbed the world of him. These words of her father were so little understood by the only well understanding *Philoclea*, that she desired him to tell her, what he meant to speake in such darke sort unto her of her lord and father, whose displeasure was more dreadfull unto her, then her punishment: that she was free in her owne conscience, she had never deserved evill of him, no not in this last fact : wherein if it pleased him to proceed with patience, he should finde her choise had not bene unfortunate. He that saw her words written in the plaine table of her faire face, thought it impossible there should therin be contained deceite : and therfore so much the more abashed : Why, said he, Madame, would you have me thinke, you are not of conspiracy with the Princesse *Pamelas* flight, and your fathers death ? with that word the sweet Lady gave a pittifull cry, having streight in her face & breast abundance of witnesses, that her hart was far from any such abhominable consent. Ah of all sides utterly ruined *Philoclea*, said she, now in deed I may well suffer all conceite of hope to dye in mee. Deare father where was I, that might not do you my last service before soone after miserably following you? *Philanax* perceived the demonstracion so lively & true in her, that he easily acquited her in his heart of that fact, and the more was moved to joyne with her in most heartie lamentation. But remembring him, that the burthen of the state, and punishment of his masters murderers, lay all upon him : Well, sayde he, Madame, I can do nothing, without all the states of *Arcadia* : what they will determine of you, I know not, for my part your speaches would much prevaile with me, but that I finde not how to excuse, your geving over your body to him, that for the last proofe of his treason, lent his garments to disguise your miserable mother, in the most vile fact she hath cõmitted. Hard sure it will be to separate your causes, with whome you have so neerely joyned your selfe. Neither do I desire it, said the sweetly weeping *Philoclea* : whatsoever you determine of him, do that likewise to me ; for I knowe, from the fountaine of vertue nothing but vertue could ever proceede ; only as you finde him faultlesse, let him finde you favourable, and build not my dishonor upõ surmises. *Philanax* feeling his hart more & more mollifieng unto her, renewed the image of his dead master in his fancy, and using that for the spurres of his revẽgefull choller, went sodainly, without any more speach, from the desolate Lady, to whome now fortune seemed to threaten unripe death, and undeserved shame among her least evils. But *Philanax* leaving good guard upon the Lodge, went himselfe to see the order of his other prisoners, whome even then as he issued, he found increased by this unhoped meanes.

The noble *Pamela* having delivered over the burthen of her fearefull cares to the naturall ease of a well refreshing sleepe, reposed both mind & body upõ the trusted support of her princely shepheard, whẽ with the brayeng cryes of a rascall company she was robbed of her quiet, so that at one instãt she opened her eyes, & the enraged *Musidorus* rose frõ her, enraged betwixt the doubt he had what these men would go about, & the spite he conceived against their ill-pleasing presence. But the clownes, having with their hideous noyse brought them both to their feet, had soone knowledge what guests they had found, for in deede these were the skummy remnant of those rebels, whose naughty minds could not trust so much to the goodnes of their Prince, as to lay their hangworthy necks upō the constancy of his promised pardon. Therfore whē the rest (who as shepe had but followed their fellowes) so sheepishly had submitted thēselves, these only cōmitted their safety to the thickest part of those desert woods, who as they were in the constitution of their mindes little better then beastes, so were they apt to degenerate to a beastly kinde of life, having now framed their gluttonish stomackes to have for foode the wilde benefites of nature, the uttermost ende they had, being but to drawe out (as much as they could) the line of a tedious life. In this sorte vagabonding in those untroden places, they were guided by the everlasting Justice, using themselves to bee punishers of theyr faultes, and making theyr owne actions the beginning of their chastizements, (unhappely both for him and themselves) to light on *Musidorus.* Whom as soone as they saw turned towards them, they full well remembred it was he, that accompanyed with *Basilius,* had come to the succour of *Zelmane*: and had left among some of them bloudie tokens of his valure. As for *Pamela,* they had many times seene her. Thus fyrst sturred up with a rusticall revenge against him, and then desire of spoyle, to helpe their miserable wants, but chiefly thinking it was the way to confirme their owne pardon, to bring the Princesse backe unto her father (whome they were sure he would never have sent so farre so sleightlie accompanyed) without any other denouncing of warre, set altogither upon the worthy *Musidorus.* Who being before hand asmuch enflamed against them, gave them so brave a welcome, that the smart of some made the rest stand further off, crying and prating against him, but like bad curres, rather barking then cloasing; he in the meane time placing his trembling Lady to one of the Pyne trees, and so setting himselfe before her, as might shewe the cause of his courage grewe in himselfe, but the effect was only employed in her defence. The villaines that now had a second proofe, how ill wordes they had for such a sword, turned all the course of their violence into throwing dartes and stones, in deede the only way to overmaister the valure of *Musidorus.* Who finding them some already touch, some fall so neere his chiefest life *Pamela,* that in the ende some one or other might happe to doo an unsuccourable mischiefe, setting all his hope in despaire, ranne out from his Lady among them. Who streight like so many swyne, when a hardy mastife sets upon them, dispersed themselves. But the first he overtooke, as he ranne away, carying his head as farre before him, as those maner of runnings are wont to doo, with one blowe strake it so cleane off, that it falling betwixt the handes, and the body falling uppon it, it made a shewe as though the fellow had had great haste to gather up his head agayne. Another the speede he made to runne for the best game, bare him full butte agaynst a tree, so that tumbling backe with a brused face, and a dreadfull expectation, *Musidorus* was streight upon him: and parting with his sword one of his legges from him, left him to make a roaring lamentation that his morter-treading was marred for ever. A third finding his feete too slowe, aswell as his handes too weake, sodaynely turned backe, beginning to open his lippes for mercye. But before hee had well entred a rudely compilde oration, *Musidorus* blade was come betweene his jawes into his throate, and so the poore man rested there for ever with a very evill mouthfull of an answere. *Musidorus* in this furious chafe would have followed some other of these hatefull wretches, but that he heard his Lady cry for helpe, whome three of this villanous crue, had (whiles *Musidorus* followed their fellowes) compassing about some trees, sodainly come upon and surprized, threatning to kill her if she cried, and meaning to convey her out of sight, while the Prince was making his bloud-thirstie chase. But she that was resolved, no worse thing could fall unto her, then the being deprived of him, on whome she had established all her comfort, with a pittifull cry fetched his eyes unto her: who then thinking so many weapons thrust into his eyes, as with his eyes he sawe bent against her, made all hartie speede to her succour. But one of them wiser then his companions, set his dagger to her Alablaster throate, swearing if hee threwe not away his sword, he would presently kill her. There was never poore scholler, that having in stede of his booke some playing toy about him, did more sodainly cast it from him, at the child-feared presence of a cruell Scholemaister. Then the valiant *Musidorus*, discharged himselfe of his only defence, whẽ he saw it stood upõ the instãt point of his Ladies life. And holding up his noble hands to so unworthy audience, O *Arcadians*, it is I that have done, you the wrong, she is your Princesse (said he) shee never had will to hurt you, and you see shee hath no power. Use your choller upõ me that have better deserved it, do not your selves the wrong to doe her any hurte, which in no time nor place will ever bee forgiven you. They that yet trusted not to his courtesie, bad him stande further off from his sword, which he obediently did. So farre was love above al other thoughts in him. Then did they call together the rest of their fellowes, who though they were fewe, yet according to their number possessed many places. And then began these savage Senators to make a consultation, what they should do: some wishing to spoile them of their Jewels and let them go on their journey, (for that if they carried them back they were sure they should have least parte of their pray) others preferring their old homes to any thing; desired to bring them to *Basilius* as pledges of their surety: and ther wanted not which cried the safest way was to kill them both; to such an unworthy thraldom were these great and excellent personages brought. But the most part resisted to the killing of the Princesse, fore-seing their lives would never bee safe after such a fact committed: and beganne to wish rather the spoyle then death of *Musidorus*: when the villaine that had his legge cut off, came scrawling towardes them, and being helped to them by one of the companie, began with a growning voice, and a disfigured face, to demaunde the revenge of his blood: which since hee had spent with them in their defence, it were no reason he should be suffered by them to die discontented. The onely contentment he required was that by their helpe with his own hands he might put his murderer to some cruel death, he would faine have cried more against *Musidorus*, but that the much losse of bloud helped on with this vehemencie, choked up the spirits of his life, leaving him to make betwixt his body and soule an ill favoured partition. But they seing their fellow in that sorte die before their faces, did swell in newe mortall rages: All resolved to kill him, but nowe onely considering what manner of terrible death they should invent for him. Thus was a while the agrement of his slaying, broken by the disagrement of the manner of it; & extremitie of cruelty grew for a time, to be the stop of crueltie. At length they were resolved, every one to have a pece of him and to become all aswell hangmen as judges: when *Pamela* tearing her heare, and falling downe among them, somtimes with al the sorte of humble praiers, mixt with promises of great good turnes, (which they knew her state was able to performe) sometimes threatning them, that if they kild him and not her, she would not onely revenge it upon them, but upon all their wives and children; bidding them consider that though they might thinke shee was come away in her fathers displeasure, yet they might be sure hee would ever shewe himselfe a father, that the Gods woulde never if shee lived, put her in so base estate, but that she should have abilitie to plague such as they were returning a fresh to prayers and promises, and mixing the same againe with threatninges, brought them (who were now growne colder in their fellowes cause, who was past aggravating the matter, with his cryes) to determine with themselves there was no way, but either to kil them both or save them both. As for the killing, already they having aunsweared themselves that that was a way to make them Cittezens of the woodes for ever; they did in fine conclude they would retourne them backe againe to the King which they did not doubt, would bee cause of a greate reward, besides their safetie from their fore-deserved punishment. Thus having either by fortune, or the force of those two lovers inward working vertue, setled their cruel harts to this gētler course they tooke the two horses, and having set upon them their princely prisoners, they retorned towards the lodge. The villaines having decked al their heads with lawrel branches, as thinking they had done a notable acte, singing and showting, ranne by them in hope to have brought them the same day againe to the King. But the time was so farre spent, that they were forced to take up that nights lodging in the middest of the woods. Where while the clownes continued their watch about them, nowe that the night, according to his darke nature, did add a kind of desolation to the pensive harts of these two afflicted lovers, *Musidorus* taking the tender hand of *Pamela*, & bedewing it with his teares, in this sort gave an issue to the swelling of his harts grief. Most excellent Lady said hee; in what case thinke you am I with my selfe, howe unmerciful judgements do I lay upon my soule, now that I know not what God, hath so reverssed my wel meaning enterprise, as in steed of doing you that honour which I hoped (and not without reason hoped) *Thessalia* should have yeelded unto you, am now like to become a wretched instrumēt of your discomfort? Alas how contrary an end have al the enclinations of my mind taken! my faith falls out a treason unto you, and the true honour I beare you, is the fielde wherein your dishonour is like to bee sowen! But I invoke that universal and only wisdome, (which examining the depth of harts, hath not his judgement fixed upon the event) to beare testimonie with me that my desire though in extremest vehemencie, yet did not so overcharge my remembrance, but that as farre as mans wit might be extended, I sought to prevent al things that might fall to your hurt. But now that all the evil fortunes of evil fortune have crossed my best framed entent, I am most miserable in that, that I cannot only not geve you helpe, but which is worst of all; am barred from giving you counsail. For how should I open my mouth to counsaile you in that, wherein by my councel you are most undeservedly fallen? The faire and wise *Pamela*, although full of cares of the unhappie turning of this matter, yet seing the greefe of *Musidorus* onely stirred for her, did so treade downe all other motions with the true force of vertue, that she thus aunswered him, having first kissed him, which before she had never done either love so cŏmaunding her, which doubted how long they should enjoy one another; or of a lively spark of noblenes, to descend in most favour to one, when he is lowest in affliction. My deere and ever deere *Musidorus* said shee, a greater wronge, doe you to your selfe, that will torment you thus with griefe, for the fault of fortune. Since a man is bound no further to himselfe, then to doe wisely; chaunce is only to trouble them, that stand upon chaunce. But greater is the wronge (at least if any thinge that comes from you, may beare the name of wrong) you doe unto me, to thinke me either so childish, as not to perceave your faithful faultlessnes; or perceaving it, so basely disposed, as to let my harte be overthrown, standing upon it selfe in so unspotted a purenes. Hold for certaine most worthy *Musidorus*, it is your selfe I love, which can no more be diminished by these showers of evill hap, then flowers are marred with the timely raynes of Aprill. For how can I want comforte that have the true and living comforte of my unblemished vertue? And how can I want honour as long as *Musidorus* in whom indeed honour is, doth honour me? Nothing bred from my self can discomfort me : & fooles opinions I wil not recken as dishonour. *Musidorus* looking up to the starres, O mind of minds said he, the living power of all things which dost with al these eies behold our ever varying actiŏs, accept into thy favorable eares this praier of mine. Yf I may any longer hold out this dwelling on the earth, which is called a life, graunt me abilitie to deserve at this Ladies handes the grace shee hath shewed unto me; graunt me wisdome to know her wisdome, and goodnes so

to encrease my love of her goodnes, that all mine owne chosen
desires, be to my selfe but second to her determinations. What
soever I be, let it be to her service, let me herein be satisfied, that
for such infinite favours of vertue, I have some way wrought her
satisfaction. But if my last time aprocheth, and that I am no
longer to be amongst mortall creatures, make yet my death serve
her to some purpose, that hereafter shee may not have cause to
repent her selfe that she bestowed so excellent a minde upon
Musidorus, Pamela, coulde not choose, but accord the conceite of
their fortune to these passionate prayers, in so much that her constant eyes yeelded some teares, which wiping from her faire face
with *Musidorus* hande, speaking softly unto him as if she had
feared more any body should be witnes of her weakenes, then of
any thing els shee had said, you see said she my Prince and onely
Lord, what you worke in me by your much greving for me. I
praye you thinke I have no joye but in you, and if you fill that
with sorrow what do you leave for mee? What is prepared for
us we know not; but that with sorrow we cannot prevent it,
wee knowe. Now let us turne from these things, and thinke you
how you will have me behave my selfe towardes you in this matter.
Musidorus finding the authoritie of her speach confirmed with
direct necessitie, the first care came to his minde was of his deare
friend and cosin *Pyrocles*: with whome long before hee had concluded what names they shoulde beare, if upon any occasion they
were forced to geve them selves out for great men, and yet not
make them selves fully knowen. Now fearing least if the Princes
should name him for *Musidorus*, the fame of their two being together, would discover *Pyrocles*; holding her hand betwixt his
handes a good while together: I did not thinke most excellent
Princesse saide hee, to have made any further request unto you,
for having bene alredie to you so unfortunate a suiter, I knowe
not what modestie can beare any further demaud. But the estate
of on young man whom (next to you, far above my selfe) I love
more then all the world, one worthy of all well being for the notable constitution of the mind, and most unworthy to receave hurt
by me, whom he doth in all faith and constancie love, the pittie
of him onely goes beyond all resolution to the contrarie. Then
did hee to the Princesse great admiration tell her the whole story
as farre as he knew of it, and that when they made the grevous
disjunction of their long company, they had concluded, *Musidorus*

should entitle himself *Paladius*, Prince of *Iberia*, and *Pyrocles* should be *Daiphantus* of *Lycia*.

Now said *Musidorus* he keeping a womans habit is to use no other name then *Zelmane*, but I that finde it best, of the on side for your honour, you went away with a Prince and not with a sheepheard: of the other side accompting my death lesse evil, then the betraying of that sweete frende of mine, will take this meane betwixt both, and using the name of *Paladius* if the respect of a Prince will stop your fathers furie, that will serve aswell as *Musidorus* until *Pyrocles* fortune being som way established, I may freely geve good proofe that the noble contrie of *Thessalia* is mine: and if that will not mitigate your fathers opinion to me wards (nature I hope working in your excellencies wil make him deale well by you) for my parte the image of death is nothing fearefull unto me: and this good I shall have reaped by it, that I shall leave my most esteemed friend in no danger to be disclosed by me. And besides (since I must confesse, I am not without a remorse of his case) my vertuous mother shal not know her sonnes violent death hid under the fame will goe of *Paladius*. But as long as her yeares now of good number be counted among the living, shee may joye her selfe with some possibilitie of my returne. *Pamela* promising him upon no occasion ever to name him, fell into extremytie of weping, as if her eyes had beene content to spend all their seing moistnes, now that there was speech of the losse of that, which they held as their chiefest light. So that *Musidorus* was forced to repaire her good counsailes, with sweete consolations, which continued betwixt them untill it was about midnight, that sleep having stolne into their heavie sences and now absolutely commaunding in their vitall powers, lefte them delicately wound on in anothers armes quietly to waite for the comming of the morning. Which as soone as shee appeared to play her parte, laden (as you have heard) with so many well occasioned lamentations. Their lobbish garde (who all night had kept themselves awake, with prating how valiant deedes they had done when they ranne away: and how faire a death their felowe had died, who at his last gaspe sued to bee a hangman) awaked them, and set them upon their horses, to whom the very shining force of excellent vertue, though in a very harrish subject, had wrought a kinde of reverence in them; *Musidorus* as he rid among them, (of whom they had no other holde but of *Pamela*) thinking it want of a well squared judgement, to leave any meane unassayed of saving their lives, to this purpose spake to his unseemly gardians, using a plaine kind of phrase to make his speach the more credible. My maisters said he, there is no man that is wise but hath in what soever hee doth some purpose whereto hee directes his doinges, which so long he followes, till he see that either that purpose is not worth the paines, or that another doinge caries with it a better purpose. That you are wise in what you take in hand I have to my cost learned: that makes me desire you to tell me, what is your ende in carying the Princesse and me backe to her father. Pardon, saide one, rewarde cried another, well saide he take both; although I know you are so wise to remember, that hardly they both will goe togeather, being of so contrary a making, for the ground of pardon is an evill, neither any man pardons but remembers an evill done, the cause of rewarde is the opinion of some good acte, and who so rewardeth that, holdes the chief place of his fancie. Now one man of one companie, to have the same consideration both of good and evill, but that the conceite of pardoning, if it bee pardoned, will take away the minde of rewarding, is very hard, if not impossible. For either even in justice will he punish the fault as well as reward the desert, or els in mercie ballance the one by the other: so that the not chastising shalbe a sufficient satisfiing. Thus then you may see that in your owne purpose, rests greate uncertaintie. But I will graunt that by this your deede you shall obtaine your double purpose. Yet consider I pray you whether by another meane, that may not better be obtained, & then I doubt not your wisdomes wil teach you to take hold of the better. I am sure you knowe, any body were better have no neede of a pardon then enjoy a pardon; for as it carries with it the suretie of a preserved life, so beares it a continuall note of a deserved death. This therefore (besides the daunger you may runne into, my Lady *Pamela* being the undoubted enheritrixe of this state, if shee shall hereafter seeke to revenge your wrong done her) shall bee continually cast in your teeth, as men dead by the lawe; the honester sorte will disdaine your company & your children shalbe the more basely reputed of, & you your selves in every slight fault hereafter, as men once condemned, aptest to bee overthrowne. Now if you will, (I doubt not you will, for you are wise) turne your course, and garde my Lady *Pamela* thither-ward, whether shee was going: first you neede not doubt to adventure your fortunes where shee goes, and there shall you be assured in a countrie as good and rich as this, of the same manners and language, to bee so farre from the conceate of a pardon, as we both shall be forced to acknowledge, we have receaved by your meanes what soever we holde deere in this life. And so for rewarde judge you whether it be not more likely, you shall there receave it where you have done no evill, but singuler and undeserved goodnes; or here where this service of yours shalbe diminished by your dutie, and blemished by your former fault. Yes I protest and sweare unto you, by the faire eyes of that Lady, there shall no Gentlemen in all that country bee preferred. You shall have riches, ease, pleasure, and that which is best to such worthy mindes, you shall not bee forced to crie mercy for a góod faĉte. You onely of all the *Arcadians*, shall have the prayse in continuing in your late valiaunt attempte, and not basely bee brought under a halter for seeking the libertie of *Arcadia*. These wordes in their mindes, who did nothing for any love of goodnes, but onely as their senses presented greater showes of proffit, beganne to make them waver, and some to clappe their hands and scratch their heades, and sweare it was the best way. Others that would seeme wiser then the rest to capitulate what tenements they should have, what subsidies they should pay, others to talke of their wives, in doubt whether it were best to send for thẽ, or to take new wher they went, most, (like fooles) not reddely thinking what was next to bee done, but imagining what cheere they woulde make when they came there, one or two of the least discourses beginning to turne their faces towards the woods which they had lefte. But being nowe come within the plaine neere to the lodges, unhappily they espied a troupe of horsmen. But then their false harts had quickly for the present feare, forsaken their last hopes, and therfore keeping on the way toward the lodge, with songes of cries and joye, the horsemen who were some of them *Philanax* had sent out to the search of *Pamela* came gallowping unto them; marveyling who they were that in such a generall mourning, durst singe joyfull tunes, and in so publicke a ruine were the lawrell tokens of viĉtorie. And that which seemed straungest, they might see two among them unarmed like prisoners, but riding like captaines.

127

But when they came neerer, they perceaved the one was a Lady,
and the Lady *Pamela*. Then glad they had by happ found that
which they so litle hoped to meete withall, taking these clownes
(who first resisted them, for the desire they had to be the de-
liverers of the two excellent prisoners, learning that they were
of those rebells, which had made the daungerous uprore, aswell
under cullour to punish that, as this their last withstanding them,
but indeed their principal cause being, because they themselves
would have the onely praise of their owne quest, they suffered
not one of them to live. Marry three of the stubbernest of them
they lefte their bodies hanging uppon the trees, because their
doing might carry the likelier forme of judgement. Such an unlooked for end did the life of justice worke, for the naughtie
minded wretches, by subjects to be executed, that would have
executed Princes: and to suffer that without lawe, which by
lawe they had deserved. And thus these yonge folkes twise
prisoners, before any due arrest, delivered of their jayloures but
not of their jayle, had rather change then respit of misery, these
souldiers that tooke them with verie fewe wordes of entertaine-
ment, hasting to carrie them to their Lorde *Philanax*: to whom
they came, even as he going out of the Lady *Philocleas* chamber,
had overtaken *Pyrocles*, whom before hee had delivered to the
custody of a noble man of that countrie. When *Pyrocles* led
towardes his prison sawe his friend *Musidorus*, with the noble
Lady *Pamela* in that in expected sorte returned, his griefe, (if
any griefe were in a minde which had placed every thing according to his naturall worthe) was verie much augmented, for besides
some small hope hee had, if *Musidorus* had once bene cleere of
Arcadia, by his dealing and aucthoritie to have brought his onely
gladsome desires to a good issue: The hard estate of his friend
did no lesse nay rather more vexe him, then his owne. For so
indeede it is ever founde, where valure and friendshipp are perfectly coopled in one hart, the reason being, that the resolute
man, having once disgested in his judgement the worst extremitie
of his owne case, and having either quite expelled, or at least
repelled, all passion, which ordinarilie followes an overthrowne
fortune, not knowing his friendes minde so well as his owne,
nor with what pacience he brookes his case, (which is as it were
the materiall cause of making a man happie or unhappie) doubts
whether his friend accomptes not him selfe more miserable, and

so indeede bee more lamentable. But assoone as *Musidorus* was brought by the souldiers neere unto *Philanax*, *Pyrocles* not knowing whether ever after hee should bee suffered to see his friende, and determining there could be no advauntage by dissembling a not knowing of him leapt sodainelie from their hands that helde him, and passing with a strength strengthened with a true affeƈtion, thorowe them that encompassed *Musidorus*, he embrased him as fast as hee coulde in his armes. And kissing his cheekes, O my *Palladius* saide he, let not our vertue now abandon us; let us prove our mindes are no slaves to fortune, but in adversitie can tryumph over adversitie. Deere *Daiphantus* aunsweared *Musidorus* (seing by his apparell his being a man was revealed) I thanke you for this best care of my best parte. But feare not, I have kept too long company with you to want nowe a thorowe determination of these things, I well know there is nothing evill but within us, the rest is either naturall or accidentall. *Philanax* finding them of so neare acquaintaunce, beganne presently to examine them a parte: but such resolution hee mett within them, that by no such meanes hee coulde learne furder, then it pleased them to deliver. So that he thought best to put them both in one place, with espiall of there wordes and behaviour, that waye to sifte out the more of these fore passed mischeifes. And for that purpose gave them both unto the nobleman, whoe before had the custodie of *Pyrocles*, by name *Simpathus*, leaving a trustie servant of his owne to geve dilligent watƈh to what might passe betwixte them. No man that hath ever passed thorow the schoole of affeƈtiõ, needs doubt what a tormenting grief it was to the noble *Pamela*, to have the company of him taken from her, to whose vertuous company she had bound her life. But waying with her self, it was fit for her honour, till her doing were clearly manifested, that they shoulde remaine seperate: kept downe the rising tokens of greefe; shewing passion in nothing but her eyes, which accompanied *Musidorus* even unto the tent, whether he and *Pyrocles* were ledde. Then with a countenaunce more princely then she was woont, according to the woont of hiest hartes (like the Palme tree striving most upwarde, when he is most burdened) she commaunded *Philanax* to bring her to her father and mother, that she might render them accompte of her doings. *Philanax* shewing a sullaine kinde of reverence unto her, as a man that honoured her as his Maisters

heire, but much misliked her for her, in his conceite, dishonorable proceedings, tolde her what was past, rather to answere her,
then that hee thought shee was ignoraunt of it. But her good
spirite did presently suffer a true compassionate affliction of those
hard adventures: which crossing her armes, looking a greate
while on the grounde, with those eyes which let fall many teares,
she well declared. But in the ende remembring howe necessarye
it was for her, not to loose her selfe in such an extremitye, she
strengthened her well created hearte, and stoutely demaunded
Philanax, what aucthoritye then they had to laye handes of her
person, who being the undoubted heyre, was then the lawfull
Princesse of that Kingdome. *Philanax* answered, her Grace
knewe the auncient lawes of *Arcadia* bare, she was to have no
swaye of government till she came to one and twentye yeares
of age, or were marryed. And marryed I am replyed the wise
Princesse, therefore I demaunde your dewe allegeaunce. The
gods forbid sayde *Philanax*, *Arcadia* shoulde be a dowery of such
marriages. Besides hee toulde her, all the States of her Countrye
were evill satisfyed, touching her Fathers death; whiche likewise
according to the Statutes of *Arcadia*, was even that daye to bee
judged of, before the bodye were removed, to receyve his princely
funeralls. After that past, she shoulde have such obedience, as
by the Lawes was due unto her, desyring God she woulde showe
her selfe better in publicke government, then she had done in
private. She woulde have spoken to the Gentlemen and people
gathered about her: but *Philanax* fearing least thereby some
commotion mighte arise, or at least a hinderaunce of executing
hys maisters murderers, which hee longed after more then any
thing, hasted her up to the Lodge, where her Sister was, and
there with a chosen companye of Souldyers to garde the place,
lefte her with *Philoclea*, *Pamela* protesting they layde violent
handes of her, and that they entred into rebellious attemptes
agaynst her. But hye tyme it was for *Philanax* so to doo, for
alreadye was all the whole multitude fallne into confused and
daungerous devisions.

There was a notable example, how great dissipations,
Monarchall governement are subject unto. For nowe theyr
Prince and guide had lefte them, they had not experience to rule,
and had not whome to obaye. Publicke matters had ever bene
privately governed, so that they had no lively taste what was

good for themselves. But every thing was eyther vehemently desirefull, or extreamely terrible. Neighbours invasions, civill dissention, crueltye of the comming Prince, and whatsoever in common sence carries a dreadfull shewe, was in all mens heads, but in fewe how to prevent : harkening on every rumor, suspecting every thing, condemning them whome before they had honoured, making strange and impossible tales of the Kings death, while they thought themselves in daunger, wishing nothing but safetye, assoone as perswasion of safetie tooke them, desiring further benefitts, as amendment of forepassed faultes, (which faultes notwithstanding none could tell eyther the groundes or effectes of) all agreeing in the universall names of liking or misliking, but of what in especiall poyntes, infinitely disagreeing. Altogether like a falling steeple, the partes whereof, as windowes, stones, and pinnacles, were well, but the whole masse ruinous. And this was the generall case of all, wherein notwithstanding was an extreame medly of diversified thoughts; the great men looking to make themselves strong by factions, the gentlemen some bending to them, some standing upon themselves, some desirous to overthrowe those few which they thought were over thē, the souldiers desirous of trouble, as the nurse of spoile, and not much unlike to them, though in another way, were all the needy sorte, the riche fearefull, the wise carefull. This composicion of conceytes, brought foorth a daungerous tumulte, which yet woulde have bene more daungerous, but that it had so many partes, that no body well knewe against whome chiefely to oppose themselves. For some there were that cried to have the state altred, and governed no more by a Prince; marry in the alteration, many would have the *Lacedemonian* government of fewe chosen Senatours; others the *Athenian*, where the peoples voyce helde the chiefe aucthoritye. But these were rather the discoursing sorte of men, then the active, being a matter more in imaginacion then practise. But they that went neerest to the present case, (as in a countrie that knewe no government, without a Prince) were they that strove, whome they should make. Whereof a great number there were, that would have the Princesse *Pamela* presently to enjoy it: some disdayning that she had as it were abandoned her owne Countrie, enclining more to *Philoclea*; and there wanted not of them, which wished *Gynæcia* were delivered, and made Regent till

Pamela were worthely marryed. But great multitudes there were, which having bene acquainted with the just government of *Philanax*, meant to establish him as Lieutenant of the state : and these were the most populer sorte, who judged by the commodities they felte. But the principall men in honor and might, who had long before envyed his greatnes with *Basilius*, did much more spurne against any such preferment of him. For yet before theyr envye had some kinde of breathing out his rancour, by layeng his greatnes as a fault to the Princes judgement, who shewde in *Damætas* he might easely be deceyved in mens valewe. But nowe if the Princes choice, by so many mouthes should be confyrmed, what coulde they object to so rightly esteemed an excellencye? They therefore were disposed, sooner to yeeld to any thing, then to his raysing: and were content (for to crosse *Philanax*) to stoppe those actions, which otherwise they could not but thinke good. *Philanax* himselfe, as much hindred by those, that did immoderatly honour him, (which brought both more envye, and suspicion uppon him) as by them that did manifestly resist him, (but standing onely uppon a constant desire of justice, and a cleere conscience) went forwarde stoutly in the action of his maisters revenge, which he thought himselfe particularly bound to. For the rest, as the ordering of the government, he accompted himselfe but as one, wherein notwithstanding he would imploy all hys loyall indeavour.

But among the Noble men, hee that most openly set himselfe against him, was named *Timantus*, a man of middle age, but of extreame ambition, as one that had placed his uttermost good in greatnes, thinking small difference by what meanes he came by it. Of commendable wit, if he had not made it a servaunt to unbrideled desires. Cunning to creepe into mens favours, which hee prized onely as they were serviceable unto him. He had bene brought up in some souldiery, which he knewe how to set out, with more then deserved ostentacion. Servile (though envious) to his betters: and no lesse tirannycallie minded to them hee had advauntage of. Counted revengefull, but in deede measuring both revenge and rewarde, as the partye might eyther helpe or hurt him. Rather shamelesse then bolde, and yet more bolde in practises, then in personall adventures. In summe, a man that could be as evill as he listed, and listed as much, as any advancement might thereby be gotten. As for vertue, hee counted it but a schoole name. Hee even at the fyrst assembling together, finding the great stroke *Philanax* carried among the people, thought it his readyest way of ambition, to joyne with him : which though his pride did hardly brooke, yet the other vice carrying with it a more apparant object, prevayled over the weaker, so that with those liberall protestacions of friendship, which men that care not for their word are wont to bestowe, he offred unto him the choise in marriage, of eyther the sisters, so he would likewise helpe him to the other, and make such a particion of the *Arcadian* estate. Wishing him, that since he loved his maister, because he was his maister, which shewed the love began in himselfe, he should rather now occasion was presented, seeke his owne good substancially, then affect the smoke of a glory, by shewing an untimely fidelitie to him, that could not reward it ; and have all the fruite he should get in mens opinions, which would be as divers, as many ; fewe agreeing to yeeld him due prayse of his true heart. But *Philanax*, who had limitted his thoughtes in that he esteemed good, (to which he was neyther carryed by the vayne tickling of uncertayne fame, nor from which he would be transported by enjoying any thing, whereto the ignorant world geves the excellent name of goodes) with great mislike of his offer, he made him so peremtorye an answere, not without threatning, if he found him foster any such fancie, that *Timantus* went with an inward spite from him, whome before he had never loved ; and measuring all mens marches by his owne pace, rather thought it some further fetch of *Philanax*, (as that he would have all to himselfe alone) then was any way taken with the lovely beawtie of his vertue ; whose image he had so quite defaced in his owne soule, that he had left himselfe no eyes to beholde it, but stayde wayting fitt oportunitie, to execute his desires both for himselfe, and against *Philanax*, which by the bringing backe of *Pamela*, the people being devided into many motions, (which both with murmuring noyses, and putting themselves in severall troupes, they well shewed) he thought apt time was layde before him, the waters being, as the proverbe sayth, troubled, and so the better for his fishing. Therefore going amongst the chiefest Lordes, whome he knewe principally to repine at *Philanax*, and making a kinde of convocation of them, he inveighed against his proceedings, drawing every thing to the most malicious interpretacion, that malice itselfe could instruct him to doe. He sayde, it was season for them to looke to such a weede, that else would overgrowe them all. It was not nowe time to consult of the dead, but of the living : since such a slye wolfe was entred among them, that could make justice the cloake of tirannye, and love of his late maister the destruction of his now being children. Do you not see, sayde hee, howe farre his corruption hath stretched, that hee hath such a number of rascalls voyces, to declare him Lieutenant, readye to make him Prince, but that he instructs them, matters are not yet ripe for it ? As for us, because we are too ritch to be bought, he thinkes us the fitter to be killed. Hath *Arcadia* bredd no man but *Philanax?* is she become a stepmother to all the rest, and hath geven all her blessings to *Philanax?* Or if there be men amongst us, let us shewe wee disdayne to bee servaunts to a servaunt. Let us make hym knowe, wee are farre worthier not to bee slaves, then hee to bee a mayster. Thinke you hee hath made such haste in these matters, to geve them over to another mans hande ? Thincke you, he durst become the gaylor of his Princesse, but either meaning to be her maister, or her murtherer ? and all this for the dere good wil forsooth he beares to the kings memory, whose authority as he abused in his life, so he would now persever to abuse his name, after his death. O notable affection, for the love of the father to kill the wife, and disenherit the children ! O single minded modestie to aspire to no lesse then to the princely Diademe ! No, no, he hath vired all this while, but to come the sooner to his affected ende. But let us remember what we be, in quallitie his equalls, in number farre before him, let us deliver the Queene, and our naturall Princesses, and leave them no longer under his authoritye; whose proceedings would rather shewe, that he himselfe, had bene the murderer of the King, then a fit Gardien of his posteritye. These wordes pearst much into the mindes, already enclined that way. Insomuch that most part of the nobilitye, confirmed *Timantus* speech, and were readye to execute it : when *Philanax* came among them, and with a constant but reverent behaviour, desired them they would not exercise private grudges, in so common a necessitye. Hee acknowledged himselfe a man, and a faultye man, to the cleering or satisfyeng of which, he would at all times submit himselfe, since his ende was to bring all things to an upright judgement, it should evill fitt him to flye the judgement. But sayde he, my Lordes, let not *Timantus* rayling speech (who whatsoever he findes evill in his owne soule, can with ease lay it uppon another) make me loose your good favour. Consider that all well doing, stands so in the middle betwixt his two contrarye evils, that it is a readye matter to cast a slaunderous shade upon the most approved vertues. Who hath an evill toong, can call severitie, crueltie, and faithfull dilligence, dilligent ambition. But my ende is not to excuse my selfe, nor to accuse him : for both those, hereafter will be time enough. There is neyther of us, whose purging or punishing may so much import to *Arcadia.* Now I request you, for your owne honours sake, and require you by the duety you owe to this estate, that you doo presently (according to the lawes) take in hande, the chastizement of our maisters murderers, and laying order for the government : by whom soever it be done, so it be done, and justly done, I am satisfyed. My labour hath bene to frame things so, as you might determine : now it is in you to determine. For my part, I call the heavens to witnesse, the care of my heart stands to repaye that, wherein both I, and most of you were tyed to that Prince ; with whome, all my love of worldly action is dead.

As *Philanax* was speaking his last wordes, there came one running to him, with open mouth, and fearefull eyes, telling him, that there were a great number of the people, which were bent to take the young men out of *Sympathus* hands, and as it should seeme by their acclamacions, were like inough to proclayme them Princes. Nay, sayde *Philanax* (speaking alowde, and looking with a just anger uppon the other noblemen) it is nowe season to heare *Timantus* idle slanders, while strangers become our Lordes, and *Basilius* murderers sit in his throne. But who soever is a true *Arcadian*, let him followe me. With that he went towarde the place he heard of, followed by those that had ever loved him, and some of the noblemen. Some other remayning with *Timantus*, who in the meane time was conspiring by strong hand to deliver *Gynæcia*, of whome the weakest guard was had. But *Philanax* where he went, found them all in an uprore, which thus was fallne out. The greatest multitude of people, that were come to the death of *Basilius*, were the *Mantineans*, as being the nearest Citie to the lodges. Among these, the chiefe man both in authoritye and love was *Kalander*, he that not long before had bene hoste to the two Princes, whome though he knewe not so much as by name, yet besides the obligacion he stood bound to them in, for preserving the lives of his sonne or nephewe, theyr noble behaviour had bred such love in his heart towardes them, as both with teares he parted from them, when they left him (under promise to returne) and did keepe their jewells and apparrell as the relicks of two demy gods. Among others, he had entred the prison, and seene them, which forthwith so invested his soule, both with sorrowe and desire to helpe them (whome he tendred as his children) that calling his neighbours the *Mantineans* unto him, he tould them, all the prayses of those two young men, swearing he thought the gods had provided for them better, then they themselves could have imagined. He willed them to consider, that when all was done, *Basilius* children must enjoy the state; who since they had chosen, and chosen so as all the world could not mende their choise, why should they resist Gods doing, and theyr Princesses pleasure? This was the only way to purchase quietnes without blood, where otherwise they should at one instant, crowne *Pamela* with a Crowne of golde, and a dishonoured title. Which whether ever she would forget, he thought it fit for them to way: such said he, heroicall greatnes shines in their eyes, such an extraordinary majestie in all their actions, as surely either fortune by parentage, or nature in creation, hath made them Princes. And yet a state already we have, we neede but a man, who since he is presented unto you by the heavenly providence, embraced by your undoubted Princesse, worthy for their youth of compassion, for their beawtie of admiracion, for their excellent vertue to be monarkes of the world, shall we not be content with our owne blisse? Shall we put out our eyes, because another man cannot see? or rather like some men, when too much good happens unto them, they thinke themselves in a dreame, and have not spirits to taste their owne goods? No no my friends, beleeve me, I am so unpartiall, that I knowe not their names, but so overcome with their vertue, that I shall then thinke, the destenyes have ordayned a perpetuall florishing to *Arcadia*, when they shall allot such a governor unto it. This spoken by a man grave in yeares, great in authoritie, neere allyed to the Prince, and knowen honest, prevayled so with all the *Mantineans*, that with one voyce they ranne to deliver the two Princes. But *Philanax* came in time to withstand them, both sides yet standing in armes, and rather wanting a beginning, then mindes to enter into a bloudy conflict. Which *Philanax* foreseeing, thought best to remove the prisoners secretly, and if neede were, rather without forme of justice to kill them, then against justice (as hee thought) to have them usurpe the state. But there agayne arose a new trouble. For *Sympathus* (the noble man that kept them) was so stricken in compassion, with their excellent presence, that as he would not falsifye his promise to *Philanax*, to geve them libertye, so yet would he not yeeld them to himselfe, fearing he would do them violence. Thus tumult uppon tumult arising, the Sunne I thinke aweary to see theyr discords, had alreadye gone downe to his Westerne lodging. But yet to knowe what the poore Shepherds did, who were the fyrst descryers of these matters, will not to some eares perchance be a tedious digression.

Heere endes the fourth booke or acte.

The fourth Eglogues.

THE Shepheards finding no place for them in these garboyles, to which their quiet hearts (whose highest ambition was in keeping themselves up in goodnes) had at all no aptnes, retired themselves from among the clamorous multitude: and as sorowe desires company, went up together to the Westerne side of a hill, whose prospect extended it so farre, as they might well discerne many of *Arcadias* beawtyes. And there looking upon the Sunnes as then declining race, the poore men sate pensive of their present miseries, as if they founde a wearines of theyr wofull wordes: till at last good olde *Geron* (who as he had longest tasted the benefites of *Basilius* government, so seemed to have a speciall feeling of the present losse) wiping his eyes and long white bearde bedeawed with greate dropps of teares, began in this sorte to complayne. Alas poore sheepe, sayde hee, which hitherto have enjoyed your fruitefull pasture, in such quietnes, as your wooll amongst other things hath made this Countrie famous, your best dayes are now past: now you must become the vittaile of an armye, and perchaunce an armye of foraine enemyes: you are now not onely to feare home Wolves, but alien Lions; now, I say now, that our right *Basilius* is deceased. Alas sweete pastures! Shall souldiours that knowe not how to use you, possesse you? Shall they that can not speake *Arcadian* language be Lordes over your Shepheards? For alas with good cause may we looke for any evill, since *Basilius* our only strength is taken from us. To that all the other Shepheards present uttered pittifull voyces, especially the very borne *Arcadians*. For as for the other, though humanitie moved them to pittie humane cases, especially in a Prince, under whome they had founde a refuge of their miseries, and justice equally administred: yet could they not so naturally feele the lively touch of sorrowe. Neverthelesse, of that number one *Agelastus*, notably noted among them, aswell for his skill in Poetry, as for an austerely mayntayned sorrow-fulnes, wherewith hee seemed to despise the workes of nature, framing an universall complaint in that universall mischiefe, uttered it in this sestine.

> SInce wayling is a bud of causefull sorowe,
> Since sorow is the follower of evill fortune,
> Since no evill fortune equalls publique damage:
> Now Princes losse hath made our damage publique,
> Sorow, pay we to thee the rights of Nature,
> And inward griefe seale up with outward wailing.
>
> Why should we spare our voice from endlesse wailing,
> Who justly make our hearts the seate of sorow?
> In such a case where it appeares that nature
> Doth add her force unto the sting of fortune:
> Choosing alas! this our theatre publique,
> Where they would leave trophees of cruell damage,
>
> Then since such pow'rs conspir'd unto our damage
> (Which may be know'n, but never help't with wailing)
> Yet let us leave a monument in publique
> Of willing teares, torne haires, & cries of sorrow.
> For lost, lost is by blowe of cruell fortune
> Arcadias gemme the noblest childe of nature,
>
> O nature doting olde, ô blinded nature,
> How hast thou torne thy selfe! sought thine owne damage!
> In graunting such a scope to filthy fortune,
> By thy impes losse to fill the world with wai'ling.
> Cast thy stepmother eyes upon our sorowe,
> Publique our losse: so, see, thy shame is publique.

O that we had, to make our woes more publique,
Seas in our eyes, & brasen tongues by nature,
A yelling voice, & heartes compos'd of sorow,
Breath made of flames, wits knowing nought but damage,
Our sports murdering our selues, our musiques wailing,
Our studies fixt upon the falles of fortune.

No, no, our mischiefe growes in this vile fortune,
That private paines can not breath out in publique
The furious inward griefes with hellish wailing:
But forced are to burthen feeble nature
With secret sense of our eternall damage,
And sorow feede, feeding our soules with sorow.

Since sorow then concludeth all our fortune
With all our deathes shew we this damage publique.
His nature feares to die who lives still wailing.

It seemed that this complaint of *Agelastus* had awaked the spirits of the *Arcadians*, astonished before with exceedingnes of sorow. For hee had scarcely ended, when diverse of them offred to follow his example, in be wayling the generall losse of that countrie which had bene aswell a nurse to straungers, as a mother to *Arcadians*. Among the rest one accounted good in that kinde, and made the better by the true feeling of sorowe, roared out a song of lamentation, which (as well as might bee) was gathered up in this forme:

SInce *that to death is gone the shepheard hie,*
  Who most the silly shepheards pipe did pryse,
  Your dolefull tunes sweete Muses *now applie.*

And you ô trees (if any life there lies
  In trees) now through your porous barkes receave
  The straunge resounde of these my causefull cries:
And let my breath upon your braunches cleave,
  My breath distinguish'd into wordes of woe,
  That so I may signes of my sorrowe leave.
But if among your selves some one tree growe,
  That aptest is to figure miserie,
  Let it embassage beare your grieves to showe.
The weeping Mirrhe I thinke will not denie
  Her helpe to this, this justest cause of plaint.
  Your dolefull tunes sweet Muses *now applie.*

And thou poore Earth, whom fortune doth attaint
  In Natures name to suffer such a harme,
  As for to loose thy gemme, and such a Sainct,
Upon thy face let coaly Ravens swarme :
  Let all the Sea thy teares accounted be :
  Thy bowels with all killing mettals arme.
Let golde now rust, let Diamonds waste in thee :
  Let pearls be wan with woe their damme doth beare :
  Thy selfe henceforth the light doo never see.
And you, ô flowers, which sometimes Princes were,
  Till these straunge altrings you did hap to trie,
  Of Princes losse your selves for tokens reare,
Lilly in mourning blacke thy whitenes die :
  O Hyacinthe *let* Ai *be on thee still.*
  Your dolefull tunes sweet Muses *now applie.*

O Echo, *all these woods with roaring fill,*
  And doo not onely marke the accents last,
  But all, for all reach out my wailefull will :
One Echo *to another* Echo *cast*
  Sounde of my griefes, and let it never ende,
  Till that it hath all woods and waters past.
Nay to the heav'ns your just complaining sende,
  And stay the starrs inconstant constant race,
  Till that they doo unto our dolours bende :
And aske the reason of that speciall grace,
  That they, which have no lives, should live so long,
  And vertuous soules so soone should loose their place ?
Aske, if in great men good men doo so thronge,
  That he for want of elbowe roome must die?
  Or if that they be skante, if this be wronge ?
Did Wisedome this our wretched time espie
  In one true chest to rob all Vertues treasure ?
  Your dolefull tunes sweete Muses *now applie.*

And if that any counsell you to measure
  Your dolefull tunes, to them still playning say,
  To well felie griefe, plainte is the onely pleasure.
O light of Sunne, which is entit'led day,
  O well thou doost that thou no longer bidest ;
  For mourning light her blacke weedes may display.

O Phœbus *with good cause thy face thou hidest,*
  Rather then have thy all-beholding eye
  Fould with this sight, while thou thy chariot guidest.
And well (me thinks) becomes this vaultie skie
  A stately tombe to cover him deceased.
  Your dolefull tunes sweet Muses *now applie.*

O Philomela *with thy brest oppressed*
  By shame and griefe, helpe, helpe me to lament
  Such cursed harmes as cannot be redressed.
Or if thy mourning notes be fully spent,
  Then give a quiet eare unto my playning :
  For I to teach the world complainte am bent.
You dimmy clowdes, which well employ your stayning
  This cheerefull aire with your obscured cheere,
  Witnesse your wofull teares with dayly rayning.
And if, ô Sinne, thou ever didst appeare,
  In shape, which by mans eye might be perceaved;
  Vertue is dead, now set the triumph here.
Now set thy triumph in this world, bereaved
  Of what was good, where now no good doth lie;
  And by the pompe our losse will be conceaved.
O notes of mine your selves together tie :
  With too much griefe me thinkes you are dissolved.
  Your dolefull tunes sweet Muses *now applie,*

Time ever old, and yong is still revolved
  Within it selfe, and never tasteth ende :
  But mankind is for aye to nought resolved.
The filthy snake her aged coate can mende,
  And getting youth againe, in youth doth flourish :
  But unto Man, *age ever death doth sende.*
The very trees with grafting we can cherish,
  So that we can long time produce their time:
  But Man *which helpeth them, helplesse must perish.*
Thus, thus the mindes, which over all doo clime,
  When they by yeares experience get best graces,
  Must finish then by deaths detested crime.
We last short while, and build long lasting places :
  Ah let us all against foule Nature *crie :*
  We Natures *workes doo helpe, she us defaces.*

For how can Nature unto this reply?
   That she her child, I say, her best child killeth?
   Your dolefull tunes sweete Muses *now apply.*

Alas, me thinkes, my weakned voice but spilleth,
   The vehement course of this just lamentation:
   Me thinkes, my sound no place with sorrow filleth.
I know not I, but once in detestation
   I have my selfe, and all what life containeth,
   Since Death on Vertues fort hath made invasion.
One word of woe another after traineth:
   Ne doo I care how rude be my invention,
   So it be seene what sorrow in me raigneth.
O Elements, by whose (men say) contention,
   Our bodies be in living power maintained,
   Was this mans death the fruite of your dissention?
O Phisickes power, which (some say) hath restrained
   Approch of death, alas thou helpest meagerly,
   When once one is for Atropos *distrained.*
Great be Physitions brags, but aid is beggerly,
   When rooted moisture failes, or groweth drie,
   They leave off all, and say, death commes too eagerlie.
They are but words therefore that men do buy
   Of any, since God Æsculapius *ceased.*
   Your dolefull tunes sweete Muses *now apply.*

Justice, justice is now (alas) oppressed:
   Bountifulnes hath made his last conclusion:
   Goodnes for best attire in dust is dressed.
Shepheards bewaile your uttermost confusion;
   And see by this picture to you presented,
   Death is our home, life is but a delusion.
For see alas, who is from you absented?
   Absented? nay I say for ever banished
   From such as were to dye for him contented?
Out of our sight in turne of hand is vanished
   Shepherd of shepherds, whose well setled order
   Private with welth, publike with quiet garnished.
While he did live, farre, farre was all disorder;
   Example more prevailing then direction,
   Far was homestrife, and far was foe from border.

His life a law, his looke a full correction :
  And in his health we healthfull were preserved,
  So in his sicknesse grew our sure infection.
His death our death. But ah; my Muse hath swarved,
  From such deepe plaint as should such woes descrie,
  Which he of us for ever hath deserved.
The stile of heavie hart can never flie
  So high, as should make such a paine notorious :
  Cease Muse therfore : thy dart ô Death applie ;
And farewell Prince, whom goodnesse hath made glorious.

Many were readie to have followed this course, but the day
was so wasted, that onely this riming *Sestine* delivered by one of
great account among them, could obtaine favour to be heard.

FArewell ô Sunn, *Arcadias clearest light:*
  Farewell ô pearl, the poore mans plenteous treasure :
Farewell ô golden staffe, the weake mans might:
Farewell ô Joy, the joyfulls onely pleasure.
Wisdome farewell, the skillesse mans direction :
Farewell with thee, farewell all our affection.

For what place now is lefte for our affection,
Now that of purest lampe is quench'd the light,
Which to our darkned mindes was best direction?
Now that the mine is lost of all our treasure ?
Now death hath swallow'd up our worldly pleasure,
We Orphans made, void of all publique might ?

Orphans indeede, depriv'd of fathers might :
For he our father was in all affection,
In our well-doing placing all his pleasure,
Still studying how to us to be a light.
As well he was in peace a safest treasure :
In warr his wit & word was our direction.

Whence, whence alas, shall we seeke our direction !
When that we feare our hatefull neighbours might,
Who long have gap't to get Arcadians *treasure.*
Shall we now finde a guide of such affection,
Who for our sakes will thinke all travaile light,
And make his paine to keepe us safe his pleasure?

No, no, for ever gone is all our pleasure;
For ever wandring from all good direction;
For ever blinded of our clearest light;
For ever lamed of our sured might;
For ever banish'd from well plac'd affection;
For ever robd of all our royall treasure.

Let teares for him therefore be all our treasure,
And in our wailfull naming him our pleasure:
Let hating of our selves be our affection,
And unto death bend still our thoughts direction.
Let us against our selves employ our might,
And putting out our eyes seeke we our light.

Farewell our light, farewell our spoiled treasure:
Farewell our might, farewell our daunted pleasure:
Farewell direction, farewell all affection.

The night beganne to cast her darke Canopie over them, and they even wearie with their woes bended homewardes: hoping by sleepe forgetting themselves, to ease their present dolours. When they were mett with a troupe of twentie horse, the chiefe of which asking them for the Kinge, and understanding the hard newes, thereupon stayed among them expecting the returne of a messenger whome with speede he dispatched to *Philanax*.

The ende of the fourth Booke.

THE FIFTH BOOKE
OF THE COUNTESSE OF
PEMBROKES ARCADIA.

THE daungerous division of mens mindes, the ruinous renting
of all estates, had nowe brought *Arcadia* to feele the pangs
of uttermost perill (such convulsions never comming, but that
the life of that government drawes neere his necessarye periode)
when to the honest and wise *Philanax*, equally distracted betwixt
desire of his maisters revenge and care of the states establishment,
there came (unlooked for) a *Macedonian* Gentleman, who in
short, but pithye maner delivered unto him, that the renowmed
Euarchus, King of *Macedon*, purposing to have visited his olde
friend and confederate the King *Basilius*, was nowe come within
halfe a mile of the Lodges, where having understoode be certayne
Shepheards, the sodayne death of theyr Prince, had sent unto
him, (of whose authoritye and faith he had good knowledge) desiring him to advertise him, in what securitie hee might rest
there for that night, where willinglye hee woulde (if safely hee
might) helpe to celebrate the funeralls of his auncient companion
and alye, adding hee neede not doubt, since hee had brought
but twentye in his companye, hee woulde be so unwise as to
enter into any forcible attempte with so small force. *Philanax*
having entertayned the Gentleman, aswell as in the middest of
so many tumultes hee coulde, pausing awhile with himselfe, considering howe it shoulde not onely be unjust, and against the
lawe of Nations, not well to receyve a Prince whome good will
had brought among them, but (in respecte of the greatnes of his
might) very daungerous to geve him any cause of due offence;
remembring withall the excellent tryalls of his equitie, which
made him more famous then his victoryes, hee thought hee might
bee the fittest instrumente to redresse the ruynes they were in,
since his goodnes put hym without suspicion, and hys greatnesse
beyonde envye. Yet weighing with himselfe howe harde many
heads were to be brideled, and that in this monstrous confusion

such mischiefe mighte be attempted, of which late repentance should after be but a simple remedie: he judged best first to knowe how the peoples mindes would sway to this determinacion. Therefore desiring the Gentleman to returne to the King his maister, and to beseech him (though with his paynes) to stay for an houre or two, where he was, till he had set things in better order to receive him: he himselfe went fyrst to the Noble men, then to *Kalander* and the principall *Mantineans*, who were most opposite unto him; desiring them, that as the night had most blessedly stayed them from entring into civill bloud, so they would be content in the night to assemble the people together, to heare some newes, which he was to deliver unto them. There is nothing more desirous of novelties, then a man that feares his present fortune. Therefore they, whome mutuall diffidence made doubtfull of their utter destruction, were quickly perswaded to heare of any newe matter, which might alter at least, if not helpe the nature of their feare. Namely the chiefest men, who as they had most to lose, so were most jealous of their owne case, and were alreadye growne as wearye to be followers of *Timantus* ambition, as before they were envyers of *Philanax* worthinesse. As for *Kalander* and *Sympathus*, as in the one a vertuous friendship had made him seeke to advaunce, in the other a naturall commiseration had made him willing to protect the excellent (though unfortunate) prisoners, so were they not against this convocation. For having nothing but just desires in them, they did not mistrust the justifyeng of them. Only *Timantus* laboured to have withdrawne them from this assemblye, sayeng, it was time to stop their eares from the ambitious charmes of *Philanax*. Let them fyrst deliver *Gynæcia*, and her daughters, which were fit persons to heare, and then then they might begin to speake. That this was but *Philanax* comming, to linke broyle upon broyle, because he might avoyd the answering of his trespasses, which as he had long intended, so had he prepared coullored speeches to disguise them. But as his words expressed rather a violence of rancour, then any just ground of accusation, so pierced they no further, then to some partiall eares, the multitude yeelding good attention to what *Philanax* would propose unto them: Who, like a man whose best building was a well-framed conscience, neyther with plausible words, nor fawning countenance, but even with the grave behaviour of a wise father,

whome nothing but love makes to chide, thus sayd unto them.
I have, said he, a great matter to deliver unto you, and thereout
am I to make a greater demaund of you: But truly such hath
this late proceeding bene of yours, that I knowe not what is not
to be demaunded of you. Me thinkes I may have reason to require of you, as men are woont among Pirates, that the life of
him that never hurt you, may be safe. Me thinkes I am not
without apparence of cause, as if you were *Cyclopes* or *Cannibals*,
to desire that our Princes body, which hath thirtie yeares maintained us in a flourishing peace, be not torne in pieces, or devoured
among you, but may be suffred to yeeld it selfe, which never
was defiled with any of your blouds, to the naturall rest of the
earth. Me thinkes, not as to *Arcadians*, renowmed for your faith
to Prince, and love of Country, but as to sworne enemyes of this
sweete soyle, I am to desire you, that at least, if you will have
straungers to your Princes, yet you will not deliver the seignory
of this goodly Kingdome to your noble Kings murtherers. Lastly,
I have reason, as if I had to speake to mad men, to desire you
to be good to your selves: For before God, what either barbarous
violence, or unnaturall follie, hath not this day had his seate in
your mindes, and left his footsteps in your actions? But in troth
I love you too well, to stand long displayeng your faults: I would
you your selves did forget them, so you did not fall againe into
them. For my part, I had much rather be an orator of your
prayses. But now (if you will suffer attentive judgement, and
not forejudging passion, to be the waigher of my wordes) I will
deliver unto you what a blessed meane the Gods have sent unto
you, if you list to embrace it. I thinke there is none among you
so young, either in yeares, or understanding, but hath heard the
true fame of that just Prince *Euarchus* King of *Macedon*. A
Prince with whom our late maister did ever holde most perfit
alliance. He, even he, is this day come, having but twenty
horse with him, within two miles of this place, hoping to have
found the vertuous *Basilius* alive, but now willing to do honor
to his death. Surely, surely the heavenly powers have in so full
a time bestowed him on us, to unite our divisions. For my part
therefore I wish, that since among our selves we can not agree
in so manifold partialities, we do put the ordering of all these
things into his hands, aswell touching the obsequies of the King,
the punishment of his death, as the mariage and crowning of

our Princesse. He is both by experience and wisedome taught
how to direct: his greatnesse such, as no man can disdaine to
obey him: his equitie such, as no man neede to feare him.
Lastly, as he hath all these qualities to helpe, so hath he (though
he would) no force to hurt. If therfore you so thinke good, since our
lawes beare that our Princes murther be chastized before his
murthered bodie be buried, we may invite him to sit to morowe
in the judgement seate; which done, you may after proceede to
the buriall. When *Philanax* first named *Euarchus* landing, there
was a muttring murmur among the people, as though in that evil
ordered weaknes of theirs he had come to conquer their country.
But when they understood he had so small a retinue, whispring
one with another, and looking who should begin to confirme
Philanax proposition, at length *Sympathus* was the first that allowed it, then the rest of the Noblemen, neither did *Kalander*
strive, hoping so excellent a Prince could not but deale graciously
with two such young men, whose authoritie joyned to *Philanax*,
all the popular sort followed. *Timantus* still blinded with his owne
ambitious haste (not remembring factions are no longer to be
trusted, then the factious may be perswaded it is for their owne
good) would needes strive against the streame, exclaiming against
Philanax, that now he shewed who it was, that would betray his
country to straungers. But well he found, that who is too busie
in the foundation of an house, may pull the building about his
eares. For the people alreadie tyred with their owne divisions,
(of which his clampring had bene a principall nurse) and beginning now to espye a haven of rest, hated any thing that should
hinder them frō it: asked one another whether this were not he,
whose evill toong no man could escape? whether it were not
Timantus that made the first mutinous oration, to strengthen the
troubles? whether *Timantus*, without their consent, had not gone
about to deliver *Gynæcia?* And thus enflaming one another
against him, they threwe him out of the assembly, and after
pursued him with stones and staves, so that with losse of one of
his eyes, sore wounded & beaten, he was faine to flye to *Philanax*
feete, for succour of his life: geving a true lesson, that vice it
selfe is forced to seeke the sanctuarie of vertue. For *Philanax*
who hated his evill, but not his person, and knewe that a just
punishment might by the maner be unjustly done; remembring
withall, that although herein the peoples rage might have hit

148

rightly, yet if it were nourished in this, no man knewe to what extremities it might extend it selfe: with earnest dealing, and employeng the uttermost of his authority, he did protect the trembling *Timantus*. And then having taken a generall oth, that they should in the noneage of the Princesse, or till these things were settled, yeeld full obedience to *Euarchus*, so farre as were not prejudiciall to the lawes, customes, and liberties of *Arcadia*: and having taken a particular bonde of *Sympathus* (under whome he had a servaunt of his owne) that the prisoners should be kept close, without conference with any man: he himselfe honorablie accompanyed, with a great number of torches went to the king *Euarchus*, whose comming in this sort into *Arcadia* had thus falne out.

The wofull Prince *Plangus* receyving of *Basilius* no other succours but only certayne to conduct him to *Euarchus*, made all possible speede towards *Byzantium*, where he understood the King, having concluded all his warres with the winning of that towne, had now for some good space made his abode. But being farre gone on his way, he receyved certayne intelligence, that *Euarchus* was not only some dayes before returned into *Macedon*, but since was gone with some haste to visit that coast of his country that lay towards *Italy*. The occasion geven by the *Latines*, who having already gotten into their hands, partly by conquest, and partly by confederacie, the greatest part of *Italie*, and long gaped to devoure *Greece* also (observing the present oportunitie of *Euarchus* absence, and *Basilius* solitarines, which two Princes they knewe to be in effect the whole strength of *Greece*) were even readye to lay an unjust gripe upon it, which after they might beawtifie with the noble name of conquest. Which purpose though they made not knowne by any solemne denouncing of warre, but contrarywise gave many tokens of continuing still their former amitie: yet the stayeng of his subjects shippes, traffiquing as Merchants into those partes, together with the dayly preparation of shipping, and other warlike provisions in Portes, most convenient for the transporting of souldyers, occasioned *Euarchus* (not unacquainted with such practizes) first to suspect, then to discerne, lastly, to seeke to prevent the intended mischiefe. Yet thinking warre never to be accepted, untill it be offred by the hand of necessitie, he determined so long openly to hold them his friends, as open hostilitie bewraied them not his enemies; not ceasing in the meane time by letters & messages to move the States of *Greece* by uniting their strength, to make timely provision against this perill : by many reasons making them see, that, though in respeƈt of place some of thē might seeme further removed from the first violence of the storme, yet being imbarqued in the same ship, the finall wrack must needs be common to them all. And knowing the mighty force of example, with the weake effeƈt of faire discourses not waited on with agreeable aƈtions, what he perswaded them, himselfe performed, leaving in his owne realme nothing either undone or unprovided, which might be thought necessary for withstanding an invasion. His first care was to put his people in a readinesse for warre, and by his experienced souldiers to traine the unskilfull to martiall exercises. For the better effeƈting whereof, as also for meeting with other inconveniences in such doubtfull times incident to the most setled states, making of the divers regions of his whole kingdome so many divisions as he thought convenient, he appointed the charge of them to the greatest, and of greatest trust he had about him : arming them with sufficient authoritie to leavie forces within their severall governments, both for resisting the invading enemy, and punishing the disordered subjeƈt. Having thus prepared the body, and assured the heart of his countrey against any mischiefe that might attaint it, he then tooke into his carefull consideration the externall parts, geving order both for the repairing and encreasing his navy, and for the fortifying of such places, especially on the sea coast, as either commoditie of landing, weakenes of the countrey, or any other respeƈt of advantage was likelyest to drawe the enemy unto. But being none of them who thinke all things done, for which they have once gevē direƈtion, he folowed everywhere his cōmandement with his presence : which witnes of every mans slacknes or diligēce, chastizing the one, & encouraging the other, suffred not the frute of any profitable counsaile for want of timely taking to be lost. And thus making one place succede another in the progresse of wisedome & vertue, he was now come to *Aulon* a principall porte of his realme, whē the poore *Plangus* extremely wearied with his long journey (desire of succouring *Erona* no more relieving, then feare of not succouring her in time aggravating his travaile) by a lamētable narratiō of his childrēs death, called home his cares frō encoūtring foraine enemies, to suppresse the insurrection of inward passions. The matter so hainous, the maner so villanous, the losse of such persons, in so unripe yeares, in a time so daungerous to the whole state of *Greece*, how vehemētly it moved to griefe & compassiō others, only not blind to the light of vertue, nor deafe to the voice of their country, might perchance by a more cunning workman in lively cullors be delivered. But the face of *Euarchus* sorow, to the one in nature, to both in affection, a father, and judging the world so much the more unworthely deprived of those excellēcies, as himselfe was better judge of so excellēt worthines, cā no otherwise be shadowed out by the skilfullest pencel, thē by covering it over with the vaile of silēce. And in deed that way himself took, with so pacient a quietnes receiving this pitifull relation, that all words of weakenes suppressed, magnanimity seemed to triumph over misery. Only receiving of *Plangus* perfit instruction of all things cōcerning *Plexirtus* & *Artaxia*, with promise not only to aid him in delivering *Erona*, but also with vehemēt protestation, never to returne into *Macedon*, til he had pursued the murtherers to death : he dispatched with speed a ship for *Byzantium*, cōmanding the governor to provide all necessaries for the war against his owne comming, which he purposed should be very shortly. In this ship *Plangus* would needs go, impacient of stay, for that in many days before he had understood nothing of his Ladies estate. Soone after whose departure, newes was brought to *Euarchus*, that all the ships detained in *Italy* were returned. For the *Latines* finding by *Euarchus* procedings their intent to be frustrate (as before by his sodaine returne they doubted it was discovered) deeming it no wisdom to shew the will, not having the abilitie to hurt, had not only in free & frendly maner dismissed them, but for the time wholy omitted their enterprise, attending the oportunitie of fitter occasion. By meanes wherof *Euarchus*, rid frō the cumber of that war (likely otherwise to have staied him longer) with so great a fleete as haste would suffer him to assemble, forthwith imbarqued for *Byzantium*. And now followed with fresh windes he had in short time runne a long course, when on a night encountred with an extreme tempest, his shippes were so scattered, that scarcely any two were lefte together. As for the Kings owne shippe, deprived of all company, sore brused, and weather-beatē, able no lōger to brooke the seas churlish entertainmēt, a litle before day it recovered the shore. The first light made thē see it was the unhappy coast of *Laconia*: for no other country could have shown the like evidēce of unnatural war. Which having long endured betwene the nobilitie and the *Helotes*, and once compounded by *Pyrocles*, under the name of *Daiphantus*, imediately upon his departure had broken out more violently then ever before. For the King taking the oportunitie of their captaines absence, refused to performe the condicions of peace, as extorted from him by rebellious violence. Whereupon they were againe deepely entred into warre, with so notable an hatred towardes the very name of a King, that *Euarchus* (though a straunger unto them) thought it not safe there to leave his person, where neither his owne force could be a defence, nor the sacred name of Majestie, a protection. Therefore calling to him an *Arcadian* (one that comming with *Plangus* had remained with *Euarchus*, desirous to see the warres) hee demaunded of him for the next place of suretie, where hee might make his staye, untill hee might heare somewhat of his fleete, or cause his ship to bee repaired. The gentleman glad to have this occasion of doing service to *Euarchus*, and honour to *Basilius* (to whom he knew hee shoulde bring a most welcome gueste) tolde him, that if it pleased him to commit himselfe to *Arcadia*, (a parte whereof laie open to their vewe) he woulde undertake ere the next night were farre spent to guide him safely to his master *Basilius*. The present necessitie much prevailed with *Euarchus*, yet more a certaine vertuous desire to trie, whether by his authoritie he might withdrawe *Basilius* from burying himselfe alive, and to imploy the rest of his olde yeares in doing good, the onely happie action of mans life. For besides the universall case of *Greece* deprived by this meanes of a principall piller, he weighed and pitied the pittyfull state of the *Arcadian* people, who were in worse case then if death had taken away their Prince. For so yet their necessitie would have placed some one to the helme: now, a Prince being, and not doing like a Prince, keeping and not exercising the place, they were in so much more evill case, as they coulde not provide for their evill. These rightly wise & vertuous cōsideratiōs especially moved *Euarchus* to take his journy towards the desert, where arriving within night, and understanding to his great griefe the newes of the Princes death, hee wayted for his safe conduct from *Philanax*: in the meane time taking his rest under a tree, with no more affected pompes, then as a man that knew, how soever he was exalted, the beginning and end of his body was earth. But *Philanax* as soone as he was in sight of him, lighting from his horse, presented himselfe unto him in all those humble behaviours, which not only the great reverence of the partie but the conceit of ones owne miserie, is woont to frame. *Euarchus* rase up unto him with so gratious a coūtenaunce, as the goodnes of his mind had long exercised him unto: carefull so much more to descend in all curtesies, as he sawe him beare a lowe representation of his afflicted state. But to *Philanax*, assoone as by neere looking on him, he might perfectly behold him, the gravitie of his countenaunce, and yeares, not much unlike to his late deceassed, but ever beloved master brought his forme so lively unto his memorie, and revived so all the thoughtes of his wonted joyes within him, that in steede of speaking to *Euarchus*, hee stoode a while like a man gone a farre jorney from him-selfe, calling as it were with his minde an account of his losses: imagining that this paine needed not, if nature had not ben violently stopped of her owne course: and casting more loving then wise conceites, what a world this woulde have bene, if this sodaine accident had not interrupted it. And so farre strayed hee, into this raving melancholy, that his eyes nimbler then his tounge let fall a floud of teares, his voice being stopped with extremitie of sobbing, so much had his friendshippe caried him to *Basilius*, that hee thought no age was timely for his death. But at length taking the occasion of his owne weeping, he thus did speake to *Euarchus*. Let not my teares most worthely renowmed Prince make my presence unpleasant, or my speach unmarked of you. For the justnes of the cause, takes away the blame of any weakenes in me; and the affinitie that the same beareth to your greatnes, seemes even lawfully to clayme pitty in you: A Prince of a Princes fall, a lover of justice, of a most unjust violence. And geve me leave excellent *Euarchus* to say, I am but the representer of all the late florishing *Arcadia*, which now with mine eyes doth weepe, with my toong doth complaine, with my knees doth lay it selfe at your feete, which never have bene unreadie to carie you, to the vertuous pro-tecting of innocents. Imagine, vouchsafe to imagine most wise and good King, that heere is before your eyes, the pittifull spectacle of a most dolorously ending tragedie: wherein I do but play the part, of all the newe miserable province, which being spoiled of their guide, doth lye like a ship without a Pilot, tumbling up and downe in the uncertaine waves, till it either runne it selfe upon the rockes of selfe-division, or be overthrowne by the stormie winde of forreine force. *Arcadia* finding her selfe in these desolate tearmes, doth speake, and I speake for her, to thee not vainly puissant Prince, that since now she is not only robbed of the naturall support of her Lord, but so sodainly robbed, that she hath not breathing time to stande for her safetie: so unfortunately, that it doth appall their mindes, though they had leisure: and so mischevously, that it doth exceede both the sodainnes and infortunatenes of it: thou wilt lend thine arme unto her, and as a man, take compassion of mankinde, as a vertuous man chastice most abhominable vice, and as a Prince protect a people, which all have with one voyce called for thy goodnes: thinking that as thou art only able, so thou art fullie able, to redresse their imminent ruines. They do therefore with as much confidence as necessitie, flie unto you for succour, they lay themselves open to you: to you, I meane your selfe, such as you have ever bene: that is to say one, that hath alwayes had his determinaciõs bounded with equitie. They only reserve the right to *Basilius* blood; the maner to the auncient prescribing of their lawes. For the rest without exception, they yeld over unto you, as to the elected protectour of this kingdome, which name and office they beseech you till you have layde a sufficient foundacion of tranquilitie, to take upon you the particularitie both of their statutes and demands, you shal presently after understand. Now only I am to say unto you, that this countrie falls to be a faire field, to proove whether the goodlie tree of your vertue, will live in all soiles. Heere I say will be seene, whether either feare can make you short, or the likorousnes of dominion make you beyond justice. And I can for conclusion say no more but this, you must thinke upon my words and your answere, depend not only the quiet, but the lives of so many thousands, which for their auncient confederacie in this their extreame necessity, desire neither the expence of your treasure, nor hazard of your subjects, but only the benefit of your wisedome, whose both glory and encrease stands in the exercising of it. The summe of this request was utterly unlooked for of *Euarchus,* which made him the more diligent in marking his speach, and after his speach take the greater pause for a perfect resolucion. For as of the one side, he thought nature required nothing more of him then that he should be a helpe, to them of like creation, and had his heart no whit commanded with feare, thinking his life well passed, having satisfyed the tyrannie of time which the course of many yeares, the expectation of the world with more then expected honour, lastly the tribute due to his own mind with the daily offring of most vertuous actions: so of the other hee wayed the just reproach that followed those, who easely enter into other folkes busines, with the opinion might be conceaved, love of seignorie rather then of justice, had made him embarke himselfe thus, into a matter nothing pertaining to him, especially in a time when ernest occasion of his owne busines so greatly required his presence: But in the ende wisedome being an assentiall and not an opinionate thing, made him rather to bend to what was in it selfe good, then what by evill mindes might bee judged not good. And therein did see, that though that people did not belong unto him, yet doing good which is not enclosed within any tearmes of people did belong unto him, and if necessitie forced him for some time to abide in *Arcadia,* the necessitie of *Arcadia* might justly demaund some fruite of abiding. To this secreat assurance of his owne worthines (which although it bee never so well cloathed in modestie, yet alwaies lives in the worthyest mindes) did much push him forward saying unto himselfe, the treasure of those inward guifts he had, were bestowed by the heavens upon him, to be beneficiall and not idle. On which determination resting and yet willing before hee waded any further, to examine well the depth of the others proffer, hee thus with that well appeased gesture, unpassionate nature bestoweth upon mankind, made answere to *Philanax* most urgent peticion. Although long experience hath made me knowe, all men (& so Princes which be but men) to be subject to infinite casualties, the verie constitution of our lives remaining in continuall change: yet the affaires of this countrie, or at least my meeting so jumply with them, makes mee abashed with the strangenes of it. With much paine I am come hither to see my long approved friend and now I finde if I will see him, I must see him dead: after, for mine owne securitie, I seeke to be waranted mine owne life: And their

sodainely am I appointed to be a judge of other mens lives, though
a friend to him, yet am I a stranger to the countrie, and now of
a stranger you would sodainely make a director. I might object
to your desire my weakenes, which age perhaps hath wrought in
mind and body: and justly I may pretend the necessitie of mine
owne affaires, which as I am by all true rules most neerely tyed
so can they not long beare the delaye of my absence. But though
I woulde and coulde dispence with these difficulties, what assurance can I have of the peoples will? Which having so many
circles of imaginations can hardly be enclosed in one pointe.
Who knowes a people, that knowes not sodaine opinion makes
them hope, which hope if it be not answered, they fall in hate?
Choosing and refusing, erecting, and overthrowing, according as
the presentnes of any fancie caries them. Even this their hastie
drawing to me, makes me thinke they wilbe as hastiely withdrawen from me, for it is but one ground of inconstancie, soone
to take or soone to leave. It may be they have hard of *Euarchus*
more thē cause: their own eies wilbe perhaps more curious judges,
out of hearesay they may have builded many conceites, which I
can not perchaunce wil not performe, then wil undeserved repentance be a greater shame and injurie unto me, then their undeserved proffer, is honour. And to conclude I must be fully
enformed, how the pacient is minded, before I can promise to
undertake the cure. *Philanax* was not of the moderne mindes,
who make suiters magistrates: but did ever thinke the unwilling
worthy man, was fitter then the undeserving desirer. Therefore
the more *Euarchus* drewe backe, the more hee founde in him
that the cunningest pilot, doth most dread the rockes, the more
earnestly hee pursued his publique request unto him. Hee desired
him not to make anye weake excuses of his weakenesse, since so
manye examples had well proved his minde, was stronge to over-
passe the greatest troubles, and his body strong enough to obey
his minde; and that so long as they were joyned together, he
knew *Euarchus* would thinke it no wearisome exercise, to make
them vessells of vertuous actions. The dutie to his countrie, he
acknowledged, which as hee had so setled, as it was not to feare
any soddaine alteration, so since it did want him, as well it might
endure a fruictfull as an idle absence. As for the doubt he conceaved of the peoples constancie in this their election, hee saide
it was such a doubt as al humane actions are subject unto: yet as

much as in politique matters, which receave not geometricall certainties, a man may assure himselfe there was evident likelyhoode to bee conceaved, of the continuance, both in their unanimitie, and his worthynes: wherof the on was apt to be held, & the other to hold, joyned to the present necessitie, the firmest band of mortall mindes. In sum hee alledged, so many reasons to *Euarchus* his minde, (alredy enclined to enter into any vertuous action) that he yeelded to take upon him selfe the judgement of the present cause, so as hee might finde in deede that such was the peoples desire out of judgement and not faction. Therefore mounting on their horses they hasted to the lodges, where they found though late in the night, the people wakefully watching, for the issue of *Philanax* embassage. No man thinking the matter would be well done, without he had his voice in it, and each deeming his owne eyes the best gardiens of his throte in that unaccustomed tumult. But when they saw *Philanax* returne, having on his right hande the King *Euarchus* on whome they had nowe placed the greatest burthen of their feares, with joyfull shoutes and applawding acclamations, they made him and the world quickly know that one mans sufficiencie is more available then ten thousands multitude. So evill ballanced be the extremities of popular mindes: and so much naturall imperiousnes there rests in a well formed spirit. For as if *Euarchus* had ben borne of the princely bloud of *Arcadia*, or that long and well acquainted proofe had engrafted him in their countrie, so flocked they about this straunger, most of them alredie, from dejected feares, rising to ambitious considerations, who should catch the first hold of his favour. And then from those crying welcomes to babling one with the other, some praysing *Philanax* for his succeeding paine, others likinge *Euarchus* aspect, & as they judged his age by his face, so judging his wisedome by his age, *Euarchus* passed thorow them like a man that did neither disdaine a people nor yet was any thing tickled with their flatteries. But alwayes holding his owne, a man might reade a constant determination in his eyes. And in that sorte dismounting among them, he forthwith demaunded the convocation to bee made, which accordingly was done, with as much order and silence: as it might appeare. *Neptune* had not more force to appease the rebellious winde, then the admiration of an extraordinary vertue hath, to temper a disordered multitude. He being raysed up uppon a place more hie then the rest, where he might be best understoode, in this sorte spake unto them. I understande saide hee, faithfull *Arcadians*, by my L. *Philanax*, that you have with one consent, chosen me to be the judge of the late evills hapned: orderer of the present disorders: and finally protector of this countrie, til therein it be seene what the customes of *Arcadia* require. He could saye no further, being stopped with a generall crie, that so it was; geving him all the honourable titles, and happie wishes, they could imagin. He beckned unto them for silence, and then thus againe proceeded, well saide hee, how good choise you have made, the attending must bee in you, the proofe in me. But because it many times falls out, we are much deceaved in others, we being the first to deceave our selves, I am to require you, not to have an overshooting expectation of mee: the most cruell adversary of all honourable doings. Nor promise your selves wonders, out of a sodaine lyking: but remember I am a man, that is to say a creature, whose reason is often darkned with error. Secondly, that you will laye your hearts voyde of foretaken opinions: els whatsoever I doe or say, will be measured by a wronge rule, like them that have the yellow Jaundise, every thing seeming yellowe unto them. Thirdly, whatsoever debates have rysen among you, may be utterly extinguished, knowing that even among the best men are diversities of opinions, which are no more in true reason to breed hatred, then one that loves black, should be angrie with him that is clothed in white, for thoughts & conceits are the verie apparel of the mind. Lastly, that you do not easely judge of your judge, but since you will have me to command, thinke it is your part to obay. And in rewarde of this, I will promise and protest unto you, that to the uttermost of my skill; but in the generall lawes of nature, especially of *Greece*, and particular of *Arcadia* (wherein I must confesse I am not unacquainted) I will not onely see the passed evills duly punished, and your weale here after established; but for your defence in it, if need shall require, I wil imploy the forces and treasures of mine owne country. In the meane time, this shalbe the first order I will take, that no man under paine of greevous punishment, name me by any other name but protector of *Arcadia*. For I will not leave any possible culloure, to any of my naturall successors, to make claime to this, which by free election you have bestowed upon me. And so I vowe unto you, to depose my self of it assoone as the judgement is passed, the King buried, and his lawfull successor appointed. For the first whereof (I meane the trying; which be guiltie of the Kings death, and these other haynous trespasses, because your customes require such haste I will no longer delay it, then till to morrowe as soone as the Sunne shall give us fit opportunitie. You may therefore retire your selves to your rest, that you may be reddier to be present, at these so great important matters. Which many allowing tokens, was *Euarchus* speech heard, who nowe by *Philanax* (that tooke the principall care, of doing all due services unto him) was offred a lodging made ready for him, (the rest of the people aswell as the small commoditie of that place, would suffer yeelding their weery heads to sleepe) when loe the night thorowly spent, in these mixed matters, was for that time banished the face of the earth, and *Euarchus*, seing the daye beginne to discloase his comfortable beauties, desiring nothing more, then to joyne speede with justice, willed *Philanax*, presently to make the judgement place bee-put in order: and assoone as the people (who yet were not fully dispersed) might be brought together, to bring foorth the prisoners and the Kings body. Which the manner was, should in such cases be held in sight, though covered with blacke velvet, untill they that were accused to be the murderers were quitted or condemned, whether the reason of the law were to shew the more gratefull love to their Prince, or by that spectacle, the more to remember the judge of his dutie. *Philanax* who now thought in himself, he approached by the just revenge he so much desired, went with all care and diligence to performe his charge. But first it shalbe well to knowe, how the poore and princely prisoners, passed this tedious night. There was never tyrante exercised his rage with more grievous torments, upon any he most hated; then afflicted *Gynecia* did crusifie her owne soule, after the guiltines of her harte, was surcharged with the sodainenes of her husbãds death, for although that effect came not frõ her minde yet her mind being evil, & the effect evill, she thought the justice of God, had for the beginning of her paines copled thẽ together. This incessantly boyled in her brest, but most of al, whẽ *Philanax* having cloasely imprisoned her, she was lefte more freely to suffer, the fierbrands of her owne thoughts, especially when it grewe darke, and had nothing left by her, but a little lampe, whose small light to a perplexed mind, might rather yeld feareful shadowes, then any assured sight. Then

beganne the heapes of her miseries, to waye downe the platforme
of her judgement, then beganne despaire to laye his ougly clawes
upon her, shee beganne then, to feare the heavenly powers (shee
was woont to reverence) not like a childe, but like an enemie,
neither kept she her selfe, from blasphemous repyning against her
creation. O Gods would she crye out, why did you make me
to destruction? If you love goodnes, why did you not geve me
a good minde? Or if I cannot have it without your gifte, why
doe you plague mee? Is it in me to resist the mightines of your
power? Then would she imagine she sawe strange sights, and
that she heard the cries of hellish ghostes, then would she skritch
out for succour, but no man comming unto her shee woulde faine
have killed her selfe, but knewe not how. At sometimes againe,
the very heavines of her imaginations, would cloase up her senses
to a little sleepe: but then did her dreames become her tormentors: One time it would seeme unto her, *Philanax* was haling
her by the heare of the head, and having put out her eyes, was
redy to throw her into a burning fornace. Another time she
would thinke she sawe her husband making the complainte of
his death to *Pluto*, and the magistrates of that infernall region,
contending in great debate, to what eternal punishment they
should allot her. But long her dreaming would not hold, but
that it woulde fall upon *Zelmane*: to whom shee would think
she was crying for mercy, and that she did passe away by her
in silence without any shew of pittying her mischief. Then
waking out of a broken sleep, and yet wishing she might ever
have slept, new formes but of the same miseries, would seaze
her minde, shee feared death, and yet desired death, shee had
passed the uttermost of shame, and yet shame was one of her
cruellest assaulters, she hated *Pyrocles* as the originall of her mortall overthrowe: and yet the love shee had conceaved to him,
had still a hie authoritie of her passions. O *Zelmane*, would she
say (not knowing how neere he himselfe was to as great a daunger)
now shalt thou glut thy eyes, with the dishonoured death of thy
enemie! Enemie alas enemie, since so thou haste wel shewed,
thou wilt have me accompt thee, couldest thou not aswel have
givē me a determinate deniall, as to disguise thy first diguising,
with a doble dissembling? Perchaunce if I had bene utterly hopelesse, the vertue was once in me, might have called together his
forces, and not have beene led captive to this monstrous thraldome

of punished wickednes. Then would her owne knowing of good enflame a new the rage of despaire: which becomming an un-resisted Lorde in her brest, shee had no other comforte but in death, which yet she had in horror, when she thought of. But the wearisome detesting of her selfe, made her long for the dayes approach, at which time shee determined to continue her former course in acknowledginge any thing, which might hasten her ende: Wherein although shee did not hope for the end of her torments, feeling alreadye the beginning of hell agonies; yet ac-cording to the nature of paine, the presente being most intollerable, shee desired to change that, and put to adventure the ensuing. And thus rested the restlesse *Gynecia*, no lesse sorrowfull, though lesse ragefull were the mindes of the Princesse *Pamela*, and the Lady *Philoclea*, whose only advantages were, that they had not consented to so much evill, and so were at greater peace with themselves: and that they were not lefte alone, but might mutu-ally beare parte of each others woes. For when *Philanax* not regarding *Pamelas* princely protestations, had by force left her under garde with her sister, and that the two sisters were matched, as well in the disgraces of fortune, as they had beene in the best beauties of nature: those thinges that till then, bashfullnes and mistrust had made them holde reserved, one from the other, now feare the underminer of all determinations, and necessitie the victorious rebell of all lawes, forced them enterchaungeably to lay open. There passions then so swelling in them, as they woulde have made Auditors of stones, rather then have swallowed up in silence, the choking adventures were falne unto them. Truely the hardest hartes, which have at any time thought womans teares to be a matter of sleight compassion (imagining that faire weather, will quickly after followe) would now have beene mollyfied: and bene compelled to confesse, that the fayrer a diamond is, the more pittie it is it shoulde receave a bleamish. Although no doubte their faces, did rather beautifie sorrow, then sorrow coulde darken that, which even in darkenes did shine. But after they had so long, as their other afflictions would suffer them, with dolefull ceremonies bemoned their fathers death: they sate downe together apparrelled as their misadventures had founde them. *Pamela* in her journying weedes nowe converted to another use: *Philoclea* onely in her night gowne, which she thought should bee the rayment of her funeralls. But when the excellent creatures, had after much panting (with their inwarde travell) gotten so much breathing power, as to make a pittifull discourse one to the other, what had befalne them; and that by the plaine comparing the case they were in, they thorowlye founde, that their greives, were not more like in regarde of themselves, then like in respecte of the subjecte (the two Princes (as *Pamela* had learned of *Musidorus*) being so minded, as they woulde ever make both their fortunes one) it did more unite, and so strengthen their lamentation: seing the one coulde not bee miserable, but that it must necessarilie make the other miserable also. That, therfore was the first matter their sweet mouths delivered, the declaring the passionate beginning, troblesome proceeding, and daungerous ending, their never ending loves had passed. And when at any time they entred into the prayses of the young Princes, to long it woulde have exercised their tonges, but that their memory foorthwith warned them, the more prayse worthy they were the more at that time they were worthy of lamentation. Then againe to crying and wringing of handes; and then a newe, as unquiet greefe sought each corner, to newe discourses, from discourses to wishes, from wishes to prayers. Especially the tender *Philoclea*, who as she was in yeares yonger, and had never lifted up her minde to any opinion of sovereignetie, so was she the apter to yeelde to her misfortune; having no stronger debates in her minde, then a man maye saye a most wittie childe-hoode is woont to nourish: as to imagine with her selfe, why *Philanax* and the other noble men, shoulde deale so cruelly by her, that had never deserved evill of any of them? And howe they could finde in their hartes, to imprison such a personage, as she did figure *Pyrocles*, whome shee thought all the worlde was bounde to love, as well as shee did? But *Pamela*, although endewed with a vertuous mildenes, yet the knowledge of her selfe, and what was due unto her, made her hart full of a stronger disdaine, against her adversitie.

So that she joyned the vexacion for her friend, with the spite to see her selfe as she thought rebelliously detayned, and mixed desirous thoughts to helpe, with revengefull thoughts if she could not helpe. And as in pangs of death, the stronger hart feeles the greater torment, because it doth the more resist to his oppressour; so her minde, the nobler it was set, and had already embraced the hyer thoughtes, so much more it did repine; and the more it repined, the more helplesse wounds it gave unto it selfe. But when great part of the night was passed over the dolefull musicke of these sweete Ladies complaints, and that leasure though with some strife, had brought *Pamela* to know, that an Eagle when she is in a Cage, must not thinke to do like an Eagle, remembring with themselves, that it was likely the next day, the Lords would proceed against those they had imprisoned. They imployed the rest of the night, in writing unto them, with such earnestnes as the matter required, but in such stiles as the state of their thoughts was apt to fashion. In the meane time, *Pyrocles* and *Musidorus*, were recommended to so strong a guard, as they might well see it was meant, they should pay no lesse prise then their lives, for the getting out of that place, which they like men in deede, (fortifying courage with the true Rampier of patience) did so endure, as they did rather appeare governours of necessitie, then servaunts to for-tune. The whole summe of their thoughts resting upon the safetie of their Ladyes, and their care one for the other: Wherein (if at all) their harts did seeme to receyve some softnes. For sometimes *Musidorus* would feele such a motion to his friend, and his unworthy case, that he would fall into such kinde speeches. My *Pyrocles* would he say, how unhappy may I thinke *Thessalia*, that hath bene as it were, the middle way to this evill estate of yours? For if you had not bene there brought up, the Sea should not have had this power, thus to sever you from your deere father. I have therefore, (if com-playntes do at any time become a mans hart) most cause to complayne, since my Countrie, which receyved the honor of *Pyrocles* educacion, should be a step to his overthrowe, if humane chances can be compted an overthrowe to him, that stands uppon vertue. Oh excellent *Musidorus* aunswered *Pyrocles*, howe do you teache me rather, to fall out with my selfe, and my fortune, since by you I have receyved all good, you only by me this affliction? to you and your vertuous mother, I in my tendrest yeares, and fathers greatest troubles, was sent for suc-cour. There did I learne the sweete mysteries of Phylosophy; there had I your lively example, to confirme that which I learned; there lastly had I your friendship, which no unhap-pines can ever make me saye, but that hath made me happy. Now see how my desteny (the gods knowe) not my will, hath rewarded you: my father sends for you away out of your land, whence but for me you had not come: what after followed, you knowe. It was my love not yours, which first stayed you heere; and therefore if the heavens ever held a just proportion, it were I and not you, that should feele the smart. O blame not the heavens, sweete *Pyrocles* sayde *Musidorus*, as their course never alters, so is there nothing done by the unreacheable ruler of them, but hath an everlasting reason for it. And to saye the truth of these things, we should deale ungratefully with nature, if we should be forgetfull receyvers of her giftes, and so diligent Auditors of the chaunces we like not. We have lived, and have lived to be good to our selves, and others: our soules which are put into the sturring earth of our bodyes, have atchieved the causes of their hether cōming: They have knowne, & honoured with knowledge, the cause of their creation, and to many men (for in this time, place, and fortune, it is lawfull for us to speake gloriously) it hath bene behovefull, that we should live. Since then eternitie is not to be had in this conjunction, what is to be lost by the separation, but time? which since it hath his ende, when that is once come, all what is past is nothing: and by the protracting nothing gotten, but labour and care. Do not me therefore that wrong, (who something in yeares, but much in all other deserts, am fitter to dye then you) as to say you have brought me to any evill: since the love of you, doth overballance all bodely mischiefes, and those mischiefes be but mischiefes to the baser mindes, too much delighted with the kennell of this life. Neither will I any more yeeld to my passion of lamenting you, which howsoever it might agree to my exceeding friendship, surely it would nothing to your exceeding vertue. Add this to your noble speech my deere Cozen said *Pirocles*, that if we complaine of this our fortune, or seeme to our selves faultie, in having one hurt the other, we showe a repentance of the love we beare to these matchlesse creatures, or at least a doubt, it should be overdeerely bought, which for my part (and so dare I aunswere for you) I call all the gods to witnesse, I am so farre from, that no shame, no torment, no death, would make me forgoe the least part, of the inward honor, essentiall pleasure, and living life, I have enjoyed in the presence of the faultlesse *Philoclea*. Take the preheminence in all things, but in true loving, aunswered

Musidorus, for the confession of that no death shall get of me. Of that aunswered *Pirocles* soberly smiling, I perceive wee shall have a debate in the other world, if at least there remayne any thing of remembrance in that place. I do not thinke the contrarye sayde *Musidorus*, although you knowe, it is greately helde, that with the death of bodye and sences (whiche are not onely the beginning, but dwelling and nourishing of passions, thoughts and immaginations) they fayling, memorye likewise fayles, which riseth onely out of them: and then is there left nothing, but the intellectuall parte or intelligence, which voide of all morall vertues, which stande in the meane of perturbacions, doth onely live in the contemplative vertue, and power of the omnipotent good, the soule of soules, and universall life of this great worke, and therefore is utterly voide, from the possibilitie of drawing to it selfe, these sensible considerations. Certenly answered *Pirocles*, I easely yeeld, that we shall not knowe one another, and much lesse these passed things, with a sensible or passionate knowledge. For the cause being taken away, the effect followes. Neither do I thinke, we shall have such a memorye, as nowe we have, which is but a relicke of the senses, or rather a print the senses have left of things passed, in our thoughtes, but it shall be a vitall power of that very intelligence; which as while it was heere, it helde the chiefe seate of our life, and was as it were the last resorte, to which of all our knowledges, the hyest appeale came, and so by that meanes was never ignorant of our actions, though many times rebelliously resisted, alwayes with this prison darkened: so, much more being free of that prison, and returning to the life of all things, where all infinite knowledge is, it cannot but be a right intelligence, which is both his name and being, of things both present and passed, though voyde of imagining to it selfe any thing, but even growen like to his Creator, hath all things, with a spirituall knowledge before it. The difference of which is as hard for us to conceave, as it had for us, when wee were in our mothers wombes, to comprehende (if any body would have tould us) what kinde of light we nowe in this life see. What kinde of knowledge we nowe have, yet nowe we do not only feele our present being, but we conceave what we were before we were borne, though remembrance make us not do it, but knowledge, and though we are utterly without any remorse of any misery, we might then suffer. Even such and much more odds, shall there be at that second delivery of ours; when voyde of sensible memorye, or memorative passion, wee shall not see the cullours, but lifes of all things that have bene or can be: and shall as I hope knowe our friendship, though exempt from the earthlie cares of friendship, having both united it, and our selves, in that hye and heavenly love of the unquenchable light. As he had ended his speeche, *Musidorus* looking with a heavenly joy upon him, sang this song unto him, he had made before love turned his muse to another subjecte.

> *SInce natures workes be good, and death doth serve*
> *As natures worke: why should we feare to dye?*
> *Since feare is vaine, but when it may preserve,*
> *Why should we feare, that which we cannot flye?*
>
> *Feare is more paine, then is the paine it feares,*
> *Disarming humane mindes, of native might:*
> *While each conceate, an ouglie figure beares,*
> *Which were not evill, well vew'd in reasons light.*
>
> *Our owly eyes, which dimm'd with passions bee,*
> *And scarce discerne the dawne of comming day,*
> *Let them be clearde, and now begin to see,*
> *Our life is but a step, in dustie way.*
> > *Then let us holde, the blisse of peacefull minde,*
> > *Since this we feele, great losse we cannot finde.*

Thus did they like quiet Swannes, sing their own obsequies, and vertuously enhable theyr mindes against all extremities, which they did thinke woulde fall uppon them, especially resolving, that the fyrst care they would have, should be by taking the faulte upon themselves, to cleere the two Ladyes, of whose case (as of nothing else that had happened) they had not any knowledge. Although their friendly hoste, the honest Gentleman *Kalander*, seeking all meanes how to helpe them, had endevored to speake with them, and to make them knowe who should be their judge. But the curious servaunt of *Philanax* forbad him the entrye, uppon paine of death. For so it was agreed uppon, that no man should have any conference with them, for feare of newe tumults. Insomuch that *Kalander* was constrayned to retire himselfe, having yet obtayned thus much, that he would deliver

unto the two Princes, their apparell and jewells, which being
left with him at *Mantinea*, (wisely considering that theyr disguised weedes, which were all as then they had, would make
them more odious in the sight of the judges) he had that night
sent for, and now brought unto them. They accepted their
owne, with great thankefulnes, knowing from whence it came,
and attired themselves in it against the nexte daye, which being
in deede ritch and princely, they accordinglye determined to
maintaine the names of *Palladius* and *Daiphantus,* as before it is
mencioned. Then gave they themselves to consider, in what
sort they might defende their causes, for they thought it no lesse
vaine to wish death, then cowardly to feare it, till something
before morning, a small slumber taking them, they were by and
by after callde up to come to the aunswere, of no lesse then
theyr lives imported. But in this sort was the judgement ordred.
As soone as the morning had taken a full possession of the
Element, *Euarchus* called unto him *Philanax,* and willed him
to draw out into the middest of the greene (before the chiefe
lodge) the throne of judgement seate, in which *Basilius* was
woont to sit, and according to their customes, was ever carried
with the Prince. For *Euarchus* did wisely consider, the people
to be naturally taken with exterior shewes, farre more then with
inward consideracion, of the materiall pointes. And therefore
in this newe entrie into so entangled a matter, he would leave
nothing which might be eyther an armour or ornament unto
him, and in these pompous ceremonyes he well knewe a secreat
of government much to consist. That was performed by the
diligent *Philanax,* and therein *Euarchus* did set himselfe all
cloathed in blacke, with the principall men, who could in that
sodainenes provide themselves of such mourning rayments. The
whole people commaunded to keepe an orderly silence of each
side, which was duly observed of them, partly for the desire they
had to see a good conclusion of these matters, and partly striken
with admiracion, aswell at the grave and princely presence of
Euarchus, as at the greatnes of the cause, which was then to
come in question. As for *Philanax, Euarchus* woulde have done
him the honour to sit by him, but he excused himselfe, desiring
to be the accuser of the prisoners in his maisters behalfe; and
therefore since he made himselfe a partie, it was not convenient
for him to sit in the judiciall place. Then was it awhile

deliberated, whether the two young Ladies, should be brought forth in open presence, but that was stopped by *Philanax*, whose love and faith, did descend from his maister to his children, and only desired, the smart should light upon the others, whome he thought guiltie of his death and dishonour, alleaging for this, that neyther wisedome would, they should be brought in presence of the people, which might hereupon growe to new uprores: nor justice required, they should be drawen to any shame, till some body accused them. And as for *Pamela*, he protested the lawes of *Arcadia* would not allowe any judgement of her, although she her selfe, were to determine nothing, till age or marriage enabled her. Then the Kings body being layde uppon a Table, just before *Euarchus*, and all covered over with blacke, the prisoners, namely the Queene, and two young Princes, were sent for to appeare in the Protectors name: which name was the cause, they came not to knowledge, how neere a kinseman was to judge of them, but thought him to be some Noble man, chosen by the Country, in this extremitye. So extraordinary course, had the order of the heavens produced at this time, that both nephewe and sonne, were not only prisoners, but unknowen, to their uncle and father, who of many yeares had not seene them. And *Pyrocles* was to pleade for his life before that throne, in which throne lately before he had saved the Kings life. But first was *Gynecia* led foorth, in the same weedes that the daye and night before she had worne, saving that in stead of *Zelmanes* garment in which she was founde, she had cast on a long cloake, which reached to the ground of russed course cloath, with a poore felt hat, which almost covered all her face, most part of her goodly heare (on which her hands had layd many a spitefull holde) so lying upon her shoulders, as a man might well see, had no artificiall carelesnes. Her eyes downe on the ground, of purpose not to looke on *Pyrocles* face, which she did not so much shunne, for the unkindnes she conceaved of her owne overthrow, as for the feare, those motions in this short time of her life, should be revived, which she had with the passage of infinite sorrowes mortified. Great was the compassion the people felt, to see their Princesse state, and beawtie, so deformed by fortune and her owne desert, whome they had ever found a Lady most worthy of all honour. But by and by the sight of the other two prisoners, drewe most of the eyes to that spectacle. *Pyrocles* came out led by *Sympathus*, cloathed after the Greeke manner, in a long coate of white velvet, reaching to the small of his legge, with great buttons of Diamonds all along uppon it : His neck without any coller, not so much as hidden with a ruffe, did passe the whitenes of his garments, which was not much in fashion unlike to the crimson rayment, our Knightes of the order first put on. On his feete he had nothing but slippers, which after the auncient manner, were tyed up with certayne laces, which were fastened under his knee, having wrapped about (with many pretty knots) his naked legs. His fayre auberne heare (which he ware in great length, and gave at that time a delightfull shew, with being sturd up and downe with the breath of a gentle winde) had nothing uppon it, but a white Ribbin, in those dayes used for a Diademe. Which rolled once or twise about the uppermost parte of his forehead, fell downe uppon his backe, cloased up at each ende with the richest pearle were to be seene in the world. After him followed an other Noble man, guiding the noble *Musidorus*. Who had upon him, a long cloake, after the fashion of that, which we call the Apostles mantle, made of purple Satten; not that purple which we now have, and is but a counterfet of the *Getulian* purple (which yet was farre the meaner in price and estimacion) but of the right *Tyrian* purple, which was neerest to a cullour betwixt our murrey and skarlet. On his head, which was blacke and curled, he ware a *Persian Tiara*, all set downe with rowes of so rich Rubies, as they were inough to speake for him, that they had to judge of no meane personage.

In this sorte with erected countenaunces, did these unfortunate Princes suffer themselves to be ledd, shewing aright by the comparison of them and *Ginecia*, how to divers persons, compassion is diversly to be sturred. For as to *Ginecia*, a Ladie knowne of great estate, and greatly esteemed, the more miserable representation was made of her sodaine ruyne, the more mens heartes were forced to bewayle such an evident witnesse of weake humanitie : so to these men, not regarded because unknowne, but rather (besides the detestacion of their facte) hated as straungers, the more they shoulde have falne downe in an abjecte semblance, the more in steed of compassion they shoulde have gotten contempt : but therefore, were to use (as I may tearme it) the more violence of magnanimitye, and so to conquer

the expectation of the lookers, with an extraordinarye vertue.
And such effecte in deede it wrought in the whole assemblye,
theyr eyes yet standing as it were in ballance, to whether of
them they should most directe theyr sight. *Musidorus* was in
stature so much higher then *Pyrocles*, as commonly is gotten by
one yeares growth. His face now beginning to have some tokens
of a beard, was composed to a kinde of manlike beawtie.
His cullour was of a well pleasing brownenes, & the features of
it such, as they caried both delight and majestie : his countenance
severe, and promising a minde much given to thinking. *Pyrocles*
of a pure complexion, and of such a cheerefull favour, as might
seeme either a womans face on a boy, or an excellent boyes face
in a woman. His looke gentle and bashfull, which bred the more
admiracion, having shewed such notable proofes of courage.
Lastly, though both had both, if there were any ods, *Musidorus* was
the more goodly, and *Pyrocles* the more lovely. But assoone as
Musidorus saw himselfe so farre forth led among the people, that
he knew to a great number of them his voyce should be heard,
misdoubting their intention to the Princesse *Pamela*, (of which
he was more carefull then of his owne life,) even as he went
(though his leader sought to interrupt him) he thus with a lowde
voyce spake unto them. And is it possible ô *Arcadians*, sayd he,
that you can forget the naturall dutie you owe to your Princesse
Pamela ? hath this soyle bene so little beholding to her noble
Auncesters ? hath so long a time rooted no surer love in your
hearts to that line ? Where is that faith to your Princes blood,
which hath not only preserved you from all daungers heretofore,
but hath spred your fame to all the nations in the world ? Where
is that justice, the *Arcadians* were wont to flourish in, whose
nature is to render to every one his owne ? Will you now keepe
the right from your Prince, who is the only gever of judgement,
the keye of justice, and life of your lawes ? Do you hope in a
fewe yeares, to set up such another race, which nothing but
length of time can establish ? Will you reward *Basilius* children
with ungratefulnes, the very poyson of manhood ? Will you
betray your long setled reputation, with the fowle name of traytors ? Is this your mourning for your Kings death, to encrease
his losse with his daughters misery ? Imagin your Prince do
looke out of the heavens unto you, what do you thinke he could
wish more at your hands then that you do well by his children ?

And what more honor I pray you can you do to his obsequies, then to satisfie his soule with a loving memorie, as you do his body with an unfelt solemnitie? What have you done with the Princesse *Pamela*? *Pamela* the just enheretrix of this Countrey, *Pamela* whom this earth may be happy, that it shall be hereafter sayde she was borne in *Arcadia*. *Pamela* in her selfe your ornament, in her education your foster childe, and every way your only Princesse, what accompt can you render to your selves of her? Truly I do not thinke that you all knowe what is become of her: so soone may a Diamond be lost? so soone may the fayrest light in the world be put out. But looke, looke unto it, O *Arcadians*, be not so wilfully robbed of your greatest treasure, make not your selves ministers to private ambitions, who do but use your selves to put on your owne yokes. Whatsoever you determine of us (who I must confesse are but strangers) yet let not *Basilius* daughters be straungers unto you. Lastly, howsoever you barre her from her publicke sovereigntie, (which if you do, little may we hope of equitie where rebellion raignes) yet deny not that childs right unto her, that she may come and do the last duties to her fathers body. Deny not that happines (if in such a case there be any happines) to your late King, that his body may have his last touch of his deerest child. With such like broken maner of questions and speeches, was *Musidorus* desirous as much as in passing by them he could, to move the people to tender *Pamelas* fortune. But at length by that they came to the judgement place, both *Sympathus* and his guider had greatly satisfied him, with the assurance they gave him, this assemblie of people had neyther meaning nor power, to do any hurt to the Princesse, whome they all acknowledged as their sovereigne Lady. But that the custome of *Arcadia* was such, till she had more yeares, the state of the country to be guided by a Protector, under whome, he and his fellow were to receive their judgement. That eased *Musidorus* hart of his most vehement care, when he found his beloved Lady to be out of daunger. But *Pyrocles* assoone as the Queene of the one side, he and *Musidorus* of the other, were stayed before the face of their judge, (having only for their barre the Table on which the Kings body lay) being nothing lesse vexed with the doubt of *Philoclea*, then *Musidorus* was for *Pamela*, in this sort with a lowlie behaviour, and only then like a suppliant, he spake to the Protector. Pardon me most honoured Judge, said he, that uncommaunded I begin my speech unto you, since both to you and me, these wordes of mine shall be most necessary. To you having the sacred exercise of justice in your hand, nothing appertaines more properly then truth nakedly & freely set downe. To me, being environed round about with many daungerous calamities, what can be more convenient, then at least, to be at peace with my selfe, in having discharged my conscience, in a most behovefull veritie. Understand therefore, and truly understand, that the Lady *Philoclea* (to whose unstayned vertue it hath bene my unspeakeable miserye, that my name should become a blot) if she be accused, is most unjustly accused of any dishonorable fact, which by my meanes she may be thought to have yelded unto. Whatsoever hath bene done, hath bene my only attempt, which notwithstanding was never intended against her chastetye. But whatsoever hath bene enformed, was my fault. And I attest the heavens, to blaspheame which I am not now in fit tune, that so much as my comming into her chamber, was wholie unwitting unto her. This your wisdome may withall consider, if I would lye, I would lye for mine owne behoofe, I am not so olde, as to be weary of my selfe; But the very sting of my inward knowledge joyned with the consideracion I must needes have, what an infinite losse it should be to all those who love goodnes in good folkes, if so pure a child of vertue should wrongfully be destroyed, compells me to use my toong against my selfe, and receive the burden of what evill was, uppon my owne doing. Looke therefore with pittifull eyes uppon so fayre beames, and that misfortune which by me hath fallen uppon her, helpe to repaier it with your publicke judgement, since whosoever deales cruelly with such a creature, shewes himselfe a hater of mankinde, and an envier of the worlds blisse. And this peticion I make, even in the name of justice, that before you proceed further against us, I may knowe how you conceive of her noble, though unfortunate action, and what judgement you will make of it. He had not spoken his last word, when all the whole people both of great and low estate, confirmed with an united murmur *Pyrocles* demaund, longing (for the love generally was borne *Philoclea*) to knowe what they might hope of her. *Euarchus* though neither regarding a prisoners passionate prayer, nor bearing overplausible eares to a many hedded motion, yet well enough content, to winne their liking with things in themselves indifferent, he was content : first, to seeke asmuch as might be of *Philocleas* behavior, in this matter : which being cleered by *Pyrocles*, & but weakely gaynesayd by *Philanax* (who had framed both his owne & *Damœtas* evidence most for her favour and in truth could have gone no further then conjecture,) yet finding by his wisedome, that she was not altogether faultlesse, he pronounced, she should all her life long, be kept prisoner among certaine women of religion like the *vestall* nonnes, so to repaye their touched honour of her house, with well observing a stryctt profession of chastitie. Although this were a greate prejudicating of *Pyrocles* case, yet was hee exceedingly joyous of it, being assured of his Ladies life ; and in the depth of his minde not sorry, that what ende soever he had, none should obtaine the after enjoying that Jewell, whereon he had set his lives happines. After it was by publicque sentence delivered, what should be done with the sweete *Philoclea*, (the lawes of *Arcadia* bearing, that what was appointed by the magistrates in the noneage of the Prince, coulde not afterwards be repealed) *Euarchus* still using to himselfe no other name but protector of *Arcadia*, commaunded those that had to say against the Queene *Gynecia* to proceede, because both her estate required shee shoulde bee first heard, and also for that shee was taken to bee the principall, in the greatest matter they were to judge of. *Philanax* incontinently stepped foorth, and shewing in his greedy eyes, that he did thirst for her bloud, beganne a well thought on discourse of her (in his judgement) execrable wickednes. But *Gynecia* standing up before the judge, casting abroad her armes, with her eyes hiddē under the bredth of her unseemely hatt, laying open in all her gestures the despairefull affliction, to which all the might of her reason was converted, with such like words stopped *Philanax*, as hee was entring into his invective oration. Staye staie *Philanax* saide shee, do not defile thy honest mouth, with those dishonourable speeches thou arte about to utter, against a woman, now most wretched, lately thy mistresse. Let either the remembraunce how great she was, move thy harte to some reverence ; or the seing how lowe she is, sturre in thee some pittie. It may be truth doth make thee deale untruely ; and love of justice frames unjustice in thee, doe not therefore (neither shalt thou neede treade upon my desolate ruines. Thou shalt have that thou seekest ; and yet shalt not be oppressoure of her, who cannot choose but love thee, for thy singular faith to thy master. I doe not speake this to procure mercie, or to prolong my life, no no I say unto you I will not live, but I am onely loth, my death shoulde bee engreeved with any wronge thou shouldest doe unto me. I have beene to painefull a judge over my selfe, to desire pardon in others judgement. I have beene to cruell an executioner of mine owne soule, to desire that execution of justice shoulde bee stayed for me. Alas they that know, how sorrow can rent the spirits, they that know what fiery hells are cōtiened in a self condemning mind, need not feare that feare can keepe such a one, from desiring to be seperated from that, which nothing but death can seperate. I therefore say to thee (O just judge) that I and only I, was the worker of *Basilius* death. They were these handes that gave unto him that poysonous potion, that hath brought death to him, and losse to *Arcadia*, it was I and none but I, that hastened his aged yeares, to an unnaturall end, and that have made all his people orphans, of their royall father. I am the subject that have killed my Prince, I am the wife that have murdred my husband, I am a degenerate woman, an undoer of this countrie, a shame of my children. What wouldest thou have saide more Oh *Philanax*? and all this I graunt, there resteth then nothing els to say, but that I desire you, you will appointe quicklie somme to ridd mee of my life, rather then these handes, which ells are destenied unto it, and that indeede it maye bee doone with such speede as I may not long dye in this life, which I have in so greate horrour: with that shee crossed her armes, and sate downe uppon the grounde, attending the judges aunswere. But a greate while it was, before anye boddye coulde bee heard speake, the whole people concurring in a lamentable crye, so much had *Gynecias* wordes and behaviour sturred their hartes to a dolefull compassion, neither in troath coulde most of them in their judgements tell, whether they shoulde bee more sorrie for her faulte or her miserie: for the losse of her estate, or losse of her vertue. But most were most moved, with that which was under there eyes: the sense most subjecte to pittie. But at length the reverent awe they stoode in of *Euarchus*, brought them to a silent wayting his determination, who having well considered the abhomination of the facte, attending more the manifest proofe of so horrible a trespasse; confessed by her selfe, and proved by others ; then any thing relenting to those tragicall phrases of hers (apter to sturre a vulgare pittie, then his minde, which hated evill, in what culloures so ever he founde it) having considered a while with the principall men of the country, and demaunded there allowannce, he definitively gave this sentence. That where as both in private and publike respectes, this woman had most haynously offēded, (in private, because marriage being the most holy conjunction that falls to mankinde, out of which all families and so consequently all societies doe proceede, which not onely by communitie goods, but communitie children, is to knit the mindes in a most perfet union, which who so breakes dissolves al humanitie, no man living free from the danger of so neere a neighbour, she had not onely broken it, but broken it with death, and the most pretended death that might be : In publike respect, the Princes persons ; being in all monarchall governmentes the very knot of the peoples welfare, and light of all their doinges to which they are not onely in conscience, but in necessitie bounde to be loyall, she had trayterously empoysoned him, neither regarding her contries profit, her owne dutie, nor the rigor of the lawes.) That therefore, as well for the due satisfaction to eternall justice, and accomplishment of the *Arcadian* statutes, as for the everlasting example to all wives and subjectes, she should presently be conveyed to cloase prison, and there be kept with such foode as might serve to sustaine her alive, untill the day of her husbands buryall, at which time, shee shoulde bee buried quicke, in the same tombe with hime. That so his murder might bee a murder to her selfe, and she forced to keepe company with the body from which she had made so detestable a severance; And lastly death might redresse their disjoyned conjunction of marriage. His judgement was receaved of the whole assemblie, as not with disliking, so with great astonishmēt, the greatnes of the matter and person as it were overpressing the might of their conceites. But when they did set it to the beame, with the monstrousnes of her ouglye misdeede, they coulde not but yeeld in their hartes, there was no overbalancing. As for *Gynecia*, who had already setled her thoughts, not only to look but long for this event, having in this time of her vexation, found a sweetnes in the rest she hoped by death, (with a countenaunce witnessing she had before hand so passed thorowe all the degrees of sorrowe, that shee had no new looke to figure forth any more) rase up and offred forth her faire handes to bee bounde or led as they would, being indeed troubled with no parte of this judgement, but that her death was as she thought long delayed. They that were appointed for it conveyed her to the place she was in before, where the guarde was relieved, and the number encreased to keepe her more sure for the time of her execution : None of them all that led her, though most of them were such, whose harts had beene long hardned with the often exercising such offices, being able to barre teares from their eyes, and others manifest tokens of compassionate sorrow. So goodly a vertue is a resolute constancie, that even in evill deservers, it seemes that partie might have beene notably well deserving. Thus the excellent Lady *Gynecia*, having passed five and thirtie yeares of her age, even to admiration of her beautifull minde and body, and having not in her owne knowledge, ever spotted her soule with any wilfull vice, but her imoderate love of *Zelmane*, was brought, first by the violence of that ill answered passion, and then by the dispayring conceite, she took of the judgement of God in her husbandes death and her owne fortune, purposely to overthrowe her selfe, and confirme by a wronge confession, that abhominable shame, which with her wisdome, joynde to the truth, perhappes shee might have refelled. Then did *Euarchus* aske *Philanax*, whether it were he that would charge the two yonge prisoners, or that some other shoulde doe it, and hee sit according to his estate, as an assistant in the judgement. *Philanax* tolde him as before hee had done, that hee thought no man coulde laye manifest the naughtines of those two yong men, with so much either truth or zeale as himselfe, and therefore he desired he might do this last service to his faithfully beloved master, as to prosecute the traiterous causers of his death and dishonour; which being done, for his parte hee ment to geve up all dealing in publicke affaires, since that man was gone who had made him love them. *Philanax* thus being redye to speake, the two Princes were commaunded to tell their names who aunswered according to their agreements, that they were *Daiphantus* of *Lycia*, and *Palladius* Prince of *Iberia*. Which when they had said, they demaunded to know by what aucthoritie, they coulde judge of them, since they were not only forryners and so not borne under their lawes, but absolute Princes and therefore not to bee touched by lawes. But aunswere was presently made them, that *Arcadia* lawes, were to have their force upon any were founde in *Arcadia*: since strangers have scope to know the customes of a contry, before they put them selves in it: and when they once are entred, they must knowe, that what by many was made, must not for one bee broken. And so much lesse for a straunger, as hee is to looke for no priveledge in that place, to which in time of neede, his service is not to be expected. As for their being Princes, whether they were so or no, the beleefe stood in their own wordes, which they had so diversly falsifyed, as they did not deserve beleefe. But what soever they were, *Arcadia*, was to acknowledge them but as private men, since they were neither by magistracy nor alliance to the princely bloud, to claime any thing in that region. Therefore if they had offended, (which now by the plaintife and there defence was to bee judged) against the lawes of nations; by the lawes of nations they were to be chastised: if against the peculiare ordinaunces of the province those peculiare ordinaunces were to laye hold of them. The Princes stoode a while upon that demaunding leasure to give perfecte knowledge of their greatnes; but when they were aunswered, that in a case of a Princes death, the lawe of that contrie had ever beene, that imediate tryall shoulde bee had: they were forced to yeelde, resolved that in those names, they woulde as much as they could, cover the shame of their royall parentage, and keepe as long as might be (if evill were determined against them) the evill newes from their carefull kinsfolke, wherein the chiefe man they considered was *Euarchus*: whom the strange and secreate working of justice, had brought to be the judge over them, in such a shadowe, or rather pit of darkenes, the wormish mankinde lives, that neither they knowe how to foresee, nor what to feare: and are but like tenisballs, tossed by the racket of the hyer powers. Thus both sides reddie, it was determined, because their cases were seperated. First *Philanax* shoulde be hard against *Pyrocles*, whome they termed *Daiphantus*, and that heard, the others cause shoulde followe, and so receave together such judgement, as they should be found to have deserved. But *Philanax* that was even shorte breathed at the first, with the extreame vehemencie he had to speake against them, stroking once or twise his forehead, and wiping his eyes, (which either wepte, or he woulde at that time have them seeme to weepe,) looking first upon *Pyrocles*, as if he had proclaymed all hatefullnes against him, humblie turning to *Euarchus*, (who with quiet gravitie, shewed great attention) he thus began his oration. That which all men, who take upon them to accuse an other, are woont to desire (most worthy protector) to have many proofes of my faultes in them they seeke to have condemned: that is to me in this present action, my greatest comber, and anoyaunce. For the number is so great, and the quallitie so monstrous, of the enormities this wretched young man hath committed, that neither I in my selfe, can tell where to begin (my thoughts being confused with the horrible multitude of them) neither doe I thinke your vertuous eares will be able to endure the reporte: But will rather imagine, you heare some tragedie invented of the extremitie of wickednes, then a just resitall of a wickednes indeed committed, for such is the disposition of the most sincere judgements, that as they can believe meane faultes, and such as mans nature may slide into, so when they passe to a certaine degree, nay when they passe all degrees of unspeakeable naughtines, then finde they in themselves a hardenes to geve credit, that humane creatures can so from all humanitie bee transformed. But in my selfe, the strength of my faith to my deade master wil helpe the weakenes of my memory; in you, your excellent love of justice will force you to vouchsafe attention: And as for the matter, it is so manifest, so pittifull evidences lie before your eyes of it, that I shall neede to bee but a breife recounter, and no rhetoricall enlarger of this most harmefull mischiefe. I will therefore, in as fewe wordes as so huge a trespasse can bee conteyned, deliver unto you the sum of this miserable fact: leaving out a great number of particular tokens, of his naughtines, and only touching the essentiall pointes, of this dolefull case. This man, whome to beginne withall I know not how to name, since being come into this contrie, unaccompanied like a loste pilgrime, from a man grewe a woman, from a woman a ravisher of wemen, thence a prisoner, and now a Prince. But this *Zelmane*, this *Daiphantus*, this what you will, (for any shape or title he can take upon him, that hath no restrainte of shame) having understoode the solitarie life my late master lived, and considering how open he had layde himselfe to any trayterous attempte, for the first maske of his falsehoode, disguised himselfe like a woman: which being the more simple and hurtelesse sexe, might easier hide his subtle harmefullnes. And presenting himselfe to my master, the most curteous Prince that lived, was receaved of him with so greate gratiousnes, as might have bounde not only any gratefull minde, but might have mollified any enemies rancoure. But this venemous serpent, admitted thus into his bosome, as contagion will easily finde a fit body for it, so had he quickly falne into so neere acquaintaunce with this naughtie woman, whom even now you have most justly condemned, that this was her right hand, shee sawe with no eyes but his, nor seemed to have any life but in him, so glad shee was to finde one more cunning then her selfe, in covering wickednes with a modest vaile. What is to be thought passed betwixt two such vertuous creatures, whereof the one hath confessed murder, and the other rape, I leave to your wise cōsideration. For my hart hastens to the miserable point of *Basilius* murder, for the executing of which with more facilitie, this yong nimph of *Dianas* bringing up, fayned certaine rites she had to performe, so furious an impietie had caried him, from all remembrance of goodnes, that hee did not onely not feare the Gods, as the beholders and punishers of so ungodly a villany, but did blasphemously use their sacred holly name, as a minister unto it. And forsooth a Cave hereby was chosen, for the temple of his devotions, a Cave of such darkenes, as did prognosticate he ment to please the infernall powers, for there this accurssed catife, upon the alter of falshood, sacrificed the life of the vertuous *Basilius*. By what meanes he trayned him thether, alas I knowe not, for if I might have knowen it, either my life had accompanied my master, or this fellowes death had preserved him. But this may suffise, that in the mouth of this Cave, where this traytor had his lodginge and chapple, when already master sheepeheard his companion, had conveyed away the undoubted enheritrix of this cuntrie, was *Gynecia* founde by the dead corps of her husband, newly empoysoned, apparelled in the garments of the young Lady, and reddy no question to have fled to some place, according to their consorte, but that she was by certaine honest shepeheards arrested: while in the meane time, because their should be lefte no revenger of this bloudy mischief, This noble *Amazon*, was violently gotten into the chamber of the Lady *Philoclea*, wherby the mingling as much as in him lay) of her shame, with his misdeede, he might enforce her to be the accessary to her fathers death, and under the countenaunce of her and her sister (against whom they knew wee woulde not rebell) seaze as it were with one gripe into their treacherous hands, the regiment of the mightie province. But the almightie eye prevented him of the end of his mischiefe, by using a villaine *Damœtas* hand, to enclose him in there, where with as much fortification as in a house could be made, he thought himselfe in most securitie. Thus see you most just judge, a shorte and simple story of the infamous misery, falne upon this contrie. In deed infamous, since by an effeminate man, we should suffer a greater overthrow, then our mightiest enemies have ben ever able to lay upon us. And that all this, which I have said is most manifest, aswell of the murdering of *Basilius*, as the ravishing of *Philoclea*, (for those two partes I establish of my accusation) who is of so incredulous a minde, or rather who will so stoppe his eyes from seing a thing cleerer then the light, as not to holde for assured so palpable a matter. For to beginne with his most cruell misdeede, is it to be imagined, that *Gynecia* (a woman though wicked, yet wittie) woulde have attempted and atchieved an enterprise, no lesse hazardous then horrible, without having some councellor in the beginning, and some comforter in the performing? Had she, who shewed her thoughtes, were so overruled with some straunge desire, as in despite of God, nature and womanhood, to execute that in deedes, which in wordes wee cannot heare without trembling, had shee I saye no practise to leade her unto it? Or had shee a practise without conspiracie? Or coulde shee conspire without some boddye to conspire with? And if one were; whoe so likelye as this, to whome shee communicated I am sure her minde, the worlde thinkes her boddye? Neither let her wordes taking the whole faulte uppon her selfe, bee heerein any thinge availeable. For to those persons who have vomited out of their soules all remnants of goodnes, there restes a certaine pride in evill, and having ells no shadowe of glorye lefte them, they glorye to bee constante in iniquitye, and that God knowes must bee helde out to the laste gaspe, without revealing their accomplices. As thinking greate courage is declared, in being neither affeard of the heavens nor ashamed of the worlde. But let *Gynecias* action dye with her selfe, what can all the earth answere for his comming hether? Why alone, if hee bee a Prince? How so richly Jewelled if he be not a prince? Why then a woman if nowe a man? Why now *Daiphantus*, if then *Zelmane*? Was all this play for nothing,

180

or if it had an ende, what ende but the ende of my deere master?
Shall we doubte so many secret conferences with *Gynecia*, such
fained favour to the over soone beguiled *Basilius*, a Cave made
a lodging, and the same lodging made a temple of his religion,
lastly such changes and traverses, as a quiet Poet coulde scarse
fill a poeme withal, were directed to any lesse scope, then to
this monstrous murder? O snakie ambition, which can winde
thyselfe in so many figures, to slyde thether thou desirest to come!
O corrupted reason of mankinde, that can yeelde to deforme
thy selfe with so filthie desires! And O hopelesse bee those
mindes, whom so unnaturall desires doe not, with their owne
ouglinesse sufficiently terrefie! But yet even of favour let us graunt
him thus much more, as to fancie that in these foretolde thinges,
fortune might be a greate Actor, perchaunce to an evill ende yet
to a lesse evill end all these entangled devises were entended.
But I beseech your Ladyshippe, my Lady *Daiphantus* tell me,
what excuse can you finde for the chaunging your lodging, with
the Queene that verie instant shee was to finish her execrable
practise? How can you cloake the lending of your cloake unto
her, was all that by chance too? Had the starres sent such an
influence unto you, as you should bee juste weary of your
lodging, and garments, when our Prince was destenied to the
slaughter? What say you to this, O shamefull and shamelesse
creature? Fit indeede to bee the dishonour of both sexes. But
alas, I spend too many words in so manifest and so miserable
a matter. They must be foure wilde horses (which according
to our lawes are the executioners of men which murdre our
Prince) which must decide this question with you. Yet see so
farre had my zeale to my beloved Prince transported me, that
I had almost forgotten my second parte, and his seconde abhomination, I meane his violence offred to the Lady *Philoclea*:
wherewith as if it had welbecome his womanhoode, he came
braving to the judgement seate, indeede our lawes appointe not
so cruell a death (although death too) for this facte as for the
other. But whosoever well wayes it, shall finde it sprenge out
of the same fountaine of mischevous naughtines, the killing of
the father, dishonouring the mother, and ravishing the child.
Alas could not so many benifites receaved of my Prince, the
justice of nature, the right of hospitalitie, be a bridle to thy lust,
if not to thy crueltie? Or if thou hadest (as surely thou haste)

a harte recompensing goodnes with hatred, could not his death, which is the last of revenges, satisfie thy mallice, but thou must heape upō it the shame of his daughter? Were thy eyes so stonie, thy brest so tygreshe, as the sweete and beautifull shewes of *Philocleas* vertue, did not astonish thee? O wofull *Arcadia*, to whom the name of this mankinde curtisan, shall ever be remembred as a procurer of thy greatest losse! But too farre I finde my passion, yet honest passion hath guided mee; the case is everie way too too much unanswearable. It resteth in you O excellent protector to pronounce judgement, which if their bee hope, that such a yonge man may prove proffitable to the world, who in the first exercise of his owne determination, farre passed the arrantest strumpet in luxuriousnesse, the conningest forger in falsehoode, a player in disguising, a Tygre in crueltie, a Dragon in ingratefulnes; let him be preserved like a jewell, to doe greater mischeefe. Yf his youth bee not more defiled with trecherie, then the eldest mans age, let I say his youth, be some cause of compassion. If hee have not every way sought the overthrowe of humaine societie, if hee have done any thing like a Prince, let his naming himselfe a Prince, breede a reverence of his base wickednesse. If hee have not broken all lawes of hospitalitie, and broken them in the most detestable degree that can be, let his being a guest, be a sacred protection of his more then savage doings: or if his whorish beawtye, have not bene as the hye waye of his wickednesse, let the picture drawne uppon so poysonous a wood, be reserved to shewe howe greatly coulours can please us. But if it is as it is, what should I saye more, a very spirit of hellish naughtines, if his acte be to be punished, and his defiled person not to be pittied, then restore unto us our Prince, by duly punishing his murderers, for then wee shall thinke him and his name to live, when wee shall see his killers to dye. Restore to the excellent *Philoclea* her honour, by taking out of the world her dishonour, and thinke that at this daye, in this matter are the eyes of the worlde uppon you, whether any thing can sway your minde from a true administracion of justice. Alas though I have much more to saye, I can saye no more, for my teares and sighes interrupt my speeche, and force me to geve myselfe over to my private sorrowe. Thus when *Philanax* had uttered the uttermost of his mallice, he made sorrowe the cause of his conclusion. But while *Philanax* was in the course of his speeche, and did with such bitter reproches defame the princely *Pyrocles*, it was well to be seene, his heart was unused to beare such injuries, and his thoughtes such, as could arme themselves better against any thing then shame. For sometimes blushing, his bloud with divers motions comming and going, sometimes cloasing his eyes, and laying his hande over them, sometime geving such a looke to *Philanax*, as might shewe hee assured himselfe, hee durst not so have spoken if they had bene in indifferent place : with some impaciencie he bare the length of his Oration : which being ended, with as much modest humblenes to the Judge, as despitefull skorne to the accuser, with words to this purpose, he defended his honour.

My accusors tale, may well beare witnes with me, most rightfull Judge, in how hard a case, and invironed with how many troubles, I may esteeme my selfe. For if hee, who shewes his toong, is not unaquainted with rayling, was in an agonye in the beginning of his speech, with the multitude of matters he had to lay unto me, wherein notwithstanding the most evill could fall unto him, was, that hee should not do so much evill as hee would; howe combred do you thinke may I acknowledge my selfe, who in things no lesse importing then my life, must be mine owne advocate, without leasure to aunswere, or foreknowledge what shoulde be objeɕted? in things I say promoted with so cunning a confusion, as having mingled truthes with falsehoodes, surmises with certaintyes, causes of no moment with matters cappitall, scolding with complayning, I can absolute neyther graunt nor denye, neyther can I tell, whether I come hether to be judged, or before judgement to be punished, being compelled to beare such unworthye woordes, farre more grievous then any death unto me. But since the forme of this government, allowes such toong libertye unto him, I will picke aswell as I can out of his inveɕtive those fewe poyntes, whiche may seeme of some purpose in the touching of mee, hoping that by your easye hearing of me, you will shewe, that though you hate evill, yet you wishe men may prove themselves not evill; so in that hee hath sayde, you will not waye so much what hee hath sayde, as what hee hath proved, remembring, that truth is simple and naked, and that if hee had guided himselfe under that banner, hee needed not out of the way have sought so vilde and false disgracings of mee, enough to make the untruest accusation beleeved. I will therefore, using truth as my best eloquence, repeate unto you as much as I knowe in this matter, and then by the only cleerenes of the discourse, your wisedome I knowe will finde, the difference betwixt cavilling supposition, and directe declaration. This Prince *Palladius* and I, being enflamed with love, (a passion farre more easely reprehended, then refrayned) to the two peerelesse daughters of *Basilius*, and understanding, howe hee had secluded himselfe from the worlde, that like Princes, there was no accesse unto him, wee disguised our selves, in such formes, as might soonest bring us to the revealing of our affections. The Prince *Palladius*, had such event of his doings, that with *Pamelas* consent hee was to convey her out of the thraldome she lived in, to receave the subjection of a greater people then her owne, untill her fathers consent might be obteyned. My fortune was more hard, for I bare no more love to the chaste *Philoclea*, then *Basilius* deceaved in my sexe, shewed to me, insomuch that by his importunacy, I could have no time to obtayne the like favour of the pure *Philoclea* : till this pollicye I founde, taking, under cullour of some devotions, my lodging, to drawe *Basilius* thether, with hope to enjoye me, which likewise I revealed to the Queene, that she might keepe my place, and so make her husband see his error. While I in the meane time, being delivered of them both, and having lockt so the dores, as I hoped if the immaculate *Philoclea* would condescend to goe with me, there should be none to hinder our going. I was made prisoner there, I knowe not by what meanes when being repelled by her devine vertue, I would faynest have escaped. Heere have you the thread to guide you in the Labyrinth, this man of his toong, had made so monstrous. Heere see you the true discourse, which hee mountbanke fashion, doth make so wide a mouth over. Heere may you conceave the reason, why the Queene had my garment, because in her going to the cave, in the Moone-shine night, she might be taken for me, which he useth as the knot of all his wise assertions : so that as this double minded fellowes accusation was double, double likewise my aunswere must perforce be, to the murder of *Basilius*, and violence offred to the inviolate *Philoclea*. For the fyrst, O heavenly gods, who would have thought any mouth could have bene founde so mercenary, as to have opened so slight proofes of so horrible matters ? his fyrst Argument is a question who would imagine that *Ginecia* would accomplish such an Acte, without some accessaries? and if any, who but I? truly I, and so farre from imagining any thing, that till I sawe these mourning tokens, and heard *Ginecias* confession, I never imagined the King was dead. And for my part so vehemently, and more like the manner of passionate, then giltie folkes, I see, the Queene persecute her selfe, that I thinke condemnation may goe too hastely over her, considering the unlikelyhood, if not impossibilitie, her wisedome, and vertue so long nourished, should in one moment throw downe it selfe, to the uttermost ende of wickednes. But whatsoever she hath done (which as I say, I never beleeved) yet how unjustly should that aggravate my fault. She founde abroade I within dores (for as for the wearing my garment I have tolde you the cause) she seeking as you say to escape, I locking my selfe in a house : without perchaunce the conspiracie of one poore straunger, might greatly enable her attempt, or the fortification of the Lodge (as the trimme man alleadged) might make me hope to resist all *Arcadia*. And see how treacherously he seeks to drawe from me, my chiefest cleering, by preventing the credit of her words, wherewith she had wholie taken the fault upon her selfe. A honest and unpartiall examiner, her words may condemne her, but may not absolve me. Thus voide of all probable allegacion, the craven crowes uppon my affliction, not leaving out any evill, that ever he hath felt in his owne soule, to charge my youth withall. But who can looke for a sweeter breath out of such a stomacke? or for honny from so filthye a Spyder? What should I say more? if, in so inhumane a matter, which he himselfe confesseth, sincerest judgements are lothest to beleeve, and in the severest lawes proofes clerer then the Sunne are required, his reasons are only the skumme of a base malice, my answeres most manifest, shining in their owne truth, there remayne any doubt of it, because it stands betwixt his affirming and my denyall, I offer, nay I desire, and humblie desire I may be graunted the tryall by combat, wherein let him be armed and me in my shirt, I doubt not Justice will be my shield, and his hart will shew it selfe as faint as it is false.

Now come I to the second part of my offence, towards the young Lady, which howsoever you tearme it, so farre forth as I have tolde you, I confesse, and for her sake hartely lament. But if herein I offred force to her, love offred more force to me.

Let her beawtie be compared to my yeares, and such effectes will be found no miracles. But since it is thus as it is, and that justice teacheth us not to love punishment, but to flye to it for necessitye: the salve of her honour (I meane as the world will take it, for else in truth it is most untouched) must be my marriage, and not my death, since the one stops all mouthes, the other becommes a doubtfull fable. This matter requires no more words, and your experience I hope in these cases shall neede no more, for my selfe me thinkes I have shewed already, too much love of my life to bestowe so many. But certainely, it hath bene love of truth, which could not beare so unworthy falsehood, and love of justice, that would brooke no wrong to my selfe nor other, and makes me now, even in that respect to desire you, to be moved rather with pittie at a just cause of teares, then with the bloudy teares this Crocodile spends, who weepes to procure death, and not to lament death. It will be no honour to *Basilius* tombe, to have guiltlesse bloud sprinckled upon it, and much more may a Judge overway himselfe in crueltie, then in clemencie. It is hard, but it is excellent, where it is found, a right knowledge, when correction is necessary, when grace doth more availe. For my owne respect, if I thought in wisedome I had deserved death, I would not desire life: for I knowe nature will condemne me to dye, though you do not; and longer I would not wish to drawe this breath, then I may keepe my selfe unspotted of any horrible crime; only I cannot nor ever will denye, the love of *Philoclea*, whose violence wrought violent effects in me: with that he finished his speeche, casting up his eyes to the Judge, and crossing his hands, which he held in their length before him, declaring a resolute pacience in whatsoever should be done with him. *Philanax* like a watchfull adversary curiously marked all that he saide, saving that in the beginning he was interrupted by two Letters were brought him from the Princesse *Pamela*, and the Lady *Philoclea*: who having all that night considered and bewayled their estate, carefull for their mother likewise, of whome they could never thinke so much evill, but considering with themselves that she assuredly should have so due tryall by the lawes, as eyther she should not neede their helpe, or should be past their helpe, They looked to that which neerelyest touched them, and each wrate in this sort for him in whome their lives joy consisted.

ARCADIA. LIB. 5.

The humble harted Philoclea *wrate much after this manner.*

" MY Lords, what you will determine of me, is to me
"uncertayne, but what I have determined of my selfe
"I am most certaine, which is no longer to enjoy my life, then
"I may enjoy him for my husband, whom the heavens for my
"hyest glory, have bestowed upon me. Those that judge him,
"let them execute me. Let my throate satisfye their hunger of
"murder. For alas what hath he done, that had not his originall
"in me? Looke uppon him I beseech you with indifferency, and
"see whether in those eyes all vertue shines not. See whether
"that face could hide a murder. Take leasure to knowe him,
"and then your selves will say, it hath bene too great an in-
"humanitie, to suspect such excellency. Are the gods thinke
"you deceaved in their workemanship? Artificers will not use
"marble but to noble uses. Should those powers be so overshot,
"as to frame so precious an Image of their owne, but to
"honorable purposes? O speake with him, ô heare him, ô knowe
"him, and become not the putters out of the worlds light. Hope
"you to joy my fathers soule with hurting him he loved above
"all the world? Shall a wrong suspicion make you forget the
"certaine knowledge of those benefits, this house hath received
"by him? Alas alas, let not *Arcadia* for his losse, be accurssed
"of the whole earth and of all posteritie. He is a great Prince,
"I speake unto you that which I knowe, for I have seene most
"evident testimonies. Why should you hinder my advancement?
"who if I have past my childhood hurtlesse to any of you, if
"I have refused no body to do what good I could, if I have
"often mitigated my fathers anger, ever sought to maintayne his
"favour towards you, nay if I have held you all as fathers and
"brothers unto me, rob me not of more then my life commes
"unto. Teare not that which is inseparably joyned to my soule;
"but if he rest misliked of you, (which ô God, how can it be)
"yet geve him to me, let me have him, you knowe I pretend
"no right to your state. Therefore is it but a private petition
"I make unto you. Or if you be hard hartedly bent, to appoint
"otherwise (which oh sooner let me dye, then knowe) then to
"ende as I began, let me by you be ordered to the same ende:
"without for more crueltie you meane to force *Philoclea* to use
"her owne hands to kill one of your Kings children."

THE COUNTESSE OF PEMBROKES

Pamelas Letter (*which she meant to send to the generall assemblie
of the Arcadian Nobilitie,*) (*for so closely they were kept, as they
were utterly ignorant of the newe taken orders*) *was thus framed.*

" IN such a state my Lords you have placed me, as I can
"neither write nor be silent; for how can I be silent, since
"you have left me nothing but my solitary words to testifie my
"miserie? and how should I write (for as for speech I have none
"but my Jaylor, that can heare me) who neither can resolve
"what to write, nor to whom to write? What to write is as
"hard for me to saye, as what I may not write, so little hope
"have I of any successe, and so much hath no injury bene left
"undone to mewards. To whom to write, where may I learne,
"since yet I wot not how to entitle you? Shall I call you my
"Sovereignes? set downe your lawes that I may do you homage.
"Shall I fall lower, and name you my fellowes? shew me I
"beseech you the Lord and mayster over us. But shall *Basilius*
"heyre, name her selfe your Princesse? Alas I am your prisoner.
"But whatsoever I be, or whatsoever you be, ô all you beholders
"of these dolefull lines, this do I signifye unto you, and signifye
"it with a hart, that shall ever remayne in that opinion. The
"good or evill you do to the excellent Prince was taken with
"me, and after by force from me, I will ever impute it as eyther
"way done to mine owne person. He is a Prince and worthie
"to be my husband, and so is he my husband by me worthely
"chosen. Beleeve it, beleeve it, eyther you shall be traytors for
"murdering of me, or if you let me live, the murderers of him
"shall smart as traytors. For what do you thinke I can thinke?
"Am I so childish, as not to see, wherein you touch him you
"condemne me? Can his shame be without my reproach? no
"nor shall be, since nothing he hath done, that I will not avowe.
"Is this the comfort you bring me in my fathers death, to make
"me fuller of shame then sorrowe? would you do this, if it were
"not with full intention to prevent my power, with slaughter?
"And so do I pray you, it is hye time for me, to be weary of
"my life too long ledd, since you are weery of me, before you
"have me? I say againe, I say it infinitely unto you, I will not
"live without him, if it be not to revenge him: eyther do justly
"in saving both, or wisely in killing both. If I be your Princesse,
"I commaund his preservation; if but a private person, then are

"we both to suffer. I take all truth to witnes he hath done no
"faulte but in going with me. Therefore to conclude, in judging
"him you judge me, neither conceave with your selves, the
"matter you treate, is the life of a stranger, though even in that
"name he deserved pittie, nor of a shepheard, to which estate
"love of me made such a Prince descend, but determine most
"assuredly, the life that is in question is of *Pamela, Basilius*
"daughter."

Many blots, had the teares of the sweet Ladyes made in their
letters, which many times they had altred, many times torne,
and written anewe, ever thinking some thing eyther wanted, or
were too much, or would offende, or which was worst, would
breede denyall: but at last, the day warned them to dispatch,
which they accordingly did, and calling one of their guard (for
no body else was suffred to come neere them) with great entreaty,
they requested him, that hee woulde present them, to the principall Noblemen and Gentlemen together. For they had more
confidence in the numbers favour, then in any one, uppon whome
they would not laye the lives they helde so precious. But the
fellowe trustie to *Philanax*, who had placed him there, delivered
them both to him, (what time *Pyrocles* began to speake) which
he sodaynly opened, and seeing to what they tended, by the first
wordes, was so farre from publishing them (whereby he feared
in *Euarchus* just minde, eyther the Princesses might be endaungered, or the prisoners preserved, of which choyse he knewe
not which to thinke the worst) that hee would not himselfe reede
them over, doubting his owne hart might be mollified, so bent
upon revenge. Therefore utterly suppressing them, he lent a
spitefull eare to *Pirocles*, and assoone as he had ended, with a
very willing hart desired *Euarchus* he might accept the combat:
although it woulde have framed but evill with him, *Pyrocles*
having never founde any match neere him, besides *Musidorus*.
But *Euarchus* made aunswere, since bodyly strength is but a
servant to the minde, it were very barbarous and preposterous,
that force shoulde bee made judge over reason. Then woulde
hee also have replied in wordes unto him, but *Euarchus* who
knewe what they coulde saye, was already saide, taking their
arguments into his minde, commaunded him to proceede against
the other prisoner, and that then he woulde sentence them both

together. *Philanax* nothing the milder for *Pyrocles* purging himselfe, but rather (according to the nature of arguing, especially
when it is bitter) so much the more vehement entred thus into
his speech against *Musidorus*, being so overgone with rage that
hee forgate in this oration his precise methode of oratory. Behold
most noble protector, to what a state *Arcadia* is come, since such
manner of men, may challenge in combat the faithfullest of the
nobilitie, and having merited the shamefullest of all deathes, dare
name in marriage the Princesses of this cuntrie. Certainely my
masters, I must saye, you were much out of taste, if you had
not rather enjoy such Ladies, then be hangd. But the one you
have as much deserved, as you have dishonoured the other. But
now my speech must be directed to you good master *Dorus*, who
with *Pallas* helpe pardie, are lately growne *Palladius*. Too much
this sacred seate of justice, grauntes unto such a fugitive bondslave
who in steede of these examinations, shoulde be made confesse,
with a whippe, that which a halter shoulde punish. Are not you
he Sir, whose sheepehooke was prepared to be our Scepter? In
whom lay the knot of all this tradgedy? or els perchaunce, they
that shoulde gaine little by it were dealers in the murder, you
onely that had provided the fruites for your selfe, knewe nothing
of it, knewe nothinge: hath thy companiõ here infected thee
with such impudency as even in the face of the world to deny
that which al the world perceaveth? The other pleades ignorance,
and you I doubt not will alleage absence. But he was ignoraunt,
when he was hard by, and you had framed your absence, just
againe the time the acte shoulde bee committed, so fit a liue-
tenante he knew he had lefte of his wickednes, that for himselfe
his safest meane, was to convey away the Lady of us all, who
once out of the contrie, he knew wee woulde come with olive
branches of intercession unto her, and fall at his feete to beseech
him to leave keeping of sheepe, and vouchesafe the tirannising
over us, for to think they are Princes, as they say (although in
our lawes it behooves them nothing) I see at all no reason. These
jewells certainly with their disguisinge sleightes, they have pilfred
in their vagabonding race. And think you such Princes should
be so long without some followers after them? Truely if they
be Princes, it manifestly shewes their vertues such, as all their
subjectes are glad to be rid of them. But be they as they are,
for we are to consider the matter, and not the men. *Basilius*

murder hath beene the cause of their comming, *Basilius* murder,
they have most trecherously brought to passe; yet that I doubte
not, you will denie as well as your fellowe. But howe will you
denie the stealinge awaie the Princesse of this Province, which is no
lesse then treason? So notably hath the justice of the gods provided,
for the punishing of these malefactors, as if it were possible, men
would not beleve the certaine evidences of their principall mischiefe, yet have they discovered them selves sufficiently for their
most just overthrowe. I saye therefore (to omit my cheefe matter
of the Kings death) This woolvish sheepheard, this counterfeite
Prince, hath trayterously contrary to his alleageaunce (having made
himselfe a servant and subjecte) attempted the depriving this
contry of our naturall Princesse: and therefore by all right
must receave the punishment of traytors. This matter is so
assured as he himselfe will not deny it, being taken and brought
backe in the fact. This matter is so odious in nature, so shamefull to the worlde, so contrarye to all lawes, so hurtefull to us,
so false in him, as if I should stande further in declaring or
defacing it, I shoulde either shewe great doubts in your wisedome, or in your justice. Therefore I will transferre my care
upon you, and attend to my learning and comfort, the eternall
example you will leave to al mankinde of disguisers, falsefiers,
adulterers, ravishers, murderers, and traytors. *Musidorus* while
Philanax was speaking against his cosin and him, had looked
rounde about him, to see whether by any meanes hee might
come to have caught him in his armes, and have killed him; so
much had his disgracing wordes filled his breste with rage.
But perceiving himselfe so guarded as hee shoulde rather showe
a passionate acte, then performe his revenge, his hande trembling
with desire to strike, and all the vaines in his face swelling;
casting his eyes over the judgement seate. O Gods saide hee,
and have you spared my life to beare these injuries of such a
drivle? Is this the justice of this place, to have such men as we
are, submitted not onely to apparent falsehood, but most shameful reviling? But marke I pray you the ungratefulnes of the
wretch, how utterly hee hath forgotten, the benefits both he
and all this contry hath receaved of us. For if ever men may
remember their owne noble deedes, it is then when their juste
defence, and other unjust unkindenes doth require it. I omit
our services done to *Basilius* in the late warre with *Amphialus*

importing no lesse then his daughters lives, and his states preservation: were not we the men that killed the wilde beastes
which otherwise had killed the Princesses, if wee had not
succourd them? Consider if it please you, where had bene
Daiphantus rape, or my treason, if the sweete beauties of the
earth, had then bene devoured? Either thinke them nowe dead,
or remember they live by us. And yet full often this telltale
can acknowledge the losse they shoulde have by their taking
away, while maliciously he over passeth who were their pre-
servers, neither let this be spoken of mee, as if I ment to ballance
this evill with that good, for I must confesse, that saving of
such creatures was rewarded in the acte it selfe: but onely to
manifest the partial jangling of this vile pickthanke. But if we
be the traytors, where was your fidelitie, O onely tonge-valliant
Gentleman, when not onely the yonge Princesse, but the King
himselfe was defended from uttermost perill, partely by me but
principally by this excellent yonge mans both wisdome and
valure? Were wee that made our selves against hundreds of
armed men, openly the shieldes of his life, like secretly to bee
his impoysoners? Did wee then shewe his life to bee dearer to us
then our owne, because wee might after robbe him of his life,
to dye shamefully? Truely truely master orator, whosoever
hath hired you to be so busie in their matters, who keepe
honester servauntes then your selfe, hee shoulde have bid you
in so manie raylings, bring some excuse for your selfe, why in
the greatest neede of your Prince, to whome you pretend a
miraculous good will, you were not then as forewarde to do like
a man your selfe, or at leaste to accuse them that were slacke
in that service, but commonlye the use their feete for there
defence whose tounge is their weapon. Certaynelye a verye
simple subtiltie it had beene in us, to repose our lives in the
daughters, when we had killed the father. But as this Gentleman thinkes to winne the reputation of a copious talker by
leaving nothing unsaide which a filthy minde can imagine, so
thinke I (or els all wordes are vaine) that to wise mens judgement, our cleerenes in the Kings death is sufficiently notorious.
But at length when the marchaunt hath set out his guilded
baggage, lastly he comes to some stuffe of importance, and
saith I conveied away the Princesse of this contrie. And is she
indeede your Princesse? I pray you then whom should I waite

of els, but her that was my mistres by my professed vow, &
Princesse over me while I lived in this soile? Aske her why she
went; aske not me why I served her. Since accounting me
as a Prince, you have not to do with me, taking me as her
servant, then take withall that I must obay her. But you will
say I perswaded her to flie awaye, certainely I will for no death
deny it, knowing to what honour I shoulde bring her from the
thraldome by such fellowes councell as you, shee was kept in.
Shall perswasion to a Prince growe treason to a Prince? It
might be error in me but falsehoode it coulde not be, since I
made my selfe partaker of whatsoever I wished her unto, who
will ever counsaill his King, if his counsaill be judged by the
event, and if it be not found wise, shall therefore be thought
wicked? But if I be a traytor, I hope you will graunt me a
correlative, to whom I shall be the traytor. For the Princesse
against whom the treasons are considered, I am sure will avowe
my faithfulnes, without you will saye that I am a traytor to
her, because I left the contrie: and a traytor to the contrie,
because I went with her. Heere do I leave out my just excuses
of loves force, which as thy narrow hart hath never had noble
roome inough in it to receave, so yet to those manlike courages,
that by experience know how subject the vertuous mindes are
to love a most vertuous creature, (witnessed to be such by the
most excellent guiftes of nature) will deeme it a veniall trespasse, to seeke the satisfaction of honourable desires. Honourable even in the curiousest pointes of honour, whereout there
can no disgrace nor disperagement come unto her. Therfore
O judge, who I hope doest know what it is to be a judge, that
your ende is to preserve, and not to destroy mankinde, that
lawes are not made like limetwigges, or nets, to catch every
thing that toucheth them, but rather like sea markes to avoide
the shipwracke of ignoraunt passingers, since that our doinge
in the extremest interpretation is but a humaine error, and that
of it you may make a proffitable event (we being of such estate,
as their parents would not have misliked the affinitie) you will
not I trust at the perswasion of this brabler, burne your house
to make it cleane, but like a wise father, turne even the fault
of your children to any good that may come of it: since that is
the fruite of wisdome, and ende of all judgements. While this
matter was thus handling, a silent and as it were astonished

attention, possest all the people. A kindely compassion moved the noble Gentleman *Simpathus*, but as for *Kalander*, every thing was spoken either by or for his own deere guestes, moved an affect in him: somtimes teares, sometimes hopefull lookes, sometimes whispering perswasions in their eares, that stoode by him, to seeke the saving the two yong Princes. But the generall multitude wayted the judgement of *Euarchus*, who shewed in his face no motions, either at the ones or other speeche, letting passe the flowers of rhetoricke, and onely marking whether their reasons tended, having made the question to be asked of *Gynecia*, who continued to take the whole faulte upon her selfe, and having caused *Damætas*, with *Miso* and *Mopsa* (who by *Philanax* order had bene helde in most cruell prison) to make a full declaration, howe much they knewe of these passed matters, and then gathering as assured satisfaction to his owne minde as in that case he could; not needing to take leasure for that, whereof a long practise had bred a well grounded habit in him, with a voice of gesture directed to the universall assemblie, in this forme pronounced sentence. This weightie matter, wherof presently we are to determine, doth at the first consideration yeeld two important doubtes. The first whether these men be to be judged. The second how they are to be judged. The first doubt ariseth because they geve themselves out for Princes absolute, a sacred name, and to which any violence semes to be an impietie. For how can any lawes, which are the bonds of all humane societie be observed if the lawe givers, and lawe rulers, bee not helde in an untouched admiration? But heereto although alredy they have beene sufficiently aunswered, yet thus much againe I will repeate unto you. That what soever they be or be not, heere they be no Princes, since betwixt Prince and subject there is as necessarie a relation, as betweene father and sonne, and as there is no man a father, but to his childe, so is not a Prince, a Prince but to his owne subjects. Therefore is not this place to acknowledge in them any principallitie, without it should at the same time, by a secreate consent confesse subjection. Yet hereto may be objected, that the universall civillitie, the lawe of nations (all mankinde being as it were coinhabitors or worlde-citizens together) hath ever required publicke persons, shoulde be of all parties especially regarded since not onely in peace, but in warre, not only Princes, but herauldes and trumpets, are with great reason exempted from injuryes. This pointe is true, but yet so true, as they that will receave the benefit of a custome, must not be the first to breake it. For then can they not complaine, if they be not helpt by that which they themselves hurte. Yf a Prince do actes of hostilitie, without denouncing warre, if he breake his oath of amitie, or innumerable such other thinges contrary to the lawe of armes, he must take heede how he fall into their hands whom he so wrongeth, for then is courtesie the best custome he can claime, much more these men, who have not onely lefte to doe like Princes, but to be like Princes, not onely entred into *Arcadia*, and so into the *Arcadian* orders, but into domesticall services, and so by making them selves private, deprived themselves of respecte due to their publicke calling. For no proportion it were of justice, that a man might make himselfe no Prince when he woulde doe evill, and might a newe create himselfe a Prince, when he would not suffer evill. Thus therefore by al lawes of nature and nations, and especially by their owne putting themselves out of the sanctuary of them, these yong men can not in justice avoide the judgement : but like private men, must have their doinges either cleared, excused, or condemned. There resteth then the second point, howe to judge well. And that must undoubtedly bee done, not by a free discourse of reason, and skill of philosophy : but must be tied to the lawes of *Greece*, and municipall statutes of this kingedome. For although out of them, these came, and to them muste indeede referre their offspringe, yet because philosophicall discourses, stande in the generall consideration of thinges, they leave to every man a scope of his owne interpretation. Where the lawes applyinge them selves to the necessary use, folde us within assured boundes, which once broken mãs nature infinitly rãgeth. Judged therfore they must be, & by your lawes judged. Nowe the action offereth it selfe to dewe ballance, betwixte the accusers two-folde accusation, and their aunsweare accordingly applied. The questions beeinge the one of a facte simplie, the other of the quallity of a fact. To the first they use direct deniall, to the second quallification and excuse. They deny the murder of the king; & mightie against presumptiõs bring forth some probable answers, which they do principally fortefie with the Queenes acknowledging her selfe only culpable. Certainely as in equallitie of conjectures, we are not to take holde of the worse, but rather to be glad we may finde any hope that mankind is not growen monstrous, (being undoubtedly lesse evill a guiltie man shoulde escape, then a guiltlesse perish) so if in the rest they be spotlesse, then is no farther to be remembred. But if they have aggravated these suspitions, with newe evills then are those suspitions so farre to showe themselves, as to cause the other pointes to be thorowly examined, and with lesse favour wayed since this no man can deny they have beene accidentall, if not principall causes of the Kinges death. Now then we are to determine of the other matters, which are laide to them, wherein they doe not deny the facte, but deny or at leaste diminish the faulte, but first I may remember (though it were not first alleaged by them) the services they had before done, truely honourable and worthy of great rewarde, but not worthy to countervaile with a following wickednes. Rewarde is proper to well doing, punishment to evill doing, which must not bee confounded, no more then good and evill are to be mingled. Therefore hath bene determined in all wisedomes, that no man because he hath done well before, should have his present evils spared, but rather so much the more punished, as having shewed he knew how to be good, woulde against his knowledge bee naught. The facte then is nakedly without passion, or partialitie to bee viewed: wherein without all question they are equallie culpable. For though he that termes himselfe *Daiphantus* were sooner disapointed of his purpose of conveying away the Lady *Philoclea*, then he that perswaded the Princesse *Pamela* to flie her countrie, and accompanied her in it: yet seing in causes of this nature, the wil by the rules of justice standeth for the deed, they are both alike to bee founde guiltie, and guiltie of hainous ravishment. For though they ravished them not from themselves, yet they ravished them from him that owed them, which was their father. An acte punished by all the *Græcian* lawes, by the losse of the head, as a most execrable thefte. For if they must dye, who steale from us our goodes, how much more they, who steale from us that, for which we gather our goodes, and if our lawes have it so in the private persons, much more forcible are they to bee in Princes children, where one steales as it were the whole state, and well being of that people, being tyed by the secret of a long use, to be governed by none but the next of that bloud. Neither let any man marvaile, our ancestours have bene so severe in these cases, since the

196

example of the *Phenician Europa* but especially of the Grecian *Helene*, hath taught them, what destroying fires have growen of such sparckles. And although *Helene* was a wife, and this but a child, that booteth not since the principall cause of marrying wives is, that we may have children of our owne. But now let us see how these yong men (truely for their persons worthy of pittie, if they have rightly pittied themselves) do goe about to mittigate the vehemencie of their errors. Some of their excuses are common to both, some peculiar onely to him that was the sheepeheard. Both remember the force of love, and as it were the mending up of the matter by their marriage, if that unbrideled desire which is intituled love, might purge such a sickenes as this, surely wee shoulde have, many loving excuses of hatefull mischiefe. Nay rather no mischiefe shoulde be committed, that should not be vailed under the name of love. For as well he that steales, might alleage the love of mony, he that murders the love of revenge, he that rebells the love of greatnesse, as the adulterer the love of a woman. Since they do in all speeches affirme they love that, which an ill governed passion maketh them to follow. But love may have no such priviledge. That sweete and heavenly uniting of the mindes, which properly is called love, hath no other knot but vertue, and therefore if it be a right love, it can never slide into any action that is not vertuous. The other and indeed more effectuall reason is that they may be married unto them and so honourably redresse the dishonour of them, whom this matter seemeth most to touch. Surely if the question were, what were convenient for the parties, and not what is juste in the never changing justice, there might much bee saide in it. But herein we must consider, that the lawes look how to prevent by due examples, that such thinges be not done: and not how to salve such things, when they are doone. For if the governors of justice, shall take such a scope, as to measure the foote of the lawe, by a show of conveniencie, and measure that conveniencie not by the publike societie, but by that which is fittest for them which offende: young men, stronge men, and rich men, shall ever finde private conveniences, howe to palliate such committed disorders, as to the publike shall not onely bee inconvenient but pestilent. The marriage perchaunce might be fit for them, but verie unfit were it to the state, to allowe a patterne of such procurations of marriage. And

thus much doe they both alleage. Further goes he that went
with the Princesse *Pamela*, & requireth the benefit of a councellor, who hath place of free perswasion; and the reasonable
excuse of a servant, that did but waite of his mistres. Without
all question, as councellors have great cause to take heede how
they advise any thing, directly opposite to the forme of that
present governement, especially when they doe it singly without
publike alowaunce, so yet is the case much more apparant : since
neither she was an effectuall Princesse, her father being then
alive, & though he had bene deade, she not come to the yeares
of authoritie, nor hee her servant, in such manner to obey her,
but by his owne preferment first belonging to *Dametas*, and then
to the Kinge, and therefore if not by *Arcadia* lawes, yet by
housholde orders, bounde to have done nothing without his
agreement. Thus therefore since the deedes accomplished by
these two, are both abhominable and inexcuseable. I doe in the
behalfe of justice, & by the force of *Arcadia* lawes pronounce,
that *Daiphantus* shalbe throwne out of a hie tower to receave
his death by his fall. *Palladius* shall bee behedded the time
before the sunne set: the place in *Mantinea* : the executioner
Dametas : which office he shall execute all the dayes of his life,
for his beastly forgetting the carefull dutie he owed to his charge.
This saide he turned himselfe to *Philanax*, and two of the other
noble men, commaunding them to see the judgement presently
performed. *Philanax* more greedie then any hunter of his praye,
went straite to laye holde of the excellent prisoners, who casting
a farewell looke one upon the other, represented in their faces
asmuch unappalled constancie, as the most excellent courage
can deliver, in outward graces. Yet if at all there were any
shewe of change in them, it was that *Pyrocles* was somthing
neerer to bashfulnes, and *Musidorus* to anger ; both over ruled
by reason and resolution. But as with great number of armed
men, *Philanax* was descending unto them, and that *Musidorus*
was beginning to saye something in *Pyrocles* behalfe. Beholde
Kalander, that with armes caste abroade, and open mouth came
crying to *Euarchus*, holding a stranger in his hãd that cried much
more then he, desiring they might be heard speake before the
prisoners were removed. Even the noble Gentleman *Simpathus*
ayded them in it, and taking such as hee coulde commaund,
stopped *Philanax* betwixt entreatie and force, from carrying away

the Princes, untill it were heard what new matters these men did bring. So againe mounting to the Tribunall, they hearkened to the straungers vehement speach, or rather appassionate exclayming. It was in deede *Kalodulus*, the faithfull servaunt of *Musidorus*, to whome his maister, when in despite of his best grounded determinations he first became a slave to affection, had sent the sheaphearde *Menalcas* to be arrested: by the helpe of whose rayment in the meane time he advaunced himselfe to that estate, which he accompted most high, because it might be serviceable to that fancy, which he had placed most high in his minde. For *Menalcas* having faithfully performed his errand, was as faithfully imprisoned by *Kalodulus*. But as *Kalodulus* perfourmed the first part of his duety in doing the commaundement of his Prince: so was he with abundance of sincere loyalty extremely perplexed, when he understood of *Menalcas* the straunge disguising of his beloved Maister. For as the actes he and his Cosen *Pyrocles* had done in *Asia*, had filled all the eares of the *Thessalians* and *Macedonians* with no lesse joy then admiration: so was the feare of their losse no lesse grievous unto them, when by the noise of report they understood of theyr lonely committing themselves to the Sea, the issue of which they had no way learned. But now that by *Menalcas* hee perceyved where he was, gessing the like of *Pyrocles*, comparing the unusednes of this act with the unripenesse of theyr age, seeing in generall conjecture they could doe it for nothing, that might not fall out dangerous: he was somewhile troubled with himselfe, what to doe, betwixt doubt of theyr hurt, and doubt of theyr displeasure. Often he was minded (as his safest and honestest way) to reveale it to the king *Euarchus*: that both his authority might prevent any domage to them, and under his winges he himselfe might remaine safe. But considering a journey to *Byzantium* (where as yet he supposed *Euarchus* lay) would require more time, then hee was willing to remaine doubtfull of his Princes estate, he resolved at length to write the matter to *Euarchus*, and himselfe the while to goe into *Arcadia*: uncertayne what to doe when he came thither, but determined to doe his best service to hys deare Maister, if by any good fortune he might finde him. And so it happened that being even this day come to *Mantinea*, and as warely and attentively as he coulde giving eare to al reports, in hope to hear some thing of them he sought, he straight receyved a straunge rumor of these thinges: but so uncertainely as popular reports cary so rare accidents. But this by all men he was willed, to seek out *Kalander* a great Gentleman of that Countrey, who would soonest satisfie him of all these occurrents. Thus enstructed he came even about the midst of *Euarchus* judgement to the desert. Where seeing great multitudes, and hearing unknowen names of *Palladius*, and *Daiphantus*, and not able to presse to the place where *Euarchus* sate, he enquired for *Kalander*, and was soone brought unto him: partly because he was generallye knowen unto all men, and partly because he had withdrawen himselfe from the presse, when he perceived by *Euarchus* words whether they tended, being not able to endure his guests condemnation. Hee enquired forthwith of *Kalander* the cause of the assembly: and whither the fame were true of *Euarchus* presence: who with manye teares, made a dolefull recitall unto him, both of the *Amazon* and sheepheard, setting forth their naturall graces, and lamenting their pittifull undoing. But his description made *Kalodulus* immediatly knowe the sheepheard was his Duke, and so judging the other to be *Pyrocles*, and speedely communicating it to *Kalander*, who he saw did favour their case, they brake the presse with astonishing every man with their cryes. And being come to *Euarchus*, *Kalodulus* fell at his feete telling him those he had judged were his owne Sunne and Nephewe; the one the comforte of Macedon, the other the onely stay of *Thessalia*. With many such like words, but as from a man that assured himselfe in that matter he shoulde neede smal speeche. While *Kalander* made it knowen to all men, what the prisoners were to whom he cried they should salute their father, and joy in the good hap the gods had sent them; who were no lesse glad, then all the people amazed at the strange event of these matters. Even *Philanax* owne revengefull hart was mollified, when he saw from diverse partes of the world so neere kinsemen should meete in such a necessitie. And with all the fame of *Pyrocles* and *Musidorus*, greatly drewe him to a compassionate conceite, and had already uncloathed his face of all shew of mallice. But *Euarchus* staide a good while upon himselfe, like a valliant man that should receave a notable encounter, being vehemently stricken with the fatherly love of so excellent children, and studying with his best reason, what his office required. At length with such a kind of gravitie, as was neere to sorrow, he thus uttred his mind. I take witnes of the immortall gods (saide he) O *Arcadians*, that what this daye I have saide, hath bene out of my assured perswasion, what justice it selfe and your juste lawes require. Though straungers then to me, I had no desire to hurt them, but leaving aside all considerations of the persons, I wayed the matter which you committed into my hands, with most unpartiall and farthest reach of reason. And thereout have condemned them to loose their lives, contaminated with so manye foule breaches of hospitalitie, civilitie and vertue. Now contrarye to all expectations, I finde them to be my onely sonne and Nephew, such upon whom you see, what guiftes nature hath bestowed. Such who have so to the wonder of the worlde heretofore behaved themselves, as might geve juste cause to the greatest hopes, that in an excellent youth may be conceaved. Lastly in fewe wordes such, in whome I placed all my mortall joyes, and thought my selfe now neere my grave, to recover a newe life. But alas shall justice halte? Or shall she winke in ones cause which had *Lynces* eyes in anothers? Or rather shall all private respectes geve place to that holy name? Bee it so, bee it so, let my graye heares bee layde in the dust with sorrow, let the small remnant of my life, bee to me an inward and outward desolation, and to the world a gazing stock of wretched misery: But never never, let sacred rightfulnes fall. It is immortal and immortally ought to be preserved. If rightly I have judged, then rightly I have judged myne own children. Unlesse the name of a child, should have force to change the never changing justice. No no *Pyrocles* & *Musidorus* I prefer you much before my life, but I prefer Justice as far before you, while you did like your selves, my body should willingly have ben your shield, but I cannot keep you from the effects of your own doing. Nay I cãnot in this case acknowledge you for mine. For never had I sheapheard to my nephew, nor ever had woman to my son, your vices have degraded you frõ being princes, & have disanulde your birthright.

Therefore if there be anie thing left in you, of Princely vertue, shew it in constant suffering, that your unprincely dealing hath purchased unto you. For my part I must tell you, you have forced a father to rob himselfe of his children. Do you therefore, O *Philanax*, and you my other Lordes of this countrie, see the judgment be rightly performed in time, place and maner, as before appointed. With that though he would have refrained them ; a man might perceive the teares drop downe his long white beard. Which moved not onely *Kalodulus* and *Kerxenus* to roaring lamentations, but al the assembly dolefully to record that pittiful spectacle. *Philanax* himselfe could not abstaine from great shewes of pittying sorrow, and manifest withdrawing from performing the kinges commaundement. But *Musidorus* having the hope of his safety, and recovering of the princesse *Pamela* : which made him most desirous to live, so sodainly dashed: but especialy moved for hys deare *Pyrocles*, for whom he was ever resolved his last speach should be, and stirred up with rage of unkindnesse, he thus spake. Enjoy thy bloudie conquest tyrannicall *Euarchus*, said he ; for neither is convenient the title of a king, to a murderer, nor the remembrance of kindred, to a destroyer of his kindred. Go home and glorie that it hath been in thy power, shamefully to kill *Musidorus*. Let thy flattering Orators dedicate Crownes of Laurell unto thee, that the first of thy race, thou hast overthrowne a Prince of *Thessalia*. But for me I hope the *Thessalians* are not so degenerate from their auncestors, but that they will revenge my injurie ; and their losse upon thee. I hope my death is no more unjust to me ; thẽ it shalbe bitter to thee, howsoever it be, my death shall triumph over thy crueltie, neither as now would I live to make my life beholding unto thee. But if thy crueltie hath not so blinded thine eyes, that thou canst not see thine own heart, if thy heart be not so divelish, as thou hast no power but to torment thy self : then look upõ this yong *Pyrocles*, with a manlike eie ; if not with a pittifull : Give not occasion to the whole earth to say, see how the gods have made the Tyrant teare his owne bowels ! Examine the eies and voices of all this people, and what all men see, be not blinde in thine owne case. Looke I say looke upon him, in whom the most curious searcher is able to finde no fault : but that he is thy sonne. Beleeve it, thy owne subjectes will detest thee, for robbing them of such a Prince, in whome they have right as well as thy selfe. Some more wordes to that purpose he would have spoken, but *Pyrocles* who often had cald to him, did nowe fully interrupt him, desiring him not to do him the wrong to geve his father ill wordes before him, willing him to consider it was their owne fault, and not his unjustice, and withall to remember their resolution of well suffering all acci-.

dents, which this impaciencie did seeme to varry frō: and then kneeling down with all humblenesse, hee tooke the speach in this order to *Euarchus*. If my dayly praiers to the Almightie Gods, had so farre prevayled, as to have graunted me the end whereto I have directed my actions; I should rather have beene nowe a comfort to your minde, then an example of your justice, rather a preserver of your memorie by my life, then a monument of your judgement by my death. But since it hath pleased their unsearchable wisedomes, to overthrow all the desires I had to serve you, and make me become a shame unto you ; since the last obedience I can shew you, is to die: vouchsafe yet O father (if my fault have not made me altogether unworthy, so to terme you) vouchsafe I say to let the few & last words your sonne shall ever speake, not be tedious unto you. And if the remembrance of my vertuous mother, who once was deare unto you, may beare any sway with you, if the name of *Pyrocles* have at any time bene pleasant, let one request of mine which shall not be for mine owne life, be graciously accepted of you. What you owe to justice is performed in my death. A father to have executed his onely sonne, wil leave a sufficient example for a greater crime then this. My bloud will satisfie the highest point of equitie, my bloud will satisfie the hardest hearted in this countrie. O save the life of this Prince, that is the onely all I will with my last breath demaund of you. With what face will you looke upon your sister, when in reward of nourishing me in your greatest neede, you take away and in such sort take away that which is more deare to her then all the world, and is the onely comfort, wherewith she nourisheth her olde age ? O give not such an occasion to the noble *Thessalians*, for ever to curse the match that their Prince did make with the *Macedon* bloud. By my losse there followes no publique losse, for you are to hold the seate, and to provide your selfe perchance of a worthier successor. But how can you or all the earth recompence that domage, that poore *Thessalia* shall sustaine ? who sending out (whom otherwise they would no more have spared then their owne eyes) their Prince to you, and you requesting to have him, by you hee should thus dishonourably be extinguished. Set before you, I beseech you, the face of that miserable people, when no sooner shall the newes come that you have met your Nephew, but withall they shall heare that you have beheaded him. How manie teares they shall spend, how many cõplaints they shal make, so manie just execrations will light upõ you. And take heede O father (for since my death answeres my fault, while I live I wil call upõ that deare name) Least seeking too precise a course of justice, you be not thought most unjust : in weakning your neighbours mightie estate, by taking away their onely piller. In me, in me this matter beganne, in me let it receive his ending. Assure your selfe no man will doubt your severe observing the lawes, when it shal be knowne *Euarchus* hath killed *Pyrocles*. But the time of my ever farewell approcheth, if you do thinke my death sufficient for my fault, and doe not desire to make my death more miserable then death. Let these dying wordes of him, that was once your sonne, pearce your eares. Let *Musidorus* live, and *Pyrocles* shall live in him, and you shall not want a childe. A childe cried out *Musidorus*, to him, that killes *Pyrocles*? with that againe he fell to intreate for *Pyrocles*, and *Pyrocles* as fast for *Musidorus*, each employing his wit how to shew himselfe most worthy to die, to such an admiration of all the beholders, that most of them examining the matter by their owne passions, thought *Euarchus* (as often extraordinarie excellencies, not being rightly conceived, do rather offend then please) an obstinate hearted man, and such a one, who being pittilesse, his dominion must needes be insupportable. But *Euarchus* that felt his owne miserie more then they, and yet loved goodnesse more then himselfe, with such a sad assured behaviour as *Cato* killed himselfe withall, when he had heard the uttermost of that their speach tended unto: he commaunded againe they should be carried away, rising up from the seate (which he would much rather have wished, should have been his grave) and looking who would take the charge, whereto everie one was exceeding backward. But as this pittifull matter was entring into, those that were next the Dukes bodie, might heare from under the velvet, wherewith he was covered, a great voice of groning. Whereat everie man astonished, (and their spirites appalled with these former miseries, apt to take anie strange conceite) when they might perfitly perceive the bodie stirre, Then some beganne to feare spirits, some to looke for a myracle, most to imagine they knew not what. But *Philanax* and *Kerxenus*, whose eies, honest love (though to diverse parties) held most attentive, leapt to the table, and putting of the velvet cover, might plainly discerne, with as much wonder as gladnesse, that the Duke lived. For so it was, that the drinke he had received, was neither as *Gynecia* first imagined, a love potion, nor as it was after thought, a deadly poyson, but a drinke made, by notable Arte, and as it was thought not without naturall magicke to procure for thirtie houres, such a deadly sleepe, as should oppresse all shew of life. The cause of the making of this drinke had first been, that a Princesse of *Cyprus*, graundmother to *Gynecia*, being notably learned, (and yet not able with al her learning, to answere the objections of *Cupid*) did furiously love a yoong noble man of her fathers Court. Who fearing the kinges rage, and not once daring either to attempt or accept so high a place, shee made that sleeping drinke, and found meanes by a trustie servaunt of hers, (who of purpose invited him to his chamber) to procure him, that suspected no such thing, to receive it. Which done, he no way able to resist, was secretly carried by him into a pleasant chamber, in the midst of a garden, she had of purpose provided for this enterprise : where that space of time, pleasing her selfe with seeing and cherishing of him, when the time came of the drinks end of working, and he more astonished then if he had falne from the cloudes, she bad him choose either then to marrie her, and to promise to flie away with her in a bark she had made readie, or else she would presently crie out, and shewe in what place he was, with othe hee was come thither to ravish her. The noble man in these straightes, her beautie prevailed, he married her, and escaped the Realme with her. And after many strange adventures, were reconciled to the king her father, after whose death they raigned. But she gratefully remembring the service, that drinke had done her, preserved in a bottle (made by singular Arte long to keepe it without perishing) great quantitie of it, with the foretold inscription, which wrong interpreted by her daughter in law the Queene of *Cyprus*, was given by her to *Gynecia* at the time of her marriage, and the drinke finding an old body of *Basilius*, had kept him some houres longer in the trance, then it would have done a yoonger. But a good while it was, before good *Basilius* could come again to himself : in which time *Euarchus* more glad then of the whole worldes Monarchie, to be rid of his miserable magistracie, which even in justice he was now to surrender to the lawful Prince of that countrie ; came from the

Throne unto him, and there with much adoe made him understand, how these intricate matters had fallen out. Many garboiles passed through his fancie before he could be perswaded, *Cleofila* was other then a woman. At length remembring the Oracle, which now indeede was accomplished (not as before he had imagined) considering all had fallen out by the highest providence, and withall waying in all these matters his owne fault had been the greatest. The first thing he did, was with all honorable pompe, to send for *Gynecia*: who poore Ladie thought she was leading forth to her living buriall: and (when she came) to recount before all the people, the excellent vertue was in her, which she had not onely maintained all her life most unspotted: but nowe was contented so miserably to die, to follow her husband. He told them how she had warned him to take heede of that drinke, and so withall the exaltinges of her that might be, he publikely desired her pardon, for those errours he had committed. And so kyssing her, left her to receive the most honourable fame of anie Princesse throughout the world, all men thinking (saving onely *Pyrocles* and *Philoclea* who never bewraied her) that she was the perfit mirrour of all wifely love. Which though in that point undeserved, she did in the remnant of her life daily purchase, with observing al dutie & faith to the example & glorie of *Greece*. So uncertain are mortall judgments, the same person most infamous, and most famous, and neither justly. Then with Princely entertainment to *Euarchus*, and many kinde words to *Pyrocles*, whom still he dearely loved though in a more vertuous kinde, the marriage was concluded, to the inestimable joy of *Euarchus*, (towardes whom now *Musidorus* acknowledged his fault) betwixt these peerelesse Princes and Princesses. *Philanax* for his singular faith ever held deare of *Basilius* while he lived, and no lesse of *Musidorus*, who was to inherite that Dukedome, and therein confirmed to him and his, the second place of that Province, with great increase of his living to maintain it: which like proportion he used to *Kalodulus* in *Thessalia*: Highly honouring *Kalander* while he lived: and after his death continuing in the same measure to love and advannce this sonne *Clitophon*. But as for *Sympathus*, *Pyrocles*, (to whom his father in his owne time gave the whole kingdome of *Thrace*) held him alwaies about him, giving him in pure gift, the great Citie of *Abdera*: But the solemnities of these marriages, with the

ARCADIA. LIB. 5.

Arcadian pastoralles, full of many comicall adventures, hapning to those rurall lovers; the straunge stories of *Artaxia* and *Plexirtus*, *Erona* and *Plangus*; *Helene* and *Amphialus*, with the wonderfull chaunces that befell them : The shepheardish loves of *Menalcas* with *Kalodulus* daughter ; the poore hopes of the poore *Philisides* in the pursuite of his affections; the strange continuance of *Klaius* and *Strephons* desire ; Lastly the sonne of *Pyrocles* named *Pyrophilus*, and *Melidora*, the faire daughter of *Pamela* by *Musidorus*, who even at their birth entred into admirable fortunes ; may awake some other spirite to exercise his penne in that, wherewith mine is already dulled.

FINIS.

[THE LADY OF MAY]

HER MOST EXCELLENT

MAJESTIE WALKING IN WANSTEED GAR-

DEN, AS SHE PASSED DOWNE INTO THE

grove, there came suddenly among the traine, one apparelled like
an honest mans wife of the countrey, where crying out for justice,
and desiring all the Lords and Gentlemen to speake a good
word for her, she was brought to the presence of her Majestie,
to whom upon her knees she offred a supplication, and used this
speech.

The Suiter.

MOst faire Lady, for as for other your titles of state state-
lier persons shall give you, and thus much mine owne
eies are witnesses of, take here the complaint of my poore wretch,
as deeplie plunged in miserie, as I wish to you the highest point
of happinesse.

One onely daughter I have, in whom I had placed all the
hopes of my good hap, so well had she with her good parts re-
compenced my paine of bearing of her, and care of bringing her
up: but now alas that she is come to the time I should reape my
full comfort of her, so is she troubled with that notable matter,
which we in countrey call matrimony, as I cannot chuse but
feare the losse of her wits, at least of her honesty. Other women
thinke they may be unhappily combred with one maister husband, my poore daughter is oppressed with two, both loving her,
both equally liked of her, both striving to deserve her. But now
lastly (as this jealousie for sooth is a vile matter) each have
brought their partakers with them, and are at this present,
without your presence redresse it, in some bloudy controversie;
now sweete Lady helpe, your owne way guides you to the place
where they encomber her: I dare stay here no longer, for our
men say in the countrey, the sight of you is infectious.

And with that she went away a good pace, leaving the

THE LADY OF MAY.

supplication with her Majestie, which very formallie contained this.

SUPPLICATION.

Most gracious Soveraigne,

To one whose state is raised over all,
Whose face doth oft the bravest sort enchaunt,
Whose mind is such, as wisest minds appall,
Who in one selfe these diverse gifts can plant;
  How dare I wretch seeke there my woes to rest,
  Where eares be burnt, eyes dazled, harts opprest?

Your state is great, your greatnesse is our shield,
Your face hurts oft, but still it doth delight,
Your mind is wise, your wisedome makes you mild,
Such planted gifts enrich even beggers sight:
  So dare I wretch, my bashfull feare subdue,
  And feede mine eares, mine eyes, my hart in you.

Herewith the woman-suiter being gone, there was heard in the woods a confused noyse, and forthwith there came out six sheapheards with as many fosters haling and pulling, to whether side they should draw the Lady of May, who seemed to encline neither to the one nor other side. Among them was Maister *Rombus* a schoole-maister of a village thereby, who being fully perswaded of his owne learned wisedome, came thither, with his authority to part their fray; where for aunswer he received many unlearned blowes. But the Queene comming to the place where she was seene of them, though they knew not her estate, yet something there was which made them startle aside and gaze upon her: till old father *Lalus* stepped forth (one of the substantiallest shepheards) and making a legge or two, said these few words.

May it please your benignity to give a little superfluous intelligence to that, which with the opening of my mouth, my tongue and teeth shall deliver unto you. So it is right worshipfull audience, that a certaine she creature, which we shepheards call a woman, of a minsicall countenance, but by my white Lambe not three quarters so beautious as yore selfe, hath disanulled the braine pan of two of our featioust yong men. And wil you wot how? by my mother *Kits* soule, with a certaine fransicall maladie *Lalus the old shepheard.*

209

THE LADY OF MAY.

they cal Love, when I was a yong man they called it flat follie. But here is a substantiall schoole-maister can better disnounce the whole foundation of the matter, although in sooth for all his loquence our young men were nothing dutious to his clarkeship; Come on, Come on Maister schoole-maister, be not so bashlesse, we say, that the fairest are ever the gentlest: tell the whole case, for you can much better vent the points of it then I.

Then came forward Maister Rombus, and with many speciall graces made this learned oration.

Now the thunderthumping *Jove* transfund his dotes into your excellent formositie, which have with your resplendent beames thus segregated the emnitie of these rurall animals: I am *Potentissima Domina*, a schoole-maister, that is to say, a Pedagogue, one not a litle versed in the disciplinating of the juventall frie, wherein (to my laud I say it) I use such geometricall proportion, as neither wanted mansuetude nor correction, for so it is described.

Parcare Subjectos & debellire superbos.

Yet hath not the pulchritude of my vertues protected me from the contaminating hands of these plebeians; for comming, *solummodo* to have parted their sanguinolent fray, they yeelded me no more reverence, then if I had bin some *Pecorius Asinus*. I, even I, that am, who am I? *Dixi verbus sapiento satum est.* But what sayd that Troian *Æneas*, when he sojorned in the surging sulkes of the sandiferous seas, *Hæc olim memonasse juvebit.* Well well, *ad propositos revertebo*, the puritie of the veritie is, that a certaine *Pulchra puella profectò* elected and constituted by the integrated determination of all this topographicall region, as the soveraigne Lady of this Dame Maias month, hath bene *quodammodo* hunted, as you would say, pursued by two, a brace, a couple, a cast of yong men, to whom the crafty coward *Cupid* had *inquam* delivered his dire-dolorous dart.

But here the May Lady interrupted his speech, saying to him:

May Lady.   Away away you tedious foole, your eyes are not worthy to looke to yonder Princelie sight, much lesse your foolish tongue to trouble her wise eares.

At which Maister Rombus in a great chafe cried out:

Rombus.   O *Tempori*, ò *Moribus!* in profession a childe, in dignitie a

210

THE LADY OF MAY.

woman, in yeares a Lady, *in cæteris* a maid, should thus turpifie
the reputation of my doctrine, with the superscription of a foole,
ô Tempori, ô Moribus!

But here againe the May Ladie saying to him,

Leave off good Latine foole, and let me satisfie the long desire   *May*
I have had to feede mine eyes with the only sight this age hath   *Lady.*
graunted to the world.

*The poore scholemaister went his way backe, and the Lady kneeling
downe said in this maner :*

Do not thinke (sweete and gallant Lady) that I do abase my   *May*
selfe thus much unto you because of your gay apparell, for what   *Lady.*
is so brave as the naturall beauty of the flowers, nor because a certaine Gentleman hereby seekes to do you all the honour he can
in his house; that is not the matter, he is but our neighbour, and
these be our owne groves, nor yet because of your great estate,
since no estate can be cõpared to be the Lady of the whole moneth
of May as I am. So that since both this place and this time are
my servants, you may be sure I wold looke for reverence at your
hands if I did not see something in your face which makes me
yeeld to you; the troth is, you excell me in that wherein I desire
most to excell, and that makes me give this homage unto you, as
to the beautifullest Lady these woods have ever received. But
now as old father *Lalus* directed me, I wil tel you my fortune,
that you may be judge of my mishaps and others worthinesse.
Indeed so it is, that I am a faire wench or else I am deceived, and
therefore by the consent of all our neighbours have bene chosen
for the absolute Lady of this mery moneth, with me have bene
(alas I am ashamed to tell it) two yong men, the one a forrester
named *Therion,* the other *Espilus* a shepheard very long even in
love forsooth, I like them both, and love neither, *Espilus* is the
richer, but *Therion* the livelier: *Therion* doth me many pleasures,
as stealing me venison out of these forrests, and many other such
like prettie and prettier services, but withall he growes to such
rages, that sometimes he strikes me, sometimes he railes at me.
This shepheard *Espilus* of a mild disposition, as his fortune hath
not bene to do me great service, so hath he never done me any
wrong, but feeding his sheepe, sitting under some sweete bush,
sometimes they say he records my name in dolefull verses. Now
the question I am to aske you faire Ladie, is, whether the many

THE LADY OF MAY.

deserts and many faults of *Therion*, or the verie small deserts and
no faults of *Espilus* be to be preferred. But before you give your
judgement (most excellent Ladie) you shall heare what each of
them can say for them selves in their rurall songs.

Thereupon Therion chalenged Espilus to sing with him,
speaking these six verses:

Therion.

Come Espilus, come now declare thy skill,
Shew how thou canst deserve so brave desire,
Warme well thy wits, if thou wilt win her will,
For water cold did never promise fire:
   Great sure is she, on whom our hopes do live,
   Greater is she who must the judgement give.

But *Espilus* as if he had bene inspired with the Muses, began
forthwith to sing, whereto his fellow shepheards set in with their
recorders, which they bare in their bags like pipes, and so of
Therions side did the foresters, with the cornets they wore about
their neckes like hunting hornes in baudrikes.

Espilus.

Tune up my voice, a higher note I yeeld,
To high conceipts the song must needes be high,
More high then stars, more firme then flintie field
Are all my thoughts, on which I live or die:
   Sweete soule, to whom I vowed am a slave,
   Let not wild woods so great a treasure have.

Therion.

The highest note comes oft from basest mind,
As shallow brookes do yeeld the greatest sound,
Seeke other thoughts thy life or death to find;
Thy stars be fal'n, plowed is thy flintie ground:
   Sweete soule let not a wretch that serveth sheepe,
   Among his flocke so sweete a treasure keepe.

Espilus.

Two thousand sheepe I have as white as milke,
Though not so white as is thy lovely face,
The pasture rich, the wooll as soft as silke,
All this I give, let me possesse thy grace,
   But still take heede least thou thy selfe submit
   To one that hath no wealth, and wants his wit.

THE LADY OF MAY.

Therion.

Two thousand deere in wildest woods I have,
Them can I take, but you I cannot hold:
He is not poore who can his freedome save,
Bound but to you, no wealth but you I would:
  But take this beast, if beasts you feare to misse,
  For of his beasts the greatest beast he is.

Espilus kneeling to the Queene.

Judge you to whom all beauties force is lent.

Therion.

Judge you of Love, to whom all Love is bent.

But as they waited for the judgement her Majestie should give
of their deserts, the shepheards and foresters grew to a great contention, whether of their fellowes had sung better, and so whether
the estate of shepheards or forresters were the more worshipfull.
The speakers were *Dorcas* an olde shepheard, and *Rixus* a young
foster, betweene whom the schoole-maister *Rombus* came in as
moderator.

Dorcas the shepheard.

Now al the blessings of mine old grandam (silly *Espilus*) light
upon thy shoulders for this honicombe singing of thine; now of
my honestie all the bels in the towne could not have sung better,
if the proud heart of the harlotrie lie not downe to thee now, the
sheepes rot catch her, to teach her that a faire woman hath not
her fairenesse to let it grow rustish.

Rixus the foster.

O *Midas* why art thou not alive now to lend thine eares to
this drivle, by the precious bones of a hunts-man, he knowes not
the bleaying of a calfe from the song of a nightingale, but if
yonder great Gentlewoman be as wise as she is faire, *Therion* thou
shalt have the prize, and thou old *Dorcas* with young maister
Espilus shall remaine tame fooles, as you be.

Dorcas. And with cap and knee be it spoken, is it your pleasure
neighbor *Rixus* to be a wild foole?

Rixus. Rather then a sleepish dolt.

Dorcas. It is much refreshing to my bowels, you have made
your choise, for my share I will bestow your leavings upon one
of your fellowes.

THE LADY OF MAY.

Rixus. And art not thou ashamed old foole, to liken *Espilus* a shepheard to *Therion* of the noble vocation of hunts-men, in the presence of such a one as even with her eye only can give the cruell punishment?

Dorcas. Hold thy peace, I will neither meddle with her nor her eyes, they sayne in our towne they are daungerous both, neither will I liken *Therion* to my boy *Espilus,* since one is a theevish proller, and the other is as quiet as a lamb that new came from sucking.

Rombus the schoole-maister.

Heu, Ehem, hei, Insipidum, Inscitium vulgorum & populorum. Why you brute Nebulons have you had my *Corpusculum* so long among you, and cannot yet tell how to edifie an argument? Attend and throw your eares to me, for I am gravidated with child, till I have endoctrinated your plumbeous cerebrosities. First you must divisionate your point, *quasi* you should cut a cheese into two particles, for thus must I uniforme my speech to your obtuse conceptions; for *Prius dividendum oratio antequam definiendum exemplum gratia,* either *Therion* must conquer this Dame *Maias* Nimphe, or *Espilus* must overthrow her, and that *secundum* their dignity, which must also be subdivisionated into three equall *species,* either according to the penetrancie of their singing, or the meliority of their functions, or lastly the superancy of their merits *De* singing *satis. Nunc* are you to argumentate of the qualifying of their estate first, and then whether hath more infernally, I meane deepely deserved.

Dorcas. O poore *Dorcas,* poore *Dorcas,* that I was not set in my young dayes to schoole, that I might have purchased the understäding of master *Rombus* misterious speeches. But yet thus much I concerne of them, that I must even give up what my conscience doth find in the behalfe of shepheards. O sweete hony milken Lommes, and is there any so flintie a hart, that can find about him to speake against them, that have the charge of such good soules as you be, among whom there is no envy, and all obedience, where it is lawfull for a man to be good if he list, and hath no outward cause to withdraw him frõ it, where the eye may be busied in considering the works of nature, and the hart quietly rejoyced in the honest using them. If templation as Clarks say, be the most excellent, which is so fit a life for

THE LADY OF MAY.

Templers as this is, neither subject to violent oppression, nor servile flatterie, how many Courtiers thinke you I have heard under our field in bushes make their wofull complaints, some of the greatnes of their Mistrisse estate, which dazled their eyes and yet burned their harts; some of the extremitie of her beauty mixed with extreame cruelty, some of her too much wit, which made all their loving labours folly. O how often have I heard one name sound in many mouthes, making our vales witnesses of their dolefull agonies! So that with long lost labour finding their thoughts bare no other wooll but dispaire, of yong Courtiers they grew old shepheards. Well sweete Lams I will ende with you as I began, he that can open his mouth against such innocent soules, let him be hated as much as a filthy fox, let the tast of him be worse then mustie cheese, the sound of him more dradfull then the howling of a wolfe, his sight more odible then a toade in ones porreage.

Rixus. Your life indeede hath some goodnesse.

Rombus the schoole-maister.

O *tace, tace*, or all the fat wil be ignified, first let me dilucidate the very intrinsicall maribone of the matter. He doth use a certaine rhetoricall invasion into the point, as if in deed he had conference with his Lams, but the troth is he doth equitate you in the meane time maister *Rixus*, for thus he sayth, that sheepe are good, *ergo* the shepheard is good, An *Enthimeme à loco contingentibus*, as my finger and my thumbe are *Contingentes*: againe he sayth, who liveth well is likewise good, but shepheards live well, *Ergo* they are good; a *Sillogisme* in *Darius* king of *Persia* a *Conjugatis*; as you would say, a man coupled to his wife, two bodies but one soule: but do you but acquiescate to my exhortation, and you shall extinguish him. Tell him his major is a knave, his minor is a foole, and his conclusion both, *Et ecce homo blancatus quasi liliŭ.*

Rixus. I was saying the shepheards life had some goodnesse in it, because it borrowed of the countrey quietnesse something like ours, but that is not all, for ours besides that quiet part, doth both strengthen the body, and raise up the mind with this gallant sort of activity. O sweet contentation to see the long life of the hurtlesse trees, to see how in streight growing up, though never so high, they hinder not their fellowes, they only enviously trouble, which are crookedly bent. What life is to be compared to ours where the very growing things are ensamples of goodnesse? we have no hopes, but we may quickly go about them, and going about them, we soone obtaine them; not like those that have long followed one (in troth) most excellent chace, do now at length perceive she could never be taken: but that if she stayed at any time neare the pursuers, it was never meant to tarry with them, but only to take breath to fly further from them. He therefore that doubts that our life doth not far excell all others, let him also doubt that the well deserving and painefull *Therion* is not to be preferred before the idle *Espilus*, which is even as much to say, as that the Roes are not swifter then sheepe, nor the Stags more goodly then Gotes.

Rombus. Bene bene, nunc de questione prepositus, that is as much to say, as well well, [n]ow of the proposed question, that was, whether the many great services and many great faults of *Therion*, or the few small services and no faults of *Espilus*, be to be preferred, incepted or accepted the former.

The May Lady.

No no, your ordinarie traines shall not deale in that matter, I have already submitted it to one, whose sweete spirit hath passed thorough greater difficulties, neither will I that your blockheads lie in her way.

Therefore ô Lady worthy to see the accomplishment of your desires, since all your desires be most worthy of you, vouchsafe our eares such happinesse, & me that particular favor, as that you will judge whether of these two be more worthy of me, or whether I be worthy of them: and this I will say, that in judging me, you judge more then me in it.

This being said, it pleased her Majesty to judge that *Espilus* did the better deserve her: but what words, what reasons she used for it, this paper, which carieth so base names, is not worthy to containe. Sufficeth it, that upon the judgement given, the shepheards and forresters made a full consort of their cornets and recorders, and then did *Espilus* sing this song, tending to the greatnesse of his owne joy, and yet to the comfort of the other side, since they were overthrowne by a most worthy adversarie. The song contained two short tales, and thus it was.

THE LADY OF MAY.

Silvanus *long in love, and long in vaine,*
At length obtaind the point of his desire,
When being askt, now that he did obtaine
His wished weale, what more he could require:
    Nothing sayd he, for most I joy in this,
    That Goddesse mine, my blessed being sees.

When wanton Pan *deceiv'd with Lions skin,*
Came to the bed, where wound for kisse he got,
To wo and shame the wretch did enter in,
Till this he tooke for comfort of his lot,
    Poore Pan *(he sayd) although thou beaten be,*
    It is no shame, since Hercules *was he.*

Thus joyfully in chosen tunes rejoyce,
That such a one is witnesse of my hart,
Whose cleerest eyes I blisse, and sweetest voyce,
That see my good, and judgeth my desert:
    Thus wofully I in wo this salve do find,
    My foule mishap came yet from fairest mind.

The musike fully ended, the May Lady tooke her leave in this sort.

Lady your selfe, for other titles do rather diminish then adde unto you. I and my litle companie must now leave you, I should do you wrong to beseech you to take our follies well, since your bountie is such, as to pardon greater faults. Therefore I will wish you good night, praying to God according to the title I possesse, that as hitherto it hath excellently done, so hence forward the florishing of May, may long remaine in you and with you.

FINIS.

NOTES

In the following references the lines are numbered from the top of the page, including titles, but not, of course, the headline. The page numbers are in heavier type. A line of verse turned over is counted as one line.

A = 1593	E = 1613	I = 1638
B = 1598	F = 1621	K = 1655
C = 1599	G = 1627	L = 1662
D = 1605	H = 1633	M = 1674

For a description of the folio editions of Arcadia, *see vol.* I, p. 522.

1. 5. *In* A—D *this last part of* Arcadia *is prefaced by the following words:*
How this combate ended, how the Ladies by the comming of the discovered forces were delivered, and restored to *Basilius*, and how *Dorus* againe returned to his old master *Damætas*, is altogether unknowne. What afterward chaunced, out of the Authors owne writings and conceits hath bene supplied, as foloweth.

In E, *it is prefaced by:*

Thus far the worthy Author had revised or inlarged that first written Arcadia of his, which onely passed from hand to hand, and was never printed: having a purpose likewise to have new ordered, augmented, and concluded the rest, had he not bene prevented by untymely death. So that all which followeth here of this Work, remayned as it was done and sent away in severall loose sheets (beeing never after reviewed, nor so much as seene all together by himself) without any certaine disposition or perfect order. Yet for that it was his, howsoever deprived of the just grace it should have had, was held too good to be lost: & therefore with much labor were the best coherencies, that could be gathered out of those scattred papers, made, and afterwards printed as now it is, onely by hir Noble care to whose deare hand they were first committed, and for whose delight and intertaynement only undertaken.

What conclusion it should have had, or how far the Work have bene extended (had it had his last hand thereunto) was onely knowne to his owne spirit, where only those admirable Images were (and no where else) to bee cast.

And here we are likewise utterly deprived of the relation how this combat ended, and how the Ladies by discovery of the approching forces were delivered and restored to *Basilius*: how *Dorus* returned to his old master *Dametas*: all which unfortunate mayme we must be content to suffer with the rest.

Then follows the passage:

How this combate ended...as foloweth. [*As in* A—D]

F—M *have the same passage as* E [Thus far...with the rest.] *then add* " A supplement of the said defect by Sir W.[illiam] A.[lexander]," *which supplement is followed by:*

From hence the History is againe continued out of the Authors owne writings and conceits, as followeth.

After that *Basilius*, &c.

NOTES

1. 15. F—M *omit* the *before* open

2. 9. KLM later danger   22. G—M *full stop instead of comma after* mee   27. KLM *omit* how *after* bent   28. BD—M then you should 31. I in my   36. KLM those two   37. C may, it shall stande

3. 5. C *inserts* hie *before* voyce   9. KLM their friend's   10. KL these last determination   M these last determinations   14. HI of *instead of* to *before* despaire   24. BD—M *comma instead of colon after* friend   31. D *omits comma after* thee   32. D (whom I love)   33. BD—HKLM *colon after* affection   I *full stop*   38. LM affliction   39. M *omits* for *after* hath

4. 2. KLM performed friendship   4. KLM shee should   6. KLM his secret   7. M utmost of   12—14. KLM *print* that friendship...dammage *in Italics*   14. G—M dammage   26. M They should   33. KLM *insert* up *after* setting

5. 3. I—M first combination   4. M fell upon them   7. GHKLM *Diaphantus*   12. I *prints* doubt and desire *in Roman type*   19. KLM he knew   27. C *has no division into stanzas*   BD—M *print* Phoebus *throughout the poem*   38. FH *omit comma after* "*possesse*"

6. 20. LM to his place in   27. C *semicolon after* place   30. B Therefore awhile   D—M Therefore a while   34. D—M *print* soyle *in Roman type* 36. LM *print* age...blood *in Italics*   38—39. KLM *print* hard...granting *in Italics*   39. I *transposes* speake *and* I

7. 1. I *comma instead of full stop after* grant   2. M to by won 4. G—M wait on him   7. E *prints* O *in Italics*   8. HI *note of exclamation instead of note of interrogation after* affraid   HI furnace!   22. I fancie 25. GH farefull *instead of* farrewell   29—30. D marble, to beautifie 30 CD *semicolon instead of full stop after* entry   33. F—M *omit* the *before* selfe-liking

8. 2. KLM effects *instead of* Affectes   E—M and *instead of* shee   3. C *has no division into stanzas*   4. BD—M "*by*" *instead of* "*of*" *before* "*beauties*" 5. BD—M *With rebell*   C *Which rebell*   KLM dungeons   6. E "*seasons*" *instead of* "*reasons*"   7. E—M "*my*" *instead of* "*mine*" *before* "*eies*" 15. BD—M *where at*   19. D sightes *instead of* sighes   20. D omits his *before* free   29. F—M *print* Lyra *in Italics*   31. C *has no division into stanzas*   33. M fatal spark   35. D Seeing (*Alas*) so   E Seeing, *Alas, so*   38. E "*my*" *instead of* "*thy*" *before* "*bosome*"

9. 7. D omits a *before* litle   M mournefull Melodie   15. F—M *griefes* HI *omit* "*me*" *before* "*best*"   BD—H *comma after* "*best*"   20. M complaint   23. BDEH—M blislesse   F blissesse   25. KLM (said hee) 26 D my musicke   BE—L *omit hyphen between* least *and* hand   D (at least hand)   25—26. G—M fellow-prentises   27. E—M rose she 28. C still-playing voyce   29. C *inserts* a *before* paper   31. C *has no division into stanzas*

10. 2. D *sorrow*   5. HI *dull pen*   8. C *has no division into stanzas* 12. G—M *torments*   21. HI feet   31. BD—M and how dim 32. D (nay blinde)   I perceiving *instead of* preventing   35. I against *instead of* unto

11. 20. F—M the *instead of* this   32. G—M estate *instead of* state 36. BD—M then in too late

12. 11. EF—M *omit* of *before* my   12. HI thorough *instead of* through 14. F—M knew   38. D but *instead of* both

219

NOTES

13. 8. D though he was   9. E—M now *instead of* how   20. FH—M accounted   28. I whom he was   37. HI *omit* a *before* ten   38. D his *instead of* the *before* Lodge   HI *omit* to *after* way   40. BD—M *insert* he *before* might

14. 2. DEFH—M between before   25. L gave to him   16. C *omits* which he had never done   32. L *omits* againe   E—M treasure   33. L hid

15. 5. LM laden with   10. KLM *print* no man...the whole *in Italics*   23. I rending up   26. E—M a greater   33. C *has no division into stanzas*   37. F *then hand see*   GH *then hand, see*

16. 9. BD—M by *instead of* me   13. KLM heard *instead of* hated   25. BD—M others sport   37. D the cause had   38. BD—M mine owne

17. 17. M *omits* her *before* hair   18. KLM *omit* the *before* free   19. D sometime   23. D as my   26. C *has no division into stanzas*   29. G—M *transpose* " better " *and* " bargaine "   37. KLM *his heart did smart*

18. 5. C *has no division into stanzas*   9. HI *promis'd due*   12. F—M *and plump*   18. C *sleeke-stone-like, it*   D *sleek stone-like, it*   E—HK—M *sleekestone, like it*   I *sleek-stone, like it*   32. M her impatient   38. D hath

19. 1. D *Oudemnian*   C as *Charitas*   7. D *Charitas*   11. C *Mantinena*   22. M whatsoever would   31. I own hand   33. F—M the sadle   37. KLM practice   38. D *omits* the *before* parting

20. 8. BD—M Princesse *instead of* Duchesse   12. LM *transpose* quickly *and* have   13. D this enterprise   14. LM *insert* so *before* absolutely   23. D sometime   27. DEFH—M mute   28. BE—M sometimes   33. KLM *note of exclamation instead of note of interrogation after* wishes   37. BDE burthen

21. 1. EFG faile   4. C far set   9. KLM *Admetus's* herdman   12. G—M *insert* a *before* little   15. E *inserts* of *before* nature   18. BD—M qualitie *instead of* equality   38. D foole although I   H—M commandements   39. L *full stop instead of comma after* self

22. 3. D *prints* since...will *in parenthesis and omits comma after* will   8. H—M *insert* of *after* enjoying   21. D have a certaine   G—M effects   23. E—M Lady in the   24. KLM on wors   26. H—M device   36. D hath bequeathed   40. M with what things shee

23. 1. C builde   28. I burthen   33. G—M he stole   37. I—M *semicolon after* unto you

24. 19. I others cates   24. BD—M changing them   G—M *Pammidorus*   34. I *eye*   39. GHKLM *barr'd my selfe*   I *barr'd from my selfe*

25. 5. LM bearer than   G—M wrote   9. KLM contemplation   M made trees.   10. E—M beare badges   B *semicolon after* passions   12. E—M *ascent*   16. KLM " *But*" *instead of* " *By*"   26. D *a-lonely*   KLM *lovely*   32. KLM *Musidorus's* ears   35. G withall   37. G her reply

26. 2. EF " *colour*" *instead of* " *colourde*"   5. BCG *whereon*   12. HI *worlds bright eye*   21. D *inserts* " *a*" *before* " *gaged*"

NOTES

27. 2. BD—M *from thy common*   5. CG—M *her sprite*   11. F—
M *fayre liddes*   23. L *omits* of *before* som   G—M stole   27. KLM
Musidorus's affects   35. LM miserably in   36. B mischiefes   38. KLM
looks   39. BDG—M Tigre EF Tiger

28. 3. EFH awhile   M with that dexterity   10. M *omits* shee *before*
thought   12. M *omits* as *before* I   17. D—M *insert* I *after* if   19. C
omits you *after* yet   35—37. LM *print* the thoughts...servant of the
thoughts *in Italics*   35. H—M overflowings   38. E *transposes* in *and* it
C wholy armies

29. 10. B my sprits   39. E—M having fought   40. G—M valour

30. 10. D *inserts* I *after* if   13. I *prints* too deeply grounded *in
parenthesis*   17. C shameful   I—M shamefac't   21. KLM have
23. C by mutuall   29. BDEFH—M *parenthesis before* as *not before* happie
33. KLM not the abusing   39. C guest, we doubt

31. 13. H—M account   16. D contention   28. D lovely place
30. C *inserts* a *before* woman-kinde   34. M *omits* cruell

32. 1. E—M hooked with others flattery   20. LM *appears*   26. I
earthy   32. M *omits* said he   38. F *dissein* G—M *designe*   39. HI
my owne

33. 9. D *"thy" instead of "my" before "long" omits full stop after "anoyes"*
10. D *"things" instead of "frends"*   17. L no fortifie   M to fortifie
19. LM so small   M *inserts a comma after* small   H—M cause of the
20. E—M pleasing   21. M *omits* all b fore his   22. M perhaps *instead
of* perchance   KLM changeable *instead of* chaunceable   24. C affections
35. E—M as *instead of* but   39. C such paine   D *omits* a *before* sacriledge

34. 8. M thought   9. M too stinging   10. F *inserts* from *after* her
selfe   11. BD—M burthen   15. BD—M her heart side   18. FGKLM
given-way   24. D—M thine owne   27—28. KLM *print* the falsest...
minde *in Italics*   37. EFHI—M *comma instead of note of interrogation
after* see *and note of interrogation instead of colon after* heart   M an heart

35. 5. BD—M *insert* to *after* but   6. D from whom   8. D *omits*
away   14. KLM thy own   18. C harts betray   25. I doings
D—M account   E—M *insert* a *before* wrong   27. DH—M happily
EF happely   35. BD—M *Lute within thy*   36. KLM *My mistress's
song*   39. DEFH—M *weeds*

36. 27. DEFH—M sweet creature *in parenthesis*   39. M *omits* a *before*
conjecture

37. 5. KLM hee *instead of* she   7. D *omits* all *before* her   8. KLM
hee *instead of* she   16. KLM *omit* in it *after* interest   31. C with
vehement   F—M matter   35. F—M subjects   39. E—M eares
40 I—M practice

38. 4. KLM Eclogue 8. F—M speciall   12. L resolutions   21. KLM
gleaning   26. I *guilty spity spite*   31. BD—M rayes   37. LM overladen

39. 7. KLM *omit* the *before* daie's   11. HI *print* Aurora *in Italics*
12. FH—M *omit parenthesis before "Which"*   D *concluding parenthesis instead
of comma after "baite"*   14. DFH—M *omit concluding parenthesis after
"waite"*   19. KLM *"neither" instead of "never"*   23. F *omits colon
after "show"*   H *comma instead of colon after "show"*   29. E—M *omit* a
before racke   33. HI objects   36. M let down   38. E things

NOTES

40. 1. D hands   2. I beaten   4. HILM device   15. BD—M
this priviledged   16. I *comma after* perfectly *not after* lesson   16—18. D
whose...countenance *in parenthesis*   17. BDEFH—M with *instead of*
which   20. KLM fitter *instead of* freer   21. LM to her

41. 5. D—M secret communing   9. I *inserts* a *before* raging
10. DEFH—M through   21. E—M she resolved by   28. H—M device
35. C *comma instead of parenthesis after* jorney   D *colon*   EFH—M *semicolon*
G *no parenthesis*

42. 5. FGH—M *omit* on *after* putting   14. D—M fortune   17. F—M
was cleared   18. D upon them.   19. HIM unfortunate   24. D the
returning of   32. DE viall   FH—M violl   DG—M ambassage   37. I
is shaked

43. 28. BD—M *insert* your *before* sweet   29. KLM *insert* and *before*
acknowledg   31. D let no   B—M imaginative   33. C whose ever failing
36—37. LM *print* hope...fear *in Italics*   39. KLM *omit* to *after* set
I what traine   B—M she should keepe

44. 3. M said hee   9. E—M you lovers   BCD *insert a colon after* it
E—M *insert a full stop*   10. D may still have   16. C withal   20. D
her ministery   21. D our live   22. HI a torment   24. I that they
escaped   27. DEFH—M accounted   32. D Thus in silence   36. DEFH—
M account   37—38. LM *print* it is a hell...resistance *in Italics*

45. 1. B—M an imaginative   11—12. C help the other-one to
14. F—M *omit* never *before* ô   BD—M *insert* never *before* looke   19. B—M
threatned deniall   36. F—M *insert* will *before* seeke   38—40. LM *print*
women are...land *in Italics*

46. 14. H—M device   KLM of it to the last   16. C enter into an
18. B—M counterfeit litle love to   30. E—M King *instead of* Duke

47. 16. D—M his daughter   30. H—M device   34. F—M *omit* to
before be   40. BD—M her mantell

48. 5. I amongst   8. D nimbly (disaraying her selfe) possesse
12. BD—M outmost apparell   24. FHKLM loves effects

49. 16. KLM arms   27. F—M beginning   FH—M breaking
29. FH—M made an   32. M *omits* a *before* reasonable

50. 1. D *parenthesis before* as *not before* I   2. D embracing   LM embraces   5. F—M *insert* such *after* yeeld   6—7. CE—M drawe on
another   9. I as he to be gone from thence   10. G—M stole   26. M
To helpless   27. H—M *omit comma after* "*Teares*"   HI "*case*" *instead
of* "*cause*"   F—M *omit concluding parenthesis after* "*cause*"   GHKLM *semicolon and concluding parenthesis instead of comma after* "*wasted*"   I *concluding parenthesis instead of comma after* "*wasted*"   32. CG *favour*   CE—
M *part*

51. 7. M in that side   8. D loving hold   13. F—M then by experience   23. KLM *Basilius*'s   25. KL *Basilius*'s   27. D they had
been   31. D surged joy   34. DH—M reckoning   36. C "*Philoclea*" *instead of* "*Pyrocles*"

52. 2. FGHKLM with his stealing   6. KLM devices   11—13. KLM
print whosoëver in...do nothing *in Italics*   LM that *whatsoëver*   13. C this
wayed   14. D part was thus   18. D *omits comma after* griefes   19. I
transposes all *and* now   26. G—M his joyous   28. E—M *omit* were
32. I entertainment   34. LM he that the extremitie   40. I the entry of

222

NOTES

53. 8—21. H—M *have no division into stanzas*   9. F *omits comma after* "*love*"   14. England's Helicon (1600) *wrongs*   16. D *taught*   F—M *thought*   20. C *nothing*   26. F—M *omit* by *after* being

54. 11. M *inserts* is *after* as   I impatiencie   12. E—M *full stop after* out   14. LM Philosopher   16. I *omits parenthesis before* for   17. C that *instead of* and *before* she   18. I heat of the countrey   24. EFH—M *parenthesis instead of comma before* as   27. I all together   F—M *insert* put *before* upon   M the *instead of* that *before* quite   33. I prettily *instead of* privilie   F—K trickle   35. C mornefull song   37. M in the best tunes

55. 4. F that disdaine   18. C—M "*hate*" *instead of* "*hath*"

56. 6—7. C because she bare former grudge   9. BD—M not, since by the

57. 2. E—M stood *instead of* should   7. BD—M please you   15. D witnes   22—23. BD—M but to bemone mine own   29. E—M broke   31. I wickedly feare no due   33. E—M conversion *instead of* conversation   34. D an other   35. KLM *Pyrocles's* form   36—37. KLM left you, to transform your self into, to inveigle   38. E—M simplicitie? Enjoy the conquest   39. LM assure thy self

58. 5. KL *Pyrocles's* mind   LM saw the time   19. KLM not giving   25. BDEFH—M hast thou   28. BD—M And *instead of* O

59. 3. M *omits* from   4. H burden   18. FG—M *omit* that   19. M caus in other   21. KLM to this action   23. I—M device   24. D *inserts* of *before* all   28. H *Evarchus*   29. D—K specially   30. D not possible   32. BD—M *omit* arguments of   39. F—M *omit* a *before* pitifull

60. 4. B—M *omit* if *after* But   5. D *omits* speech: which   6. KL *Pyrocles's*   10. M by his unexpected   F any any degree   14. G—M *omit* so *before* to   18. LM against such   28. KLM bee mended   31. LM consider what was   38. LM might run to

61. 2. B—M at first   6. BD—M of his owne   7. M burdens   21. F—M *print* The third *in Italics*   F Eclogues   G—M Eclogue   24. CD *comma after* not   EFKLM *comma after* her   HI *semicolon after* her

62. 5. KLM *Thyrsis's* carefulness   6. I *transposes* one *and* of   12. HI won   15. KLM fell down   17. DM great persons   21. B—M brought   25. B—M all joyfull   26. E *Klaias*   33. HI bower made   34. KLM *Thyrsis's* hous   35. HI *insert* was *before* placed

63. 8. C *has no division into stanzas*   18. KLM *beauty*   36. KLM Thyrsis's *musick*   BDEKLM *your praise*

64. 6. KLM *Wors care*   18. KLM *shall allow*   19. C *Like Oxe*

65. 3. E—M *the house*   8. BD *wholesome*   E—M *whole your*   29. C—M prize   G—M won   36. E—M longer, than a

66. 14. C *has no division into stanzas*

67. 23. E—M *transpose* "*did*" *and* "*her*"   26. KL enclining   27. D her hart

68. 10. F—M *ill becomes*   12. M *thereof*   15. BD—M *further*   29. E *little had*   30. I Yours must   31. H—M *Th' epistle*   32. EFG *spirite*

69. 15. KLM *that in him no grief*   EFG *be bread*   H—M *be bred*   31. FGHKLM he had   33. I was enough

NOTES

70. 1. *This poem was first published by Sir John Harington* (Orlando Furioso, 1591, *note to Book XI*, p. 87) C *has no division into stanzas* 3. Harington *Then be he such* 4. Harington *And alwayes one credit with her preserve:* 10. Harington *Tone doth enforce, the tother doth entice* BD—GKLM *latter* 11. Harington *but drive fro thence* 14. Harington *To nature, fortune* 20. F *resolving* 21. M *fortune* 23. I *good matters* 24. E—M *his cunning* 30. E—M *river side* 33. E—M *beside* 34. BD—M *root* 35. BD—M *boot*

71. 10. KL *the 'author* M *the author* 18. C—M *cunning* 30. BD—G *Cowslop* 34. C *children by*

72. 1. BD—M *Wither* 5. LM *thy cherries* 11. BDEFH—M *Thy* 33. LM *breasts* 34. KLM *of greedie* 40. KLM *comma after "death"*

73. 9. M *Th'adst* 10. F—M *"Cabin" instead of* Caban 11. BDEFM *Then want* G—L *Than want* 13. KLM *had better* 15. E—M *Which Ciprus sweet* 18. KLM *weight* 19. I *Masters* 25. BD *no legs* E—M *on legs with faintnesse* 29. G—M *rose* 30—31. C *prints these two lines as one line*

74. 1—**81.** 33. *See* vol. I, *notes to* **132.** 19—**140.** 30.

81. 33. *After this line* E—M *add:*

> *Perchance I will, but now me thinks it time,*
> *To goe unto the Bride, and use this day:*
> *To speake with her while freely speake we may.*

F—M *insert* Histor *in margin before "Perchance"* 35—36. *Cf.* vol. I, *note to* **140.** 32—33 35. E—M *"Lalus" instead of "Thyrsis"* KLM *Lalus's fortune* 38. DEFHIK *comma instead of full stop after* wassalling LM *semicolon*

82. 1. E—M *"Lalus" instead of "Thyrsis"* 8. D—M *print this line in Italics*

83. 8. F—M *omit* in *after* brought 22. E—M discontentment 26. KLM *Midas's* 27. I between the gods

84. 6. DEFH—M accounted 10. E—M before night 16. M *omits* so *after* were 18. D an house 34. E—M man that would 36. B—M *omit* of *after* light 40. E—M for her wit

85. 2. HI *omit concluding parenthesis after* gallows? 3. M hee would 4. CKLM *omit colon after* tydings EFG *colon after* her *not after* tidings HI *no colon after* tidings *but colon and concluding parenthesis after* her 6. E—M *insert* yet *before* never 12. M *omits* light 13. BD—M *full stop after* prevaile 15. E—M *omit* and *before* did 18. I began throw 22. B—M her armes 31. HI when *instead of* then 34. E—M *omit* him *after* tell 35. C didst love *Phaetons* mother

86. 13. DEFH—M the other 14. M will declare thee a 27. KLM *Dorus's* 36. F this duty 37. BD—M Oudemian

87. 2. KLM *print* panick *in Roman type* 9. DEFH—M *omit comma after* being 10. M nor age 10—11. H mitigate 11. G—M suffi-cient remedy 21. D her pray 23. EFH—M *insert a parenthesis before* thinking 24. D *comma instead of semicolon after* nowle EFH—M *concluding parenthesis instead of semicolon after* nowle 25. D minds parts 26. L the cholor M the choler 40. H—M bastanado's

NOTES

88. 4. KLM what in the world shee   7. D her of *Charita*   11. LM *omit* a *before* rude   13. M *omits* the *before* opportunitie   14. F of the there, hee   20. D possible   36. B—M negligence   39. G—M were falne

89. 7. *See* List of Misprints etc., which have been corrected   BCE—M somersaults D somerfaults   10. M know   21. HI *omit* O *before* Wife   28. E—M villaine   29. B—M thinking to run away   31. D *semicolon after* death   EFH—M *insert a colon*   33—34. KLM *print* fear is…courage *in Italics*

90. 2. C barren *instead of* barred   H—M trap   3. HI into the vault   6. G passing softly   8—9. B—M one on the bed by her   11. C—FH—M went hard to   14. B—M to the destined   16. DEFH—M *comma instead of parenthesis after* sleepe   19. C—FH—M *omit parenthesis after* mind   20. KLM *Psyce*   23. I *omits* same   25. BDEFH—M *semicolon after* opinion   27. KLM *Pyrocles's* sword   33. BD—M negligence   34—35. KLM *print* the more rage…punishment *in Italics*

91. 3. G—M all the while   6. BDEFH—M *full stop instead of comma after* "*Philoclea*"   11. BD—M from the one crie   15. I *inserts* a *before* spectator   21. KLM promises   22. BD—M made to *Zelmane*   F—M true orders   26. FHI—M *semicolon instead of comma after* himselfe   *omit* in *before* which   35. C *has no division into stanzas*   36. E—M harvest of

92. 6. DKLM sencelesse sleepe   I "*wisedomes mother*" *in parenthesis*   10. HIM *is blest*   C *since joyde*   11. E—M *further*   21. FGHKLM Alabaster   22. BD—M such a title   23. M *omits* alas   26. M shee come   27. M Cave entry   30. EFHI—M *concluding parenthesis after* "*Zelmane*"   33. E—HKLM if she would

93. 20. LM *omit* the *before* mother   34. E—M himselfe overtaken

94. 5. D you to governe   16. DKLM you are the cause   30. HI pardon unto you   31. D for the fained   39. H—M *Basilius's* owne

95. 7. D that he had wrought   10. KL *Basilius's* great   11. D this hard   12. E—M lickour meant for   14. D whome *instead of* home   19. E—M King *instead of* Duke   20. D drough   28. BD—M burthen   29. I *inserts* a *before* heavie   30. EFHKL whither   F portion   38. M that *instead of* what

96. 2. C so horrible   12. F—M unto from somthing   14. K *comma after* laws   L *semicolon*   M *colon*   16. C supportable *instead of* insupportable   17. G—M *omit* her *after* as   24. BD—M For whither   26. D ashamed   31. BD—M Whither then   32. C *omits* this *after* was   LM was this thee

97. 3. B—M lover *instead of* loves   4. D were dried   6. D detestination   9. KLM *omit* had *before* some   15. M no way seek   17. LM so well I   20. F—M *insert* And *before* as   23. KLM *Basilius's* death   37. KLM in those woods

98. 6. D mortifications against   12. F—M taken her   13. D had possessed   18. F—I *semicolon instead of full stop after* admiration   KL *comma*   FGHKL They I they   40. FGHKLM *omit* I *before* was

NOTES

99. 3. DLM no pittie   4. F—M *insert* to *before* some   E—M other
E—M desiring them   7. C arbitrers   9. HI *comma after* once   BD—M
whither   11. D *omits* a *after* not   12. F—M so much the more
15. C *omits* yet *before* let   16. D—M whither you   32—33. C all-to-
gether KLM altogether   34—35. LM the access of

100. 5. BD—M yet all men naturally   14. ILM others   16—17. KLM
print men are...cours *in Italics*   18. C—M how easie a   19. M likely
monument   21. HI the resounding   26. I was come   27. M the
place   28. KLM *Basilius*'s solitariness   29—30. KLM Prince's return
37. I dove *instead of* love   38. D *omits* ever *before* over-soone

101. 10. F pleaseath   16. BD—M *insert* I *after* words   C in the
most faithful   21. I fitteth in me   22. M *omits* to *before* womanish
28. BD—M murtherers   29. D the *instead of* this   36. B—M vindi-
cative

102. 8. DF—M but as a traitor   K *Basilius*'s wife   LM *Basilius*'s his
wife   8—9. KLM *Basilius*'s murtherer   15. D in his bitter   25. D
countries   26. CI order   28. *See* List of Misprints etc., which have been
corrected   B—M in

103. 5. B—M locked the   6. M poisoners for   HI prisones to   10. D
his sence   11. DFG *salue*   H—M *salve*   18. I chiefest nurse   20. D
doth never make   23. I on the outside   24. KLM for the force
26. GKLM escape of him   36. C that this being

104. 7. KLM heavy grief   B—M fellowlesse *Philoclea*   8. C enjoyn-
ing   13. D burden   19. B—M vice *instead of* voice   20. M how oft
26. B—M negligence   E—M had no more

105. 9. F to be better end   G—M to a better end   13. D *omits* shall
19. I *omits parenthesis before* which   G—M somewhat *instead of* something
21. B—M breake off the feeble threed   22. LM well preserved   BD—I
that will   29. I and now againe   36. D my leave   37. D *omits* so
before doe   39. D *omits* a *before* short

106. 4. D *omits* not *before* be   5. I *omits parenthesis before* And   6. I
parenthesis before as   *omits* and *before* when   10. BD—M with all   HI *insert* it *after* upon   12. C—M doe the effect   28. M straying   29. E—M
embracements   32. I *omits* a *before* death   36. D terrible   38. C
omits I *before* for

107. 2. C newe-teller   6. D *parenthesis instead of comma before* that   *no
parenthesis before* though   9. C *transposes* then *and* that   15. KLM *insert* a *before* new   20. E—M unshaken   21. I guiltinesse   28. E—M
by his hand   30. KLM *insert* of *after* doing   36. E—M *omit* my *before*
minde   39. M with *instead of* within

108. 3. G—M killing of ones self   4. BE—M of a feare   5. E—M
transpose a *and* not   10. GHI valour   KLM valor   13. CM God hath
20. E—M humble   23. BE—M burthen   33. F—M as I cannot
38. G—M *insert* to *before* see

109. 4. KLM that they may bee   20. B—M further   22. E—M
can never   23. B—M I call the   32. M or *instead of* of *after* title
F—M *omit* a *before* passion   35. *See* List of Misprints etc., which have been
corrected   B—M resolution   KL a way   35—36. C with the wonder
38. F—M which in an assured

NOTES

110. 7. LM had the one   13. GHI valour KLM valor   20. F—M *omit* for   29. D breds   30. F—M God had   32. FGKLM at your owne

111. 3. D in scope D to provoke   9. D bee matters of   10. D or claime   14. F—M preserving of all   17. C truely my deare *Pyrocles* 23. B—M valures   24. D owne part   29. HI others mens   39. D now making it

112. 14. FGHKLM shee would have   19. D reproaching death   36. D that this ende

113. 6—7. HI very worthily   9. EFK deprived off   10. C I preferred   16. KLM *omit* in *before* recompence   19. D *transposes* am *and* I 24. KLM the later   28. F—M to stay   34. D a while   36. D with all 40. DEFH—M waited on

114. 3. C a straunger   14. K *transposes* it *and* be   25. BD—M errand   26—27. E—M inexcusable   29. DF—M thus much   37. KLM *transpose* then *and* be

115. 9. KLM of the truth   11. F—M house that she   14. BD—K unto *instead of* to *after* owe   15. EFH—M *omit* you *after* come   17. LM disdaining with   18. E—M *omit* I *before* would   21. LM by oath 22. D leave his wife   23. BD—M inward scorne   28. KLM said poor *Pyrocles*   32. GHKLM valor I valour   34. G—M of his former

116. 1. D shee as so surprized   14—15. M faith he so much   25. M *omits* in deede

117. 2. E—M falling to tender   10. FGH under *instead of* unto   15. I benefits   17. D *omits* now   30. EF him to [*end of line*] to proceed 38. C witnesse KLM far from such

118. 4. KL *omit* he *before* easily   M *omits* that he   5. D her in his hartie   7. KL murders D lay upon him   12. D garment   13. KLM *omit* hath *after* shee   14. KLM *transpose* it *and* will   30. F naturall case   31. D reposed with mind

119. 13. KLM *omit* and *before* making   16. D *transposes* full *and* well 19. BD—I valour KLM valor   25. D set together H—M set all together   33. BD—M ill wards they had   36. BD—I valour KLM valor

120. 1. M disperses   3. F running   8. C *omits* a *before* dreadfull 16. BD—M mouth full   20. HI *comma instead of parenthesis after* fellowes 21. HI *concluding parenthesis instead of comma after* trees   29. CHI Alabaster   34. BD—M *comma instead of full stop after* Scholemaister

121. 1. BD—M time or place   4. EFH—M other things in him 19. BDEFKLM groning HI groaning   20. D *omits* a *before* disfigured 24. BD—M murtherer   27. C leaving them to   32. BD—M broken by disagreement   38. D her estate   39. C sometime

122. 7. EFH—M *omit parenthesis before* who   8. EFHI *parenthesis instead of comma before* who KLM *parenthesis before* who   14. F—M be the cause   15. D from this fore-deserved   16. D of these two

123. 3. KLM *omit* as *after* far   D mans wil   D extĕded as I sought 7. C helps   14. BD had never love so commanding   E had never love commanding F—M had never, love commanding   21. KLM that stand's   29. C *prints* Aprill *in Italics*   30—31. HI of thy unblemished 34—35. KLM O mind of mine   35. D withall

NOTES

124. 2. KLM determination   3. H let it to her   9. DEFH—M
full stop instead of comma after " Musidorus "   15. BD—M your too much
grieving   22. D of hir deare   24. K any any occasion   26. KLM
insert to *before* make   29. KLM think, excellent   32. LM the state
33. D *no parenthesis before* next *but parenthesis instead of comma before* far
34—35. C noble constitution   35. BD—M of his mind   40. E—M
combination *instead of* company

125. 4. CKLM *transpose* I *and* that   6. DEFH—M accounting
13. KLM excellencie   14. D well with you   18. BD—M of her case
25. D their was speech   E—M there was a speech   26. I the *instead of*
their *before* chiefest   33. E—HKLM *semicolon instead of full stop after*
lamentations I *comma*   36. D at the last

126. 1. M in *instead of* it *before* want   E—M *omit* a *before* well   17. BD—M
comma after rewardeth *not after* that   30—31. KLM *print* better have...
enjoy a pardon *in Italics*   35. HI the wrong   39. D as man

127. 2. BD—M whither   3. KLM fortune   4. D and as rich as
this   13. CDLM Gentleman   18. M *transposes* basely *and* be   25. D
other to   27. D was the next   29. FH—M the last   F—M discoursers
34. F—M songs & cryes of joy   35. *See* List of Misprints etc., which have
been corrected   BD—M them *Philanax*   C them, *Philanax*   38. F—M
token

128. 25. DEFHI inexpected   KLM unexpected   32. GHI valour
KLM valor   37. BD mindes   38. KLM which as it   40. KLM
account's

129. 9. D *Plaudius*   15—17. KLM *print* there is...or accidental *in
Italics*   19. IM with in   20. BD—M further   C it pleaseth them
31. I doings   32. C keepe downe   34. DEFH—M whither   35. M
than hee   37. BD—M burthened   39. DEFH—M account

130. 5. BD—M *insert* with *after* which   8. DEFKLM to lose   HI to
love   10. CH—M hands on her   13. HI *Arcadia* were   15. I
answered *instead of* replyed   22. M self obedience   28. HI murtherers
32. CG—M handes on her   37. C Monarchicall   BD—M is subject

131. 3. D crueltie comming of the Prince   14. HI the part   16. G—M
general cause   30. BD—M of a few

132. 11. F valure   GHI valour   KLM valor   19. FH—M *parenthesis
before* standing *not before* but   20. C *omits* a *before* cleere   23. DEFH—M
accounted   27. BDEG—M *Timautus*   F *Tamautus*   36. C Contende
revengefull   39. EF practise   G—M practice

133. 15. C shewing of an untimely   16. M he could get   19. C in
that esteemed good   25. BD—M *Timautus*   28. B *omits* he *before* would
40. F—M proceeding

134. 12. D be brought   19. I anothers mans hand   26. M *omits* to
before no lesse   32. BD—M murtherer   35. BD—I *Timautus* speech
KLM *Timautus's* speech

135. 2. BD—I *Timautus*   KLM *Timautus's*   3. I in his soule
15. BD—HKLM murtherers   25. FH—M that there was   26. KLM
Sympathus's hands   29. F—M upon the Noblemen   29—30. G—M it
is no season   30. BD—I *Timautus*   KLM *Timautus's*   31. BD—G
Basilius murtherers   H—M *Basilius's* murtherers   35. BD—M *Timautus*

228

NOTES

136. 5. BD—M sonne & nephew   13. HI of these   14. F—M
had promised for   16. M *Basilius*'s children EF the estate   17. FGH
world would not   33. F—M no *instead of* not *after* have   38. G—M
by a grave man in yeares

137. 17. BD—M *print this line in Italics* F—M *endeth*   18. DF—M
print The fourth *in Italics* G—M Eclogue   21. M *omits* had *before* at
E—M any aptenesse   24. M an hill   29. KLM *Basilius*'s government
33. LM hath enjoyed   34. I among

138. 2. F—M *insert* the *before* "*Arcadian*" DE *print* Arcadian *in
Roman type*   6. BDE *print* Arcadians *in Roman type*   7. KLM humane
causes   21. KLM *with inward wailing*   25. *her forces*   26. BD
threatre   34. LM *O blinde dead nature*   35. F—M "*danger*" *instead of*
"*damage*"

139. 16. D *Agelastes*   17. KLM the exceedingness   19. DEFHI—
M bewayling   21—**143.** 10. See vol. I, *notes to* **498.** 30—**502.** 19

143. 12. KLM onely his riming   23. D *the mind is*   37. I *his paines*

144. 4. I *surest*   8. IM *in our wailing*   20. LM *omit* and *before*
understanding   23. F—M *print this line in Italics*

145. 1. KLM *have the following title:*
   The | Countess | of | Pembroke's Arcadia. | *The Fifth Book.*
6. F—M of the uttermost   9. BD—I estates KLM estate's   10. K
Gentlemen   11. H—M renowned   12. HI *Evarchus*   14. B—M by certaine

146. 8. C *Kalandar*   20. BD—I *Timautus* KLM *Timautus's*
26. BD—M *Timautus*   31. E—I *Philanax* cunning   KLM *Philanax's*
cunning   36. G—M eare

147. 4. G—M *omit* not *after* is   8. D appearance   13. H—M renowned   20. E—M day his seate   29. D had heard   30. H *Evarchus*

148. 4. F equalities   9. H *Evarchus*   14. KLM *Philanax's* proposition   18. BD—M *Timautus*   20. M factions *instead of* factious
23—24. KLM *print* who is...ears *in Italics*   28. E—M asking   30. BD—
M *Timautus*   31. BD—M *Timautus* KLM her consent   36—37. LM
print vice...of vertue *in Italics*   38. C *omits* a *before* just

149. 4. BD—M *Timautus*   6. H *Evarchus*   12. H *Evarchus*
14. GKLM received of *Basilius*   15. H *Evarchus*   16. D possible speech
20. H *Evarchus*· D unto *instead of* into   21. D *Macedonia* C visit the
coast   26. H *Evarchus*   33. C in those partes   36. E *prints* Euarchus
in Roman type H *Evarchus*   37. HIM practices

150. 1. D hospitality *instead of* hostilitie   FGHKLM nor *instead of* not
before ceasing   20. F government   21. LM for the resisting   23. C
might attaine it   31. G—M which witnessed of   38. C not succouring him in

151. 7. C colour H *Evarchus*   14. G—M all the words   25. H
Evarchus   26. H *Evarchus*   26—27. KLM *Euarchus's* proceeding   28. M
omits no *before* wisdom   30. M no friendly D for that time   32. H *Evarchus*   36. F—M *insert* a *before* short

152. 6. D *Dalphantus* E—HKLM *Diaphantus*   7. F—M taking opportunitie   10. D to warre   12, 16, 20, 26. H *Evarchus*   30. KLM
cases of   34. M place som   38. H *Evarchus* D deserts

NOTES

153. 3. K beginning an end   4. K as shee was   7. H *Evarchus*   8. G—M rose up   10. D saw them beare   13. D not much liked to   16. H of a speaking to *Evarchus*   23. BD—M into his raving   28. H *Evarchus*   29. H—M renowned   34. H *Evarchus*

154. 9. KLM Lords   20. F—M open unto you   22. E—M *omit* one *before* that   26. D of his kingdome   28. D—M *semicolon after* you   33. M licourishness   35. G—M *semicolon after* words   G—M and on your answer   G—M *omit comma after* answer   CI depends

155. 1. H *Evarchus*   7. BD—M with *instead of* which *after* time   9. KLM *omit* own *before* mind   10. KLM action   14. LM unto a   19. F—M though the people   30. D other proffer   31. E—M welpoysed gesture   C inpassionate   38. I *transposes* I *and* am   40. C warranted mine owne releife

156. 6. E—M *insert* to *before* which   D which was I am   10. M imagination   11. D nor sudden   12. E hope if be   I into hate   17. H *Evarchus*   25. I who makes   25—26. KLM *print* the unwilling...desirer *in Italics*   26. KLM *"unworthie" instead of* undeserving   27. H *Evarchus*   34. H *Evarchus*   35. C duty of his

157. 5. M joyned the present   KLM bands   6. H *Evarchus*   13. KLM *Philanax*'s Embassage   15—16. KLM that accustomed   17. H *Evarchus*   20—21. KLM *print* one...multitude *in Italics*   20. M man's sufficient   21. I thousand of the multitude   23. C *omits* as *after* For   H *Evarchus*   29. F—M for his excceeding paine   30. H *Evarchus*   31. LM *omit* so *before* judging   H *Evarchus*   32. BD not yet   37. B—HKLM *comma instead of full stop after* appeare   I *omits full stop*

158. 6. K could no say further   LM could not say further   7. D him all his   13. D any overshooting   22. I diversitie   26. M that thou do not   29. F—M that the uttermost   F—M *comma instead of semicolon after* skill   BD—M both *instead of* but *before* in   30. DILM and particularly of   34. EFH—M force   40. C to despose my selfe

159. 2. DEFH—M *comma instead of parenthesis after* whereof   HI *comma after* meane   C *concluding parenthesis instead of semicolon after* trying   DEFH—M *omit semicolon after* trying   LM tyring *instead of* trying   6. EFH—M your selfe   D *omits* that *after* rest   7. BD—M With many   8. H *Evarchus*   9. DLM service   11. G—M as a small   13. C in the mixed   14. H *Evarchus*   21. C in blacke velvet   21—22. BD—M murtherers   25. E—M approched to the   26. D with care   39. M *omits* by *before* her

160. 5. M blasphemously   6. KLM O God   9. D Is it to mee to M the naughtiness of your   18. KLM her in a   24. D he *instead of* she *before* was   26. LM *omit* ever   30. E—M assaultes   32. LM *insert* and *before* had   C *omits* a *after* still   D passion   36. DEFH—M account   37. L determined denial

161. 13. LM where the minds   30. C would not have   37. D disadventures

162. 6. M Princesse   EFH—M *comma instead of parenthesis before* as   7. EFH—M *comma instead of concluding parenthesis after "Musidorus"* M they could ever   33. LM her adversarie   34. HI vexation of her   38. HI *omit* to *after* resist

230

NOTES

163. 1. C wounde   2. I when a great   5—6. KLM *print* Eagle
when...an Eagle *in Italics*   5. KLM *omit* a *before* Cage   12. LM so
strange a guard   13. D—M price   23. D that had beene   25. C
his power   26. KLM *omit* you *after* sever   29. KLM *Pyrocles's* education   30. DEFH—M counted   39. LM can never make   BD make
you say   LM that had made

164. 3. KLM which stayed   10. EFH—M gift   BD—M *omit* so *before*
diligent   13. KLM hath *instead of* have   14. F—M thither   19. D
omits note of interrogation after time   20. G—M all that is past   22. C
therefore the wrong   23. KLM but all in other deserts   26. KLM bee
but mischief   32. C hurt to the   35. M so dear I

165. 16. LM that we should not know   19. BD—M effects followe
21. EFH—M past   24. KL *transpose* of *and* all   M *omits* of *after* which
34. E—M as it was for us   36. BD—M *comma instead of full stop after* see

166. 4. C *omits* the *before* cullours   11. C *has no division into stanzas*
14. E—M *comma after* "*that*" *not after* "*feare*"   19. E—M *only* eyes
23. M *Then let let us*   30. E—I else that happened   33. D know who
shall be

167. 8. D richly   9. FGK *Diaphantus*   13. D that *instead of* they
before were   17. H *Evarchus*   19. I throne or judgement seat   21. KLM
print Prince *in Italics*   H *Evarchus*   25. KLM or an ornament   28. F
Philinax   H *Evarchus*   35, 36. H *Evarchus*

168. 13. H *Evarchus*   18. F—M extraordinarie a course   25. C
that indeede of *Zelmanes*   27. D—M russet   35. KLM should be received   39. HI *transpose* other *and* two

169. 5. D was not so much   13. .F—M *omit* a *before* white   22. D
omits of *after* but   25. M wore

170. 12. E—M face in a boy   19. F—M whom *instead of* which
28. D nations of the world   34. LM *Basilius*'s children   38. F—M
Prince doth

171. 8. DEFH—M account   25. D to the tender   36. D *omits
parenthesis before* having   37. D *parenthesis before* on   HI Table on the
which   39—40. C *omits* and only then like a suppliant   D onely with such
a suppliant

172. 1. C most honorable   BD—M saith he   13. C have *instead of*
hath   20. M for my own   26. C burthen   B—M upon mine owne
38. H *Evarchus*

173. 3. LM manner *instead of* matter   5. M no farther   6—7. D
wisedome, that shewes not altogether   9. BD—M repay the touched
11. LM *Pyrocles*'s case   12. KLM exceeding joyous   19. H *Evarchus*
L to himself to no other name   23. F—M greater matter   37. D truth
both make me deale   39. C *omits parenthesis before* neither   EFH—M *concluding parenthesis after* need   40. I have what thou

174. 4. D with my wrong   14. G—M unto him the   18. D that
hath   37. H *Evarchus*

175. 5. BD—M whereas   7. C *concluding parenthesis instead of comma
after* private   9. B—M communitie of goods   10. B—M communitie
of children   15. C monarchicall   16. KLM of all her doings   18. D
parenthesis instead of comma before neither   23. F—M there kept   40. G—
M rose up

NOTES

176. 2. D of his judgement   9. B—M other manifest   13. F—M to the admiration   G—M of a *instead of* of her *after* admiration   21. I joyned with the   22. H *Evarchus*   23. D that will charge   25. LM of the judgment   26. D could say manifest   35. GK *Diaphantus* L *prints* Iberia *in Roman type*   40. HIM *Arcadian* Lawes

177. 19. D *omits* a *after* case of   26. H *Evarchus*   30. F—M *omit* but *before* like   32. FH—M *comma instead of full stop after* separated   33. GK *Diaphantus*

178. 1. H *Evarchus*   4. B—M proofes of faultes   8. D I my selfe   13. I recitall of wickednesse   14. D that they can   25. D enlarger of the most harmelesse mischiefe   D *omits* as *after* in   31. LM accompanied like   33. FGK *Diaphantus*   34—35. C *omits* (for any shape…of shame)   39. D hurtfull sexe   LM his subtile

179. 5. GHI neat *instead of* neere   9. KLM *transpose* shee *and* was   12. CEF murther   14. C murther   18. C did not only feare the   37—38. C *omits* as much as in him lay)   37. DEFH—M *parenthesis before* as   39. F—M be accessary   40—180. 1. C *omits* (against whom…rebell) *and inserts a comma after* sister

180. 1. D wee would rebell   2. F—M of this mightie   3. C preventing him   4. D *Damatas*   F—M *Dametas* his hand   5. D as in the house   22. D *prints* God *in small capitals*   24. GHIM no practice to   H—M a practice without   33. D *prints* God *in small capitals*   35. HIM affraid   40. FGK *Diaphantus*

181. 5. E changes and treasures   F—M changes and trecheries   6. D *omits* to *after* then   7. GHK murther   L murtherer   M murderer   8. F—M to *instead of* in *before* so many   11. I meanes *instead of* mindes   15. HIM devices   16. FGK *Diaphantus*   17. G—M *transpose* can *and* you   19. H—M practice BD of our cloake   G of you cloake   20. D such a   22. BCD your Prince   26. E with according   27. C which murther   37. D dishonouring of the   38. D Alas would not so many

182. 3. D Where thy eyes   C so stone   6. C name this mankind   7. C procurer thy greatest   8. E—M cause *instead of* case   11. C may proofe   21. F—M all the lawes   28. D if this act   30. C for when we shall think   32. C *Philoclea* that honour   35. C Alas although

183. 6. B—M sometimes   8—9. KLM in an indifferent   17. KLM of the matters   24. B—M so cunning confusion   26. F—M absolutely   29. I compelled to heare   30—31. D of his government   32. D his invective speech those fewe point   39. CEFH—M so vile   40. G—M disgracing

184. 1. C be beleeved   22. D see her error   D *omits* I *after* While   28. LM *transpose* have *and* you   29. C *prints* Labyrinth *in Italics*   30. F—M *transpose* see *and* you   34. C all the wise   35. EFGKLM accusations   36. B—M murther

185. 2—3. B—M Truely I am so farre   13. D *parenthesis before* as *not before* for   21. B—M An honest   25. G—M for a sweete   27. EFH—M *omit comma after* matter   28. EFH—M *parenthesis before* which   31. EFH—M *concluding parenthesis instead of comma after* truth

186. 15. FGKLM *omit* the *before* bloudie   21. BD—M For mine owne   24. KL *transpose* I *and* may   39. DG—M wrote

232

NOTES

187. 1. LM *print this line in Roman type with the exception of* Philoclea *which is in Italics* C *prints* Philoclea *in Italics* DG—K *wrote* L wrote 2—39. CDHI *omit inverted commas in margin* LM *print this letter in Italics with the exception of* Arcadia *and* Philoclea *which words are in Roman type* 2. HI *bracket before* My B—M it is to me 8. I its originall 24. D *omits* for *before* I have 29. M *if I have told you* 34. F—M *transpose* is *and* it 36. KL *insert* the *after* to 39. HI *bracket after* children

188. 1—3. LM *print these lines in Roman type* 1. CLM *print* Pamelas *in Italics* 2. C *Arcadians* M *prints* Arcadian *in Italics* I *kept, that they* 3. D *omits* "thus" *before* "framed" 4—189. 8. CDHI *omit inverted commas in margin* LM *print this letter in Italics with the exception of* Basilius *and* Pamela *which words are in Roman type* 4. HI *bracket before* In 7. KLM how shall I KLM for as speech 9. D not to whome 9—10. D What to write it is hard for mee LM *What to write is hard for mee* 20. F—M *transpose* shall *and* ever 36. F—M indefinitely

189. 4. I you treat of is the 5. GHKLM not of a shepheard 7—8. KLM *Basilius's* daughter 8. HI *bracket after* daughter 9. E—M of these sweet 12. F—M was too much 28—29. F—K he sent a spitefull care to 30, 33, 36. H *Evarchus*

190. 3. F—M so much more vehement 27. F—M against the time 34. F—M I see it no reason

191. 18. D if I would 37. LM his countrey 39. EFH—M others unjust

192. 5. G *Diaphantus* KLM *Diaphantus's* 14. F—M *omit* the *before* traytors 18. GHIM valour KL valor 23. C have hired you 29—30. LM *print* commonly...weapon *in Italics* 29. B—M they use 36. G King death 38. HI at last hee comes

193. 1. G—M on else, but 21. E—M *omit* to *before* those 22. GHKL that experience know 23. C witnessed to such by 30. KLM *insert* the *before* laws 34. C may marke a profitable 36. M babler

194. 3. M *inserts* that *before* was 4. CDG—M effect in him 7. H *Evarchus* 8. B—M others speech 9. BD—M whither 12. F—M called *instead of* caused 13. H in a most 17. H—M practice 18. B—M voice and gesture 19—20. F—M whereof we are presently 28. I *transposes* I *and* will 30. KLM subjects 31. HI necessary relation K relation between father 40. HI trumpeters

195. 6. M breaks 22. C And that most undoubtedly 24. FH—L *print* Greece *in Roman type* 36. B—M murther 37. E—M *transpose* mighty *and* against

196. 4. F—M then is this no I further 14. F—M countervaile a following 17. F—M hath it beene 20. F—M *insert* yet *before* would 21. KLM *transpose* then *and* is 24. *See* Corrigenda GK *Diaphantus* 27. C seeing the causes of 32. B—L *print* Grecian *in Roman type* 35. M in private 36. M forcibly

197. 1. B—M *omit* the *before* Grecian M *prints* Grecian *in Italics* 7. E—M if they had 17. C murthers 29. E—M *transpose* much *and* be 31. F—M to save such

198. 1. L thus much doth 8. F—M *transpose* so *and* yet 13. HI *Arcadian* 17. HI *Arcadian* 18. GK *Diaphantus* 30. B—M somewhat *instead of* somthing 31. KLM to a bashfulness 34. M *Pyrocles's* 36. H *Evarchus*

233

NOTES

199. 3. M rather a passionate   4. F—M friend *instead of* servaunt
9. H—M accounted   14. KLM of the Prince   20. E their lovely
29. H *Evarchus*   30. I damage unto them   32, 34. H *Evarchus*

200. 3. D of this Countrie   4. E—M of all occurrents   5. H *Evarchus*
7. GK *Diaphantus*   8. H *Evarchus*   11. H *Evarchus*   11—12. LM
Euarchus's words   12. BD—M whither they   13. KLM Hee requireth
14. BD—M whether   D the same H *Evarchus*   14—15. LM *Euarchus*'s presence   15. KLM doubtfull recital   18. F—M this description
24—25. B—M *print* Macedon *in Italics*   36. H *Evarchus*   40. C such kinde of

201. 7. B—M with my most   HI impartiall   18. D in one cause

202. 3. B—M *"Kalander" instead of "Kerxenus"*   11. BCD with the rage of   13. H *Evarchus*   14. B—HKLM murtherer   25. B—M hurt *instead of* heart *after* owne   26. E *omits* but *after* power   27. G—M with a manly eie   31. B—M owne cause   32. D searchers

203. 3. H *Evarchus*   14. E—M not to be tedious   18. M my own life   36. LM your requesting

204. 4. M upon that name   LM lest seeing too   9. H *Evarchus*   16. B—M that he fel againe to   20. H *Evarchus*   22. B—M such an one
24. H *Evarchus*   26. C when he heard   32. KLM *print* Dukes *in Italics*   39. BD—M *" Kalander" instead of "Kerxenus"*   C *Kalandar*

205. 2. F—M *omit* had *after* he   19. KLM pleased her self   32. H—M wrongly interpreted   36. F—M But a while it was   HI the good *Basilius*   37. H *Evarchus*

206. 4. B—M *" Zelmane" instead of "Cleofila"*   7. D weighing all these
10. LM lively burial   13. G—M was content so   15. E—M *omit* he
19. F—M betrayed her   21. EFH—M duely *instead of* daily   25, 28. H *Evarchus*   29. B—M betwixt the peerelesse   D princesse & princesses
32. B—M Kingdome *instead of* Dukedome   33. I place in that   35. CI *Kalandar*   36. B—M his son

207. 5. H *Manalcas*   12. BEF *The end of the fifth and last booke of* Arcadia   D The end of the fifth and last part of Arcadia   G—M *The end of the fift Booke of* Arcadia

208. 1. *The folios have no title*   2—338. *First published in the Folio of* 1598.   12. E you titles   14. D—M of me poore   17. FH—M Onely one daughter   19. F—M bearing her   22. F—M in the countrey
24. M *inserts* may *before* think   31. D incomberd   33. F a good peace

209. 1. D very formerly   H—M containeth   8. M *ones self*   11. LM *your shield*   13. M *wise, but still it makes you*   18. E—M wood   21. D one or other side   KLM one nor the other side   24. KLM autoritie
30. *After this line* F—M *insert the following:*
           Lalus the old Shepheard.
31. CF—M *omit* "Lalus &c...." [margin]   F—M your dignitie   H no give
36. KLM your   37. KLM brain-pain   38. I fansicall

210. 7. KLM *omit* it *after* of   11. CI with you   12. HIL enmity
12—13. KLM *Potentissma*   14. F—M juvenall   20. D *solummdo*   26. M that certain   D *porfecto*   28. G—M Maies   LM mouth *instead of* month
33. FH—M *omit* " May Lady." [margin]   37. CFH—M *omit* " Rombus." [margin]

NOTES

211. 5. CFH—M *omit* "*May Lady.*" [*margin*]   6. KLM sight of this age hath   10. CFH—M *omit* "*May Lady.*" [*margin*]   16. KLM month   20. M truth   27. KLM month   36. K to to mee great   LM to mee great

212. 20. *Published in* England's Helicon (1600)   21. Eng. Hel. *conceite*   23. Eng. Hel. *live and die*   30. D *plowed in thy*

213. 8. *Instead of this line* Eng. Hel. *has the following:*
Both kneeling to her Majestie
18. F—M *insert* a *before* moderator   20. KL blessing   KLM of my   22. D mine honestie   26. HI *Roxus*   27. KLM art not thou   28. KLM bone   33. KL it is your   35. F—M sheepish

214. 1. D art thou not   3. KL such an one   6. LM they fain   8. KLM quiet as lamb   11. G—M *Incitium*   14. D gravitated   18. LM obtruse   19. C *comma after* "*definiendum*"   FH—L *semicolon*   20. FHIK *Mayas*   LM *Mydas*   30. D conceive *instead of* concerne

215. 2. G—M have I heard   3. I under bushes in our field   8. G—L of her dolefull   M of our doleful   14. KLM of him bee more   18. D *omits* all *before* the fat   22. KLM that the sheep   23—24. C *contingentibus*   26. E—M *omit* a *before* "*Sillogisme*"

216. 8. LM doth not so far   10. D *omits* is *after* which   KLM *insert* as *after* much   13. HI *propositus*   29. D *Esphilus*   34. D *Esphilus*

217. 3. KL *that hee obtain*   14. KLM *such an one*   15. I—M *blesse*   16. C *desart*   17. G—M *Thus wofull I in*

3.	20.	in warde	29.	beloved	39. it harh
16.	24.	alittle			
22.	4.	desirons			
23.	20.	to wardes			
32.	37.	*unrefram'd*			
40.	24.	aprologue			
45.	1.	and Imaginatife			
73.	15.	*hollandsweet*			
85.	36.	*no full stop after* husband			
86.	23.	weight of of a			
87.	4.	withall			
89.	7.	somerfaults			
91.	31.	allliving			
102.	28.	concurring s			
109.	35.	resoluti			
113.	21.	whtsoever			
116.	2.	e of *omitted*			
122.	40.	judgement			
127.	1.	thither ward	35.	*full stop after* them	
142.	24.	*Muses*			
155.	37.	a bashed			
156.	16.	form me			
158.	26.	of yonr			
159.	26.	withall			
160.	13.	her helfe			
178.	35.	solitatie			
189.	38.	cammaunded			
190.	14.	Toomuch			
194.	1.	compssion	7.	judgēment	
331.	23.	*Æneas*			
336.	29.	extingnish			
338.	24.	willl			
349.	7.	once mynde			

INDEX OF FIRST LINES OF POEMS

INDEX OF FIRST LINES OF POEMS